BRITISH GEOLOG

CW00688381

Geology in south-west Scotland

Scotland

An excursion guide

BRITISH GEOLOGICAL SURVEY

Geology in south-west Scotland
An excursion guide

In memory of Byron Charles Lintern
1948–1993

Editor
P Stone
with assistance from A D McAdam and J I Chisholm

Contributors

M C Akhurst	J A McCurry
R P Barnes	A A McMillan
M P Boland	R J Merriman
P J Brand	S K Monro
R F Cheeney	E R Phillips
J I Chisholm	B Roberts
E N K Clarkson	A W A Rushton
D J Fettes	P Stone
J D Floyd	C M Taylor
M J Gallagher	S P Tunnicliff
R A Hughes	J A Weir
A D McAdam	D E White

supported by the Edinburgh Geological Society

Keyworth, Nottingham   British Geological Survey   1996

Editor
P Stone
British Geological Survey
Edinburgh

Contributors
M C Akhurst
R P Barnes
P J Brand
D J Fettes
J D Floyd
M J Gallagher
R A Hughes
A D McAdam
A A McMillan
S K Monro
E R Phillips
P Stone
British Geological Survey
Edinburgh
M P Boland
J I Chisholm
R J Merriman
A W A Rushton
S P Tunnicliff
D E White
British Geological Survey
Keyworth, Nottingham
R F Cheeney
E N K Clarkson
C M Taylor
University of Edinburgh
J A Weir
University of St Andrews
B Roberts
Birkbeck College, University of London
J A McCurry
Scottish Natural Heritage, Edinburgh

BRITISH GEOLOGICAL SURVEY

Keyworth, Nottingham NG12 5GG
0115-936 3100

Murchison House, West Mains Road,
Edinburgh, EH9 3LA   0131-667 1000

London Information Office, Natural History Museum, Earth Galleries, Exhibition Road, London SW7 2DE
0171-589 4090

The full range of Survey publications is available through the Sales Desks at Keyworth and at Murchison House, Edinburgh, and in the BGS London Information Office in the Natural History Museum (Earth Galleries). The adjacent bookshop stocks the more popular books for sale over the counter. Most BGS books and reports can be bought from HMSO and through HMSO agents and retailers. Maps are listed in the BGS Map Catalogue, and can be bought together with books and reports through BGS-approved stockists and agents as well as direct from BGS.

The British Geological Survey carries out the geological survey of Great Britain and Northern Ireland (the latter as an agency service for the government of Northern Ireland), and of the surrounding continental shelf, as well as its basic research projects. It also undertakes programmes of British technical aid in geology in developing countries as arranged by the Overseas Development Administration.

The British Geological Survey is a component body of the Natural Environment Research Council.

C20   1/96
ISBN 0 85272261 3

Printed in England by Linneys Colour Print Ltd

Contents

vi

Tables

Front cover photograph Cleaved, steeply dipping Hawick Group strata on the west side of Brighouse Bay, Kirkcudbrightshire. D4402.

Back cover photograph by J E Cavill, digitally reprocessed by P M Green.

Preface

This excursion guide, the first to detail the varied geology of south-west Scotland, is dedicated to the memory of Byron Charles Lintern who died, after a short illness, on 12 January 1993, aged 44 years. Byron was born in Willington, County Durham and graduated in geology from Bristol University in 1970. He began his career investigating base metal deposits in Botswana; the structural geology of these deposits was the theme of his PhD study completed at Leeds University in 1978. From Leeds, Byron moved to the British Geological Survey, working in Wallingford and Swindon before joining the Edinburgh Office in 1984. There he applied his considerable expertise in structural geology to the reassessment of regional models for Southern Scotland. His mapping contributions in this area include the Kirkcudbright (5W) and Dalbeattie (5E) 1:50 000 sheets published in 1993. His research interests were focused on the major shear zones of the region; it is particularly appropriate that this volume contains an itinerary for the Moniaive Shear Zone, recognised and defined by Byron shortly before his death.

This selection of geological excursions within south-west Scotland has been compiled by Byron's friends and colleagues as a tribute to his scientific achievements. It provides a fitting memorial to an outstanding field geologist and will hopefully pass on to others his enthusiasm for the rocks of Galloway. It contains an introduction to the geology of the region, and 18 excursion itineraries which between them describe examples of most geological features that can be appreciated in the field. The first eight excursions are of general interest and are intended for the non-specialist, whereas the last ten concentrate on specific themes and are of a more specialised nature. Mineralisation in the region is separately reviewed and a final section considers geological conservation with an appended list of Sites of Special Scientific Interest.

The British Geological Survey and the Edinburgh Geological Society are happy to join in producing this tribute to Byron.

Peter J Cook, DSc, CGeol, FGS
Director, British Geological Survey

S Ian Hogarth, DRTC
President, Edinburgh Geological Society

7 April 1995

Geological column for the Mesozoic and Palaeozoic eras. IUGS time scale after Cowie and Bassett (1989).

Era	Approximate age (Ma)	System (Period)		Series (Epoch)	Orogenic episode
MESOZOIC		CRETACEOUS			
	135	JURASSIC			
	205	TRIASSIC			
	250	PERMIAN			
	290	CARBONIFEROUS	Silesian	Stephanian Westphalian Namurian	HERCYNIAN
			Dinantian	Viséan Tournaisian	
PALAEOZOIC	355	DEVONIAN		Upper (Late) Middle (Mid) Lower (Early)	ACADIAN
	410	SILURIAN		Přídolí Ludlow Wenlock Llandovery	CALEDONIAN
	438	ORDOVICIAN		Ashgill Caradoc Llandeilo Llanvirn Arenig Tremadoc	
	510	CAMBRIAN			
	540				

Introduction

The rolling hills of south-west Scotland are underlain principally by Lower Palaeozoic clastic sedimentary rocks and Caledonian granitic plutons. Drainage in the region is controlled in the main by Permo-Carboniferous faults trending SSE, which define the margins of half-graben sedimentary basins. The Upper Palaeozoic basin infills have been preferentially eroded so that they now coincide with the main river valleys. Rivers such as the Cree, Ken and Nith flow generally southwards to the Solway Firth, the site of another major Upper Palaeozoic basin. The Lower Palaeozoic rocks are exposed on the west coast of the Rhins of Galloway and along much of the Solway coast westward from about Dalbeattie. The lower-lying part of the region, mainly in the south along the Solway coast, carries an extensive cover of glacial deposits, with drumlins particularly well developed between Wigtown and Glenluce.

The main population centres are Dumfries and Stranraer. Local service buses link the main towns and villages, but independent transport will be required for most of the excursions described in this guide. Information on travel and accommodation may be obtained from the Dumfries and Galloway Tourist Board, Whitesands, Dumfries DG1 2SB (Tel. 01387 253862). The Gretna Gateway office (Tel: 01461 38500) is also open all year and from April to October the following Tourist Board local offices are open: Castle Douglas (Tel: 01556 502611), Dalbeattie (Tel: 01556 610117), Gatehouse of Fleet (Tel: 01557 814212), Kirkcudbright (Tel: 01557 330494), Newton Stewart (Tel: 01671 402431) and Stranraer (Tel: 01776 702595).

Many of the routes recommended in the excursions cross private land. Users of this guide are reminded that access arrangements are their own responsibility, and local advice and entry permission should be sought where necessary. Some sites are designated as Sites of Special Scientific Interest (SSSIs), a comprehensive list of which is included in Appendix 2. Most of these are in private ownership and their designation does not confer automatic rights of entry; indeed, access to some may require advance written permission. The geological visitor should be particularly conscious of the need to conserve geological sites in general, and to keep the use of hammers to a minimum. There is usually loose debris around rock exposures and patient use of a hand lens is likely to be far more rewarding than vigorous but indiscriminate hammering. A comprehensive *Code of Practice* for geological fieldwork has been prepared by the Geologists' Association (copies available from the GA, c/o Burlington House, Piccadilly, London WIV 9AG) and all visitors to geologically important sites are urged to familiarise themselves with its contents.

The geological features described in the excursions can be studied with the minimum of equipment. A hand lens is essential and a compass-clinometer will be needed to check bedding and cleavage attitude in areas of complex structure. A geological hammer will be useful but should be used sparingly.

The excursions are arranged into three sections on the basis of their duration and geological specialisation. Excursions 1 to 8 will each provide a day of general geological interest and are particularly recommended for parties with a mixture of geological experience and/or background. Excursions 9 to 14, also each of one day's duration, focus on particular geological themes and develop them in some detail; a measure of specialist interest is needed if full advantage is to be taken of these. Excursions 15 to 18 are planned to cover two or three days each and develop specific geological themes in their regional context. These longer excursions are likely to appeal most to specialist groups. As a supplement to the excursions two appendices provide regional reviews of metalliferous mineralisation and geological conservation sites.

A word of warning: severe weather can develop over the Scottish hills at any time

of the year. **Always check weather forecasts and wear appropriate clothing and boots.** For the coastal outcrops always **check the local tidal conditions and be aware of the potential dangers both of the rising tide and of wave-swept rock areas.** Particular safety warnings are indicated in **bold type** in the text.

Maps and general publications

National Grid references are used extensively for location throughout the guide. They fall into five 100 km-grid squares, NS, NT, NW, NX and NY. However, as most excursions lie within one 100 km-square the relevant letters are usually only given at the start of each excursion.

ORDNANCE SURVEY MAPS

Landranger maps at a scale of 1:50 000 are advised for route-finding for the excursions. The following cover the relevant part of South-west Scotland:

Sheet 71   Lanark and Upper Nithsdale area
Sheet 72   Upper Clyde Valley
Sheet 76   Girvan and surrounding area
Sheet 77   Dalmellington to New
            Galloway
Sheet 78   Nithsdale and Annandale area
Sheet 79   Hawick and Eskdale area
Sheet 82   Stranraer, Glen Luce and
            surrounding area
Sheet 83   Newton Stewart and
            Kirkcudbright area
Sheet 84   Dumfries, Castle Douglas and
            surrounding area
Sheet 85   Carlisle and The Solway Firth

Bartholomew's 1:100 000 scale Sheet 37 Galloway and Sheet 38 Solway Firth also cover the whole region.

GEOLOGICAL SURVEY MAPS

British Geological Survey maps at 1:50 000 or 1:63 360(*) scales are available for most of the region. Maps indicated ‡ are reconstituted at 1:50 000 scale from earlier surveys. Maps indicated † are currently available as electrostatic plots, prior to publication. Published maps can be purchased from BGS at Murchison House, West

Mains Road, Edinburgh, EH9 3LA, or from Ordnance Survey stockists.

Sheet 1 & 3   Rhins of Galloway Solid
                1992
Sheet 1   Kirkmaiden Drift 1982‡
Sheet 2   Whithorn Solid & Drift 1987
Sheet 3   Stranraer Drift 1982‡
Sheet 4W   Kirkcowan Solid 1992, Drift
             1982‡
Sheet 4E   Wigtown Solid 1992, Drift
             1981‡
Sheet 5W   Kirkcudbright Solid, 1993,
             Drift 1980‡
Sheet 5E   Dalbeattie Solid 1993, Drift
             1980‡
Sheet 6   Annan Drift 1983‡
Sheet 7   Girvan Solid 1988, Drift
             1981‡
Sheet 8W   Carrick Solid 1978‡ , 1994†,
             Drift 1981‡
Sheet 8E   Loch Doon Solid 1977‡ ,
             1994†, Drift 1980‡
Sheet 9W   New Galloway Solid 1978‡ ,
             Drift 1979‡
Sheet 9E   Thornhill Solid 1978‡ , Drift
             1980‡
Sheet 10W   Lochmaben Drift 1983‡
Sheet 10E   Ecclefechan Drift 1982‡
Sheet 11*   Langholm Solid 1968, Drift
             1968
Sheet 14W   Ayr Solid 1978, Drift 1978
Sheet 14E   Cumnock Solid 1976, Drift
             1980
Sheet 15W   New Cumnock Solid 1986‡,
             Drift 1982‡
Sheet 15E   Leadhills Solid 1987‡, Drift
             1981‡
Sheet 16W   Moffat Drift 1987‡
Sheet 24W   Biggar Solid 1980‡, Drift
             1980‡

There is also a 1:25 000 Sheet NX08, 18 and 19 (in part), Ballantrae, Solid, 1988.

The 1:250 000 solid geological sheets give a synoptic coverage of south-west Scotland and the surrounding land and sea areas.

Borders   Sheet 55N 04W 1986
Clyde   Sheet 55N 06W 1986
Lake District   Sheet 54N 04W 1980
Isle of Man   Sheet 54N 06W 1982

Geological maps at 1:10 560 or 1:10 000 scale are available for much of the region and may be consulted at the Library, British

Geological Survey, Murchison House, Edinburgh, EH9 3LA. Dyeline copies can be purchased from the Sales Desk.

PUBLICATIONS

The geology of Scotland, 3rd edition, 1991, gives an introduction to Scottish geology. The third edition of the BGS regional geology, *The south of Scotland*, 1971, provides a more detailed, though somewhat dated, account. Sheet memoirs or explanations are available for Sheets 1 and 3 (The Rhins of Galloway) 1995, Sheet 2 (Whithorn) 1989, Sheet 7 (Girvan) 1986 and Sheet 11 (Langholm) 1967. Memoirs for several other sheets should be published shortly. *The Ballantrae area*, 1988, is described in the *Classical areas of British geology* series.

Lower Palaeozoic regional geology: P Stone

The geology of south-west Scotland testifies to processes active at the margins of a major ocean some 400 to 500 million years ago. This precursor to the Atlantic has become known as the Iapetus Ocean and its vestiges can be traced from the American Appalachians, through the maritime provinces of Canada, across Ireland and Scotland and into Scandinavia. The Iapetus Ocean probably spread to its maximum size during the Cambrian Period, and the Ordovician and Silurian rocks of the Scottish Southern Uplands record its later evolution and eventual destruction by oblique collision between the bordering continental plates. The one to the north is referred to as Laurentia, that to the south as Avalonia.

The oldest rocks seen form the early Arenig ophiolitic assemblage of the Ballantrae Complex, cropping out over about 75 km[2] on the Ayrshire coast south of Girvan (Figure 1). In broad terms ophiolites represent relics of the oceanic crust and mantle; their most complete development would show an upward sequence from ultramafic rock to gabbro, both layered and homogeneous, then through a dyke complex feeding spilitic pillow lavas with the whole pile topped by abyssal sedimentary rocks, typically black shale and chert. The Ballantrae example is fragmentary and only the ultra-

mafic rocks and pillow lavas are well preserved. However, sufficient evidence can be gathered from these, particularly in respect of their geochemistry, to show that the Ballantrae ophiolite was not generated at a mid-ocean spreading centre, but instead is a tectonic mixture of supra-subduction zone island arc and oceanic island components (Thirlwall and Bluck, 1984; Smellie and Stone, 1992; Stone and Smellie, 1988 and references therein). The oldest volcanic components formed in an oceanic island arc above a subduction zone about 500 million years ago, but the oceanic crust forming the foundations of that arc might have been 70 or 80 million years older. Volcanic arc activity continued through the Arenig epoch, changing in character subtly as the arc evolved. Volcanic activity of different character occurred simultaneously, probably in the back arc region. This phase was brought to a close towards the end of the Arenig, about 478 million years ago, by collision of the arc with the Laurentian continental landmass. The volcanic arc, with its oceanic crust and mantle foundations, was structurally imbricated and emplaced on the continental margin, a process known as obduction. The subsequent foundering of the continental margin allowed a marine sedimentary sequence to be deposited above the deformed ophiolite. Conglomerates and shallow-marine limestone commonly form the base of the succession but sedimentary facies becomes more deep-water upwards as marine conditions transgressed northwards. The succession is almost complete from the Llanvirn to the lower Wenlock, with only a small break at the Ordovician–Silurian boundary.

The continuity of sedimentary sequence found above the obducted Ballantrae ophiolite is in stark contrast to the fragmented situation seen farther south in the Southern Uplands, where the Lower Palaeozoic rocks are divided by major strike faults into a series of blocks, each with only a limited stratigraphical range. These successions are dominated by turbidite deposits of greywacke, siltstone and shale. Graptolites, found most commonly in black shales, are important in establishing the ages of these, and prove that an upward lithological change from black shale to greywacke, present in each of the fault-bounded blocks, is diachronous,

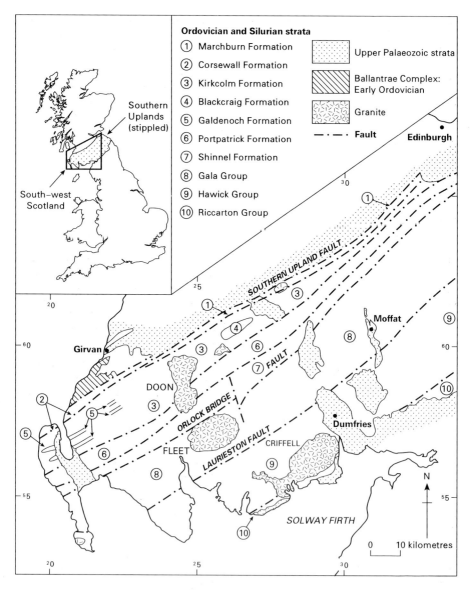

Figure 1 Principal features of Lower Palaeozoic geology in south-west Scotland.

becoming sequentially younger southwards. Graptolite evidence for the age of the overlying greywacke formations is much more limited but generally proves the greywacke to be the same age or only slightly younger than the youngest shale. This emphasises the differences in sedimentation rates; within a single biozone (lasting very roughly a million years) a few metres of black shale may have been deposited but in the same time interval repeated turbidity current flows may have built up several thousand metres of greywacke. The mechanism of turbidity current action, and details of graptolites and their biostratigraphy, are discussed more fully below.

Throughout the Southern Uplands the greywacke turbidite beds are for the most part steeply inclined with a fairly uniform strike of about 060°. From the assemblage of sedimentary features it is clear that most of the succession youngs towards the NW, though many beds are slightly overturned to dip steeply SE. Folded zones consist of tight anticline–syncline pairs which do not interfere with the overall trend of younging. The dominance of NW-directed younging is at odds with the overall age relationships across the Southern Uplands; a glance at any geological map of the area shows that the oldest rocks crop out in the NW and the youngest in the SE. This paradox has been created by the major strike faults, all of which downthrow to the SE (Figure 1). In each fault-bounded block the oldest rocks lie at the SE side and youngest at the NW, but progressively older strata form the base of each block sequentially across the Southern Uplands from SE to NW (Figure 2) to produce the overall stratigraphical pattern. In the northernmost structural blocks spilitic lavas, chert and black shale form the base of the sequence, overlain by greywacke; in the more southerly blocks only shale is seen below the greywacke. From a comparison with the equivalent sequence now preserved in Newfoundland it seems likely that the volcanic component was originally much more extensive (Colman-Sadd et al., 1992) and represents arc and back arc material formed within the Iapetus Ocean.

The structural and stratigraphical relationships seen in the Southern Uplands have been explained by the 'accretionary prism' model formulated by Leggett et al. in 1979 and refined by Leggett (1987). This envisaged the greywackes being deposited in a deep ocean trench at an active continental margin of the Iapetus Ocean where the oceanic plate was subducting north-westwards. As the oceanic plate descended, its covering of sediment was scraped off and stacked at the continental margin in a series of underthrust slices. Since greywackes would only be deposited above the hemipelagic (black shale) sediments covering the oceanic plate as it approached the trench, the age of the greywacke in each thrust slice is younger than that in the pre-viously accreted slice. Final rotation of the thrust stack to the vertical was caused by continental collision as the ocean closed completely in the late Silurian or early Devonian.

The accretionary prism model elegantly explains the overall geological relationships within the Southern Uplands but many details are still difficult to reconcile. In particular, a close examination of the compositions of individual sand grains within the greywackes shows marked differences between adjacent beds in the same structural block and between the blocks themselves. These differences are particularly marked in the Ordovician sequence and form the basis of the lithostratigraphical divisions shown in Figures 1 and 2. Two distinct provenances are indicated and palaeocurrent analyses of sole marks suggests a mature continental margin to the north and NE and an active volcanic island arc to the south and SW. The palaeogeographical indications have led to an alternative interpretation, namely that the early history of the Southern Uplands was within a back arc basin which Stone et al. (1987) propose developed into a sequential back arc to foreland basin thrust system following collision between continent and arc in the early Silurian. Whichever model is preferred the thrust geometry is fundamentally the same and has one important rider; the thrust-related deformation was diachronous, with structures in the NW formed before those in the SE. This process has been partly quantified by Barnes et al. (1989) and its understanding remains dependent on graptolite biostratigraphy.

Within the Ordovician Leadhills Group (Figure 2) the compositional variation in the greywackes, when viewed in the light of the graptolite biostratigraphy, allows a stratigraphical division into defined formations. The same is possible in the mid-Silurian Hawick Group where the presence or absence of interbedded red mudstone provides a key lithostratigraphical indicator. However, the early Silurian Gala Group is more compositionally uniform and the units shown in Figure 2 are arranged on the basis of biostratigraphy and deduced structural position. These units are regarded as tectonostratigraphical blocks or tracts and

6

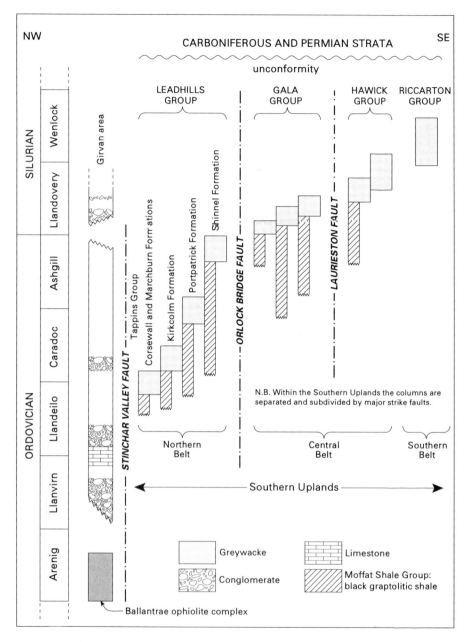

Figure 2 Schematic representation of stratigraphical relationships in south-west Scotland.

are numbered, from north to south, Gala 1 to Gala 9. Some formation names have been applied locally and are used informally.

Various fold geometries will be seen during the excursions, and most can be linked into a general picture of southward-propagating thrust development followed by superimposed sinistral shear. The thrust-related structures can be grouped into three styles which, at outcrop, form distinct structural domains:

Type 1 Uniform, usually steeply inclined or vertical bedding younging consistently NW. The regular pattern of strike and dip is only locally interrupted by sporadic fold pairs.

Type 2 Continuous sequences of small- to medium-scale folds separated by minor shears and/or narrow unfolded units of steeply inclined bedding younging NW. Most of the folds are tight or close with axial planes steeply inclined and fold hinges which generally plunge gently; some folds are periclinal.

Type 3 Continuous sequences of close to open folds, ranging considerably in wavelength and amplitude. Axial planes are upright or steeply inclined and fold hinges plunge gently.

Figure 3 shows how, in an idealised example, the three styles interrelate. Note that they may form at various depths within the thrust stack and therefore have no absolute implications in terms of structural depth. There are also local reversals of the regional trend, for example at the southern end of the Rhins of Galloway, where younging is dominantly southwards and the sense of thrust movement is towards the north (McCurry and Anderson, 1989).

Overall the regional (burial-related) metamorphic grade throughout the Lower

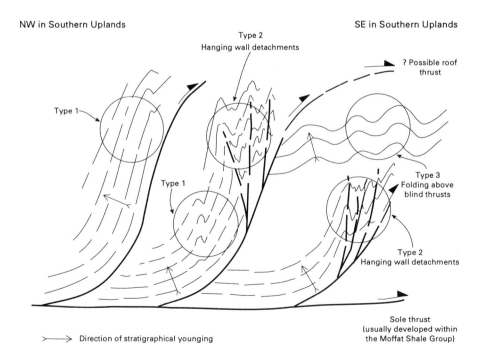

Figure 3 Variable fold style developed within an idealised thrust sequence: examples are seen in the Southern Uplands.

Palaeozoic sequence of south-west Scotland is fairly low. The prehnite–pumpellyite facies is the maximum developed with many parts of the succession still at diagenetic grade. The clear implication is that thrusting occurred at relatively shallow depths as a thin-skinned tectonic phenomenon. Details of the techniques used to assess metamorphic grade and a discussion of its regional variation are given below.

The thrust deformation was a diachronous process, becoming progressively younger southwards. The NW part of the Lower Palaeozoic outcrop was affected in the late Ordovician and the SE part in the mid-Silurian. The first phase of deformation at the thrust front was accompanied by refolding within the thrust hinterland to accommodate the progressive steepening of the thrust sheets. However, a different factor came into play in the mid-Silurian with the increased importance of sinistral shear. Prior to that time deformation seems to have been more or less orthogonal and early-formed fold hinges generally have only a gentle plunge to NE or SW and an axial planar cleavage. However, from the mid-Silurian onwards, steeply plunging folds with an S-shaped down-plunge profile were superimposed on the thrust hinterland to refold earlier structures and cleavage. Simultaneously the deformation at the thrust front, by then coincident with the SE part of the Southern Uplands, changed in character so that the first folds formed there have variable, locally steeply plunging hinges; cleavage formed at this stage may transect the folds markedly. This diachronous tectonic history, spanning much of the Silurian or more, is the local manifestation of the Caledonian Orogeny, the mountain-building episode which accompanied the destruction of the Iapetus Ocean.

A numbering system has been widely applied to the Southern Uplands fold sequence. The early, thrust-related deformation is deemed D1, accommodation structures in the thrust hinterland are grouped together as D2, and the late sinistral shear is identified as D3. When specifically discussing fold hinges or cleavage planes D may be replaced by F or S respectively. Thus the D1 deformation produced F1 fold hinges and an S1 slaty cleavage. This short-hand will be used in many of the excursion accounts.

During the final stages of deformation a widespread dyke swarm was intruded into the region. Felsites, porphyritic microdiorites and lamprophyres are all present and some have been foliated by the later tectonic episodes. Other dykes are entirely post-tectonic and have been radiometrically dated at about 395–418 Ma (Rock et al., 1986). The climax of igneous activity was reached as deformation ended with the intrusion of the major granitic plutons. These have all been dated radiometrically to within a few million years of 400 Ma (Halliday et al., 1980). Evidence pertaining to the timing of deformation and intrusion is summarised in Figure 4.

Graptolite biostratigraphy: R A Hughes

Graptolites are a long extinct group of tiny colonial animals which formed the greater part of the Ordovician and Silurian oceanic plankton. They are the most useful fossil group in Southern Uplands biostratigraphy. Each graptolite colony was composed of many (over 1000 in some cases) polyp-like animals (zooids) which lived in linked cup-like structures (thecae). These collectively comprised a single skeletal structure, called a rhabdosome, made of a protein-like material. Graptolite rhabdosomes are normally a few centimetres in length, but range from almost microscopic to a metre or so in extreme cases; all are slender and delicate. During Ordovician and Silurian times the graptolites evolved an extraordinary variety of shapes (Figure 5), which may have been adaptations to differing feeding strategies or to life in various parts of the water column. When the graptolites are well preserved, this variety enables today's palaeontologists to distinguish different groups and species, essential to the practice of biostratigraphy.

Graptolites inhabited the waters of the ancient oceans, and many different species co-existed at any one time. After death the graptolites sank to the sea bed. Graptolites today can be extremely abundant in 'hemipelagite' rock sequences, such as the Moffat Shale, formed mainly of very fine-grained sediment. Some Moffat Shale bed-

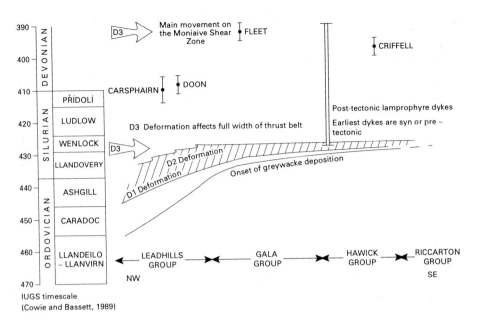

IUGS timescale
(Cowie and Bassett, 1989)

Figure 4 Summary of information used to establish controls on the timing of Caledonian deformation in the Southern Uplands (cf. Barnes et al., 1989, fig. 1)

Ages of post-tectonic plutons (in million years):

Carsphairn:	410 ± 4, Rb-Sr, Thirlwall (1988).
Loch Doon:	408 ± 2, Rb-Sr, Halliday et al. (1980).
Fleet:	392 ± 2, Rb-Sr, Halliday et al. (1980).
Criffell:	397 ± 2, Rb-Sr, Halliday et al. (1980).
Dyke ages (range):	Rb-Sr and K-Ar, Rock et al. (1986b).

ding planes are covered with graptolite remains. In marked contrast, graptolites are generally rare within the thick greywacke sequences, where hemipelagic sedimentation was mostly overwhelmed by coarse-grained sediment from continental sources, transported and deposited by frequent turbidity currents.

The different graptolite species on a Moffat Shale bedding plane constitute a sample of the graptolite population which existed at the time of deposition, and collectively are called an assemblage. Distinct assemblages of graptolite species are unique to individual graptolite zones, each of which represents a small slice of geological time. By calibrating the sequence of Silurian graptolite zones against the radiometric time-scale for the Silurian, we know for example that the duration of some of the Silurian grapto-

lite zones was considerably less than one million years. The graptolites were a rapidly evolving group, especially in the Silurian, and different assemblages of species representing different zones are therefore indicative of different geological time periods.

In the latter half of the last century Charles Lapworth, working in the Moffatdale area of the Southern Uplands (now the type area for the Moffat Shale Group) first recognised that graptolites occur in distinct assemblages, and established the sequence of assemblages and zones which record the evolution of the graptolites through geological time (Figure 5). Lapworth was the first person to demonstrate the use of graptolites as a biostratigraphical tool, and his work has survived the test of time to the extent that his sequence of zones (Lapworth, 1878) remains almost entirely unchanged, and is today used

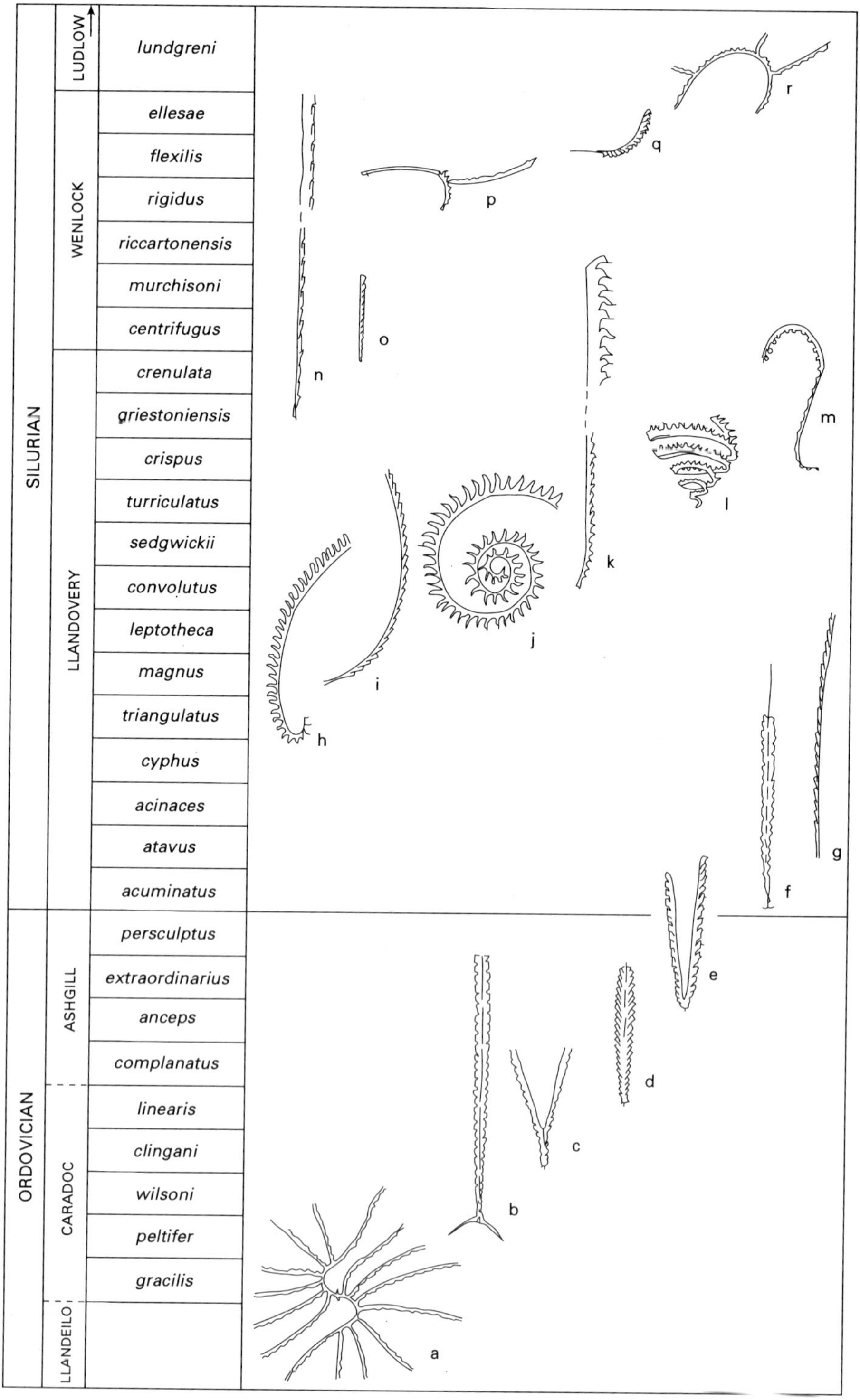
SILURIAN
LUDLOW
WENLOCK
LLANDOVERY
ORDOVICIAN
ASHGILL
CARADOC
LLANDEILO
lundgreni
ellesae
flexilis
rigidus
riccartonensis
murchisoni
centrifugus
crenulata
griestoniensis
crispus
turriculatus
sedgwickii
convolutus
leptotheca
magnus
triangulatus
cyphus
acinaces
atavus
acuminatus
persculptus
extraordinarius
anceps
complanatus
linearis
clingani
wilsoni
peltifer
gracilis
a
b
c
d
e
f
g
h
i
j
k
l
m
n
o
p
q
r

throughout the world. His achievement was extraordinary, and without the tool of graptolite biostratigraphy the recognition of the gross structure of the Southern Uplands as an imbricate thrust stack would have been impossible. It is no exaggeration to state that graptolite biostratigraphy has been and will remain entirely fundamental to solving the great geological complexity of the Southern Uplands. Excursion 18 gives a selection of localities where they can be found. Further information on this fascinating group of animals is given by Palmer and Rickards (1991).

Turbidite sedimentology: M C Akhurst

Exposures of Lower Palaeozoic rocks in south-west Scotland are predominantly of interbedded greywacke, siltstone, mudstone, shale and, more rarely, conglomerate. The term greywacke refers to hard, poorly sorted sandstones containing grains of quartz, feldspar, dark ferromagnesian minerals and rock fragments set in a clay matrix which constitutes more than about 15 per cent of the rock. The sandstone beds may range from a few centimetres to more than 2 m thick. Bedding relationships are consistent:

Figure 5   The sequence of Ordovician and Silurian graptolite biozones present in south-west Scotland, with line-drawings of selected graptolites, arranged in stratigraphical order. The graptolites are approximately × 1, and the species are:

a. *Nemagraptus gracilis* (Hall)
b. *Climacograptus bicornis* (Hall)
c. *Dicranograptus clingani* Carruthers
d. *Orthograptus abbreviatus* Elles & Wood
e. *Dicellograptus anceps* (Nicholson)
f. *Parakidograptus acuminatus* (Nicholson)
g. *Atavograptus atavus* (Jones)
h. *Monograptus triangulatus* (Harkness)
i. *Coronograptus gregarius* (Lapworth)
j. *Monograptus convolutus* (Hisinger)
k. *Monograptus sedgwickii* (Portlock)
l. *Monograptus turriculatus* (Barrande)
m. *Monograptus crispus* Lapworth
n. *Monoclimacis griestoniensis* (Nicol)
o. *Monoclimacis crenulata* (Elles & Wood)
p. *Cyrtograptus rigidus* Tullberg
q. *Monograptus flexilis* Elles
r. *Cyrtograptus lundgreni* Tullberg

the sandstone has a sharp base and grades up into siltstone and shale, reflecting their origin in a single depositional event. Sediment is transported downslope as a turbulent current. As the current slows, first coarse-grained then fine-grained sediment is deposited. The resulting graded bed is called a turbidite and shows a characteristic set of sedimentary structures forming a 'Bouma sequence' (Figure 6) (Bouma, 1962). Turbidity currents can flow very fast; one generated by an earthquake off eastern Canada in 1929 flowed at up to 20 metres/second (about 45 mph). Turbidity currents can erode the sea bed prior to deposition of the coarse-grained sediment. The erosive patterns, preserved as positive casts or 'sole structures' on the base of a turbidite bed, will then give a clear indication of way-up in the sedimentary sequence. Flute casts are distinctive sole structures, deepest and narrowest at the up-current end, which can be used to deduce the flow direction of the turbidity current. Linear groove casts are not quite so useful in this respect; they lie parallel to the current trend but do not show which way it flowed. Loading of sand into the underlying turbidite may also produce sole structures; sand at the base of the bed sinks into the underlying mud to form distinctive bulbous structures called load casts. Tapered 'flames' of mobile mud may penetrate up into the sand between the load casts.

Large volumes of sediment can be carried in suspension within the turbid flow. As current velocity wanes the coarsest sand and pebbles are deposited, followed by progressively finer-grained sand to form a graded bed (Figure 6). Deposition of fine sand and silt follows and is associated with the development firstly of planar lamination and then of ripple cross-lamination, reflecting changes in the flow regime of the current. Bedding in the fine sandstone and siltstone may also be contorted or convoluted where the rapidly deposited sediment was very wet and unstable. The ripple cross-laminated sediment (another indication of way up) grades into finely laminated or homogeneous siltstone and mudstone. These finest-grained sediments, which are darker in colour, accumulated much more slowly. The resulting mudstone or shale beds include both the finest sediment from the turbidity current

12

Figure 6 Divisions within an idealised turbidite bed after Bouma (1962) and Pickering et al. (1989).

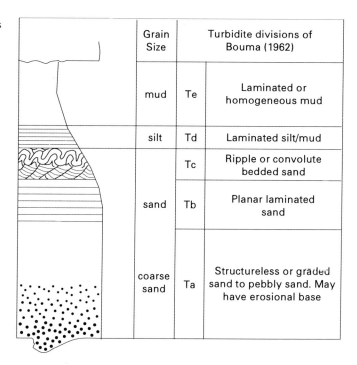

Grain Size		Turbidite divisions of Bouma (1962)
mud	Te	Laminated or homogeneous mud
silt	Td	Laminated silt/mud
sand	Tc	Ripple or convolute bedded sand
sand	Tb	Planar laminated sand
coarse sand	Ta	Structureless or graded sand to pebbly sand. May have erosional base

and hemipelagic deep-sea sediment. The turbidites are predominantly unfossiliferous, although graptolites may be preserved in the finer-grained bed tops, perhaps only as broken pieces. However, if time is available between flows for a hemipelagic interval to develop, the resulting shale bed may carry a rich graptolite fauna.

Generation and flow of turbidity currents and subsequent deposition of turbidite beds, are sudden, catastrophic events. Turbidity currents can be initiated, for example, by collapse of unstable sediments on a submarine slope or by an earthquake shock. The resuspended sediment may be transferred for hundreds of kilometres on to the deep ocean floor. Currents are first funnelled down the continental slope via submarine canyons. Most sediment is then deposited as the current slows at the foot of the slope and spreads out from the confinement of the canyon. Accumulated deposits from many turbidity currents form a fan that has its apex at the canyon mouth (Figure 7). Submarine fans can be very large structures; modern examples are tens to hundreds of kilometres across.

The sediments deposited from a single turbidity current are not of uniform character along the length of the flow. Close to the source the turbidite bed will be dominated by coarse-grained graded sandstone, the lowest of the Bouma divisions (Figure 6), but far away from the source only fine-grained siltstone and mudstone of the higher divisions will occur. The complete Bouma sequence will only be deposited at intermediate positions. Studies of many ancient and modern submarine fan sequences have recognised inner, middle and outer fan divisions (Figure 7). The inner fan, nearest the sediment source, is crossed by a single channel within which turbidite deposition is mostly confined. Fine-grained sediment in suspension is deposited laterally to the channel. Inner fan deposits are, therefore, made up of coarse-grained sandstones and conglomerates forming lenses within a background of laminated mudstone. Down-current, in the middle fan setting, the channel divides and becomes much shallower. Turbidites dominated by the graded and planar-bedded divisions are deposited as more extensive, sheet-like beds. In the outer fan setting turbidity currents

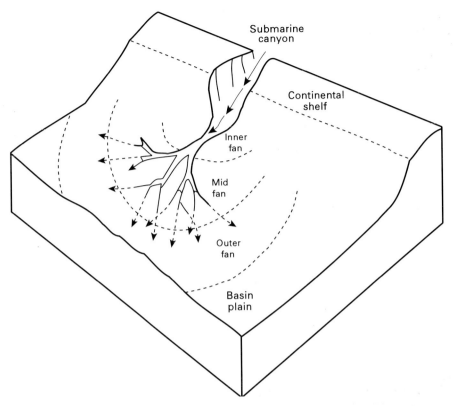

Figure 7 Depositional environments on a submarine fan.

spread out over the fan surface to give laterally extensive beds with complete Bouma sequences. Finally, at locations farthest from the submarine canyon mouth, turbidite units may consist of only laminated siltstone and mudstone. Thus, by noting the style of bedding and sedimentary structures in a sequence of turbidites, it is possible to recognise where on a submarine fan they were deposited.

An extensive review of this remarkable group of sedimentary rocks is given by Pickering et al. (1989). Detailed sedimentological analyses are provided by Nilsen (1978) and Walker and Mutti (1973).

Metamorphism of the Lower Palaeozoic rocks: R J Merriman and B Roberts

The development of the imbricate thrust system of the Southern Uplands was accompanied by regional low-grade metamor-phism. Studies of this metamorphism have used the occurrence of hydrous Ca-Al silicate minerals in greywacke (Oliver and Leggett, 1980) and the white mica (illite) crystallinity of clay mineral assemblages in mudstone, shale and slate (Kemp et al., 1985) to assess the grade of metamorphism. These studies generally show that the prehnite–pumpellyite facies is widely developed in volcaniclastic greywacke and basic volcanic rocks; associated mudstones have white mica crystallinity indices typical of the anchizone. As deformation and metamorphic grade increase, mudstone and shale transform to slate, which commonly shows cleavage subparallel with bedding lamination. The grades detected suggest that across much of the Southern Uplands metamorphic temperatures did not exceed 300°C.

In the SW of the region, and in particular along the Rhins of Galloway, white mica crystallinity studies have been closely linked with the stratigraphy and structure (BGS, 1992a). X-ray diffraction (XRD) analysis was used to determine the Kubler index of white mica crystallinity and the mineralogy of the less than 2 µm fractions of mudstone samples (Merriman and Roberts, 1993). The Kubler index (KI in $\Delta°2\theta$) measures very small changes in the profile of the 10Å XRD peak which occur when authigenic clay micas recrystallise in response to advancing metamorphic grade. Metamorphism ranges from the zone of diagenesis (KI > 0.42) through the anchizone (KI 0.42–0.25) to the epizone (KI < 0.25). Metamorphic maps showing contours of equal crystallinity value (isocrysts) have been generated using Kubler indices (KI) from all mudstone samples and are shown as insets on the BGS solid geology maps of the region (e.g. BGS, 1992a, b, c). The metamorphic maps show that the isocrysts commonly trend subparallel to the traces of the strike-parallel faults. In many places the contours (which coincide with the diagenetic/anchizone and anchizone/epizone boundaries) are discontinuities marking abrupt changes in grade across the tract-bounding faults. There is therefore a close relationship between the imbrication of the succession and the regional metamorphism. Isocrysts which cut across the tract-bounding faults mostly reflect contact overprinting of the regional metamorphism by igneous intrusions. Contact metamorphism typically reaches high-anchizone or epizonal grade and gives isocrysts broadly concentric with igneous outcrops, as seen around the Portencorkrie and Cairngarroch intrusions on the Rhins of Galloway. These concentric isocryst patterns are generally wider than aureoles delineated by recognisable hornfelsing. Such a pattern is also developed around the geophysically delineated but concealed intrusion at Sandhead (Kimbell and Stone, 1992). The concentric patterns developed around the Cairngarroch and Sandhead intrusions extend across the Orlock Bridge Fault, indicating that igneous emplacement occurred after the sinistral strike-slip fault movement proposed by Anderson and Oliver (1986). A similar relationship between metamorphism and fault movement is seen in the aureole of the Cairnsmore of Fleet granite (Merriman et al., 1991).

In relation to the tectonostratigraphy, the distribution of KI values shows distinctive trends of grade rising and falling from north to south through sequentially younger tracts of strata (Merriman and Roberts, 1993, Figure 3; Stone, 1995 Figure 32). For example, on the Rhins of Galloway the oldest strata sampled from the Corsewall Formation (Figure 1) are mostly of late diagenetic grade. To the SE of the Glen App Fault the metamorphic grade increases abruptly into younger Leadhills Group strata so that most samples from the Kirkcolm, Portpatrick and Shinnel formations (Figure 1) are in the mid- or high-anchizone. South of the Orlock Bridge Fault in the Kirkcowan district (BGS, 1992b) the grade intially falls on crossing southwards into Gala 1, but then increases into the Gala 2 tract. Farther south, grade generally falls across sequentially younger tracts so that diagenetic mudstones occur widely in the southern part of the group's outcrop around Port Logan. Grade generally increases abruptly in the Hawick Group (Figure 1) where both slates and interbedded sandstones have a penetrative cleavage.

The pattern of regional metamorphism found in south-west Scotland cannot easily be modelled in terms of a stratigraphical burial pattern whereby grade increases into older strata with increasing thickness of overburden (Roberts et al., 1991). Had the succession initially acquired such a pattern of burial metamorphism and subsequently been imbricated and rotated, older strata would still show higher grades than younger strata, whatever the final structure. The regional pattern in the Ordovician and parts of the Llandovery outcrop is the reverse of that generated by stratigraphical burial, in that grade may increase into younger tracts of strata. Such a pattern indicates that, from time to time, younger strata were buried beneath older strata, and in turn this suggests that the metamorphic pattern was generated by thrust-related tectonism. In the Ordovician outcrop the metamorphic pattern suggests that tracts comprising NW-younging Kirkcolm, Portpatrick and Shinnel formations were sequentially underthrust and buried beneath the older Corsewall

Formation, which formed the upper unit of a thrust stack. It appears that a depth-related pattern of metamorphism was acquired after the strata were steepened, but imbrication continued to modify the pattern after burial. On the Rhins of Galloway, the widespread occurrence of diagenetic grade mudstones and shales in the SE-younging strata of the southernmost Gala Group outcrop is consistent with overthrusting to the upper part of the thrust stack (McCurry and Anderson, 1989). The outcrop of diagenetic zone strata has an abrupt southern termination at a significant metamorphic discontinuity across which grade and probable depth of burial increase sharply into the Hawick Group.

Upper Palaeozoic to Quaternary regional geology: A A McMillan and A D McAdam

Following the Caledonian Orogeny and intrusion of the Galloway granitic plutons, the Southern Upland region was subjected to uplift and erosion. Extension of the crust from late Devonian times led to the development of major sedimentary basins in the Midland Valley to the north and the Northumberland–Solway Trough to the south. Associated north- and NW-trending normal faults, which can be traced through the Southern Uplands, may have been active during early Carboniferous times, perhaps initiated by minor dextral movement on existing faults of Caledonoid (NE) trend (McMillan and Brand, 1995). Small half-graben basins defined by these faults as at Thornhill, Sanquhar and Loch Ryan (Figure 8), preserve a fragmentary record of fluviatile, estuarine and marginal marine sedimentation from Devonian to late Carboniferous times. A subsequent extensional event in early Permian times, generated a short-lived volcanic episode as arid climatic conditions developed and extensive desert dune sandstones and associated breccia fans covered much of the region.

The north Solway coast, effectively the northern margin of the Solway Basin, pro-

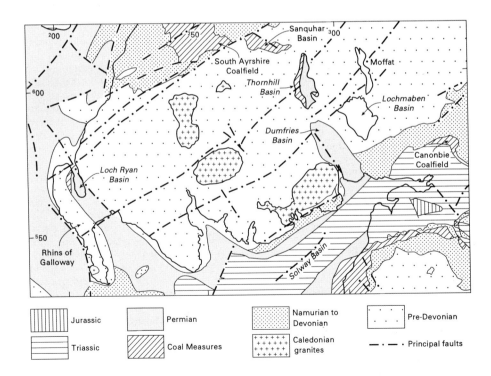

Figure 8   Principal features of Upper Palaeozoic geology in south-west Scotland.

Table 1 Lower Carboniferous stratigraphy correlated along the northern margin of the Solway Basin.

Age		Langholm (after Lumsden et al., 1967)	Kirkbean Glen (after Craig, 1956; BGS, 1993)	Southerness–Borron Point–Hogus Point (after Craig, 1956; BGS, 1993)		Castlehill Point–Gutcher's Isle (after BGS, 1993)
DINANTIAN (LOWER CARBONIFEROUS)	BRIGANTIAN	Upper Liddesdale Group				
	ASBIAN	Lower Liddesdale Group		?		
		Upper Border Group		Arbigland Limestone Formation		
		Glencartholm Volcanic Beds				
	HOLKERIAN	Middle Border Group			Thirlstane Sandstone Member	?
				Powillimount Sandstone Formation		Rascarrel Formation
				Gillfoot Sandstone Formation		
	ARUNDIAN	Harden Beds		Southerness Limestone Formation		
					Syringothyris Limestone	
	CHADIAN	Lower Border Group	Kirkbean Cementstone Formation	?		
	COURCEYAN	Birrenswark Volcanic Formation				
LATE DEVONIAN		Upper Old Red Sandstone				
SILURIAN		Riccarton Group	Hawick Group			Hawick Group

This table does not show relative thickness of different groups, formations and members.

vides the best exposed record of early Carboniferous sedimentary rocks, together with remnants of late Devonian red beds (Table 1). The latter comprise conglomerates and arenites deposited in fans and braided channels under hot, arid conditions. Calcareous palaeosols developed locally (Leeder, 1976). Following deposition of the Devonian strata, short-lived volcanic activity produced the lavas of the Birrenswark Volcanic Formation. The volcanism may be related to the extensional event which formed the Solway Basin (Leeder, 1982, 1988).

The NE-trending North Solway Fault which forms the northern boundary to the

Table 2 Upper Carboniferous and Permian stratigraphy in south-west Scotland.

AGE		THORNHILL BASIN (Permian after Brookfield, 1978)	LANGHOLM (after Lumsden et al., 1967)	DUMFRIES BASIN (after Brookfield, 1978)	BALLANTRAE & LOCH RYAN (after Stone, 1988)
Early Permian		Thornhill Sandstone Durisdeer and Locherben breccias Carron Basalt	'New Red Sandstone' strata (Permian to Triassic)	Locharbriggs Sandstone Doweel Breccia	Corseclays Sandstone Park End and Loch Ryan breccias
Silesian (Late Carboniferous)	Westphalian	Upper Coal Measures		strata not proven	Upper Carboniferous rocks with interbedded basalt at Loch Ryan
		Middle Coal Measures			
		Lower Coal Measures			
	Namurian	Passage Formation	Stainmore Group		

This table does not show relative thickness of different groups, formations and members.

Solway Basin is probably a reactivated Caledonoid structure. Coarse clastic rocks of Dinantian age in the Rerrick (Wall Hill to Rascarrel Bay) and Colvend (Castlehill Point to Portling Bay) outliers provide evidence for periodic syn-sedimentary dip-slip movement on the fault (Deegan, 1973; Ord et al., 1988). Syn-sedimentary deformation of hanging-wall strata increases towards the fault. Cyclicity within alluvial fan deposits of the Rerrick Outlier may be attributed to the interplay between tectonic subsidence and changing sea level. Further away from the margin, Lower to Upper Border Group strata (Courceyan to Asbian, Table 1) of the Kirkbean-Southerness area (Craig, 1956) and at Langholm (Lumsden et al., 1967) also show evidence of changing sea level. Cyclically interbedded mudstones, siltstones and sandstones with thin cementstones and thin coals with seatearths reflect changing depositional environments in low-lying coastal areas. Locally, as at Powillimount on the Solway coast, there is convincing evidence in the Thirlstane Sandstone Member of syn-sedimentary seismic activity (Ord et al., 1988).

Marine inundations are also recorded at higher stratigraphical levels in the Lower and Upper Liddesdale groups (Asbian to Brigantian) at Kelhead near Annan, and at Langholm and Thornhill. At Thornhill, the Closeburn Limestone Formation records a marginal and probably quite short-lived marine incursion. These strata represent the earliest record of a breach through the Southern Uplands linking the Solway Basin to Sanquhar and the Midland Valley. Later Carboniferous sedimentation in the Southern Uplands was probably also restricted, particularly during Namurian times, but an attenuated Coal Measures sequence at Thornhill (Table 2) can be correlated with those at Canonbie and Sanquhar. At Thornhill, late-Carboniferous to Permo-Triassic oxidation has resulted in reddening of strata and replacement of coal. A fragmentary Upper Carboniferous sequence is also present at Loch Ryan. There has long been speculation on the extent of late Carboniferous to Permian sedimentation over the Southern Uplands. Pringle and Richey (1931) opined that it was once much more extensive and considered that the present distribution of strata could be attributed to post-Carboniferous downfaulting.

Crustal shortening and basin inversion took place in the Solway Basin during late

Carboniferous times (Leeder and McMahon, 1988) resulting in the folding of Lower Carboniferous strata. The effects of deformation are particularly well seen on the Southerness coast where there are many examples of NE-orientated anticline–syncline fold pairs, structures probably controlled by inheritance of the Caledonian tectonic grain. Folding attributed to late Carboniferous inversion is also well displayed in the Liddel Water at Langholm.

Renewed extension activated N- and NW-trending normal faults during early Permian times to rejuvenate the Carboniferous basins of the Southern Uplands. At the same time the climate changed from tropical or semitropical to arid, and desert deposits of alluvial fans and aeolian dunes accumulated at Loch Ryan, Thornhill, Dumfries, Lochmaben and Moffat (Brookfield, 1978; 1980) (Table 2). In the Dumfries Basin, more than 1000 m of aeolian sandstones (Locharbriggs Sandstone Formation) and flash-flood breccias (Doweel Breccia Formation) conceal any remnant of Carboniferous strata. The extensive accumulation of breccia fan deposits on the western side of this basin may be attributed to synsedimentary activity on NW-trending faults, enhanced by relative uplift of the low-density crustal block of the Criffell granodiorite pluton (Bott and Masson-Smith, 1960). Evidence of a brief episode of volcanic activity associated with extension is seen at Loch Ryan, Thornhill and Lochmaben, as well as at Mauchline farther north in the Midland Valley. At Thornhill, this episode is represented by the Carron Basalt Formation which is succeeded by a series of fan breccias of the Durisdeer Formation and Locherben Formation, passing up into aeolian desert dune deposits of the Thornhill Sandstone Formation.

There are no strata preserved to record the geological history of the region between the Triassic and the Quaternary. The only rocks from this interval are Tertiary dykes, part of the swarms associated with igneous centres in Arran and Mull and thought to be about 55–60 million years old (Harrison et al., 1987; Hitchen and Ritchie, 1993).

During the last two million years Scotland has been repeatedly covered by ice sheets, which formed during glacial episodes and disappeared during periods of milder climate. Clear evidence is only preserved of the latest (Late Devensian) glaciation when ice accumulated on high ground in central Galloway and radiated out towards the lower ground. This merged with ice from the Highlands, which flowed down the Firth of Clyde and periodically encroached onto the Rhins of Galloway. The ice ground down the rocks, preferentially eroding softer lithologies, leaving striations on ice-smoothed rock surfaces, crag-and-tail features and oval drumlins as evidence of ice-flow direction. Particularly fine drumlin fields were developed in the south of Wigtownshire and Kirkcudbrightshire.

Glacial tills, the ground moraine of the ice sheet, blanket much of the lower ground. The colour and composition of the tills reflects the local rock type so that grey tills are common in the areas of greywacke outcrop whereas red sandy tills characterise the Permian basins. Marine shells are found in some of the tills deposited from Highland ice on the Rhins of Galloway. This suggests that the ice sheets scoured the sea floor of the Firth of Clyde.

Some 15 000 years ago the ice sheets began to melt. The higher hills became free of ice while glaciers still filled valleys. Meltwater from the ice cut channels, many now left as dry valleys, and deposited sand and gravel as eskers and kames and as raised beaches along the coast. Rivers have continued this process, depositing alluvial clay, silt, sand and gravel in their floodplains. However, the drainage pattern has been fundamentally influenced by the underlying

Figure 9 A selection of characteristic Carboniferous fossils.

a. *Latiproductus latissimus* (Sowerby) × 1.
b, c. *Syringothyris cuspidata* (Sowerby) × ¹/₂, dorsal valve and posterior view.
d, e. *Lithostrotion* sp. × ¹/₂ with cross-section × 1.
f. *Siphonodendron junceum* (Fleming) × 1
g. *Schellwienella* × 1, dorsal view.
h. *Prothyris* sp. × 3
i. *Gigantoproductus giganteus* (Sowerby) × ¹/₂

Illustrations b, d, e, g, h and i are reproduced by permission of the Natural History Museum, London.

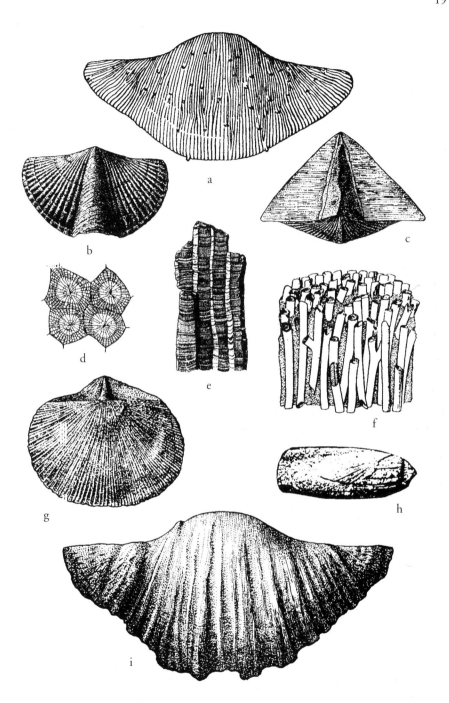

a

b

c

d

e

f

g

h

i

geology. The main river valleys follow the trend of the Upper Palaeozoic basins, the softer rocks of which were preferentially eroded by the ice.

Carboniferous palaeontology: P J Brand

Carboniferous faunas (Figure 9) reflect the changing environments which affected south-west Scotland. Faunas in the Lower Border Group, for example, are of low diversity, the bivalve *Modiolus latus* being the dominant form. It appears to have flourished in restricted environments, possibly saline, such as lagoons which had only limited access to the sea and periodically dried up. The algal limestones which are a feature of the transition between the Lower and Middle Border groups are indicators of clear waters, no deeper than the photic (daylight) zone with limited access to marine conditions. Here the colonies could grow to large size. An exception to this restricted regime was the marine incursion represented by the Harden Beds of the Langholm area, with probable correlatives at Southerness and Orroland. At this horizon *Syringothyris cuspidata*, a distinctive spiriferoid brachiopod, and several species of productoid make their earliest appearance in the area. Current and wave action has disturbed and broken up the larger shells to some extent. Peculiar conditions prevailed during the deposition of the Glencartholm Volcanic Beds and these led to the preservation of a varied biota including numerous species of shrimps and fish. These comprised part of an offshore marine community periodically overwhelmed and buried by mud. Also present are rare pectinaceans and other marine bivalves a few of which appear to have been preserved in the bottom mud where they actually lived.

The faunas of the overlying Carlyle Beds at Langholm and in the corresponding beds at Southerness are much more varied, illustrating features associated with a habitat in soft bottom mud. Thus *Megachonetes papilionaceus* with its wide flat shell was able to lie on the mud without sinking, and the species of *Prothyris* were able to live partially buried in these conditions. Some horizons are composed of materials which formed a harder substrate and colonies of *Lithostrotion* were able to establish themselves on these. However, current or wave action was sufficient to disturb the colonies from their growth positions, at least in the Southerness area.

The thick limestones of the late Dinantian Upper Liddesdale Group (as at Penton Linns) contain species of *Gigantoproductus*, which could have lived partially buried in the bottom sediment. Their thick shells, however, required an abundant carbonate supply, and this had a limiting effect on their distribution. Other brachiopods and the abundance of colonial corals, species of *Siphonodendron*, point to the availability of an abundant food supply, plenty of current movement and a low mud content in the water.

In the Namurian, conditions altered following the deposition of the Blae Pot Limestone and its correlatives resulting in the formation of a coal-bearing sandy sequence. In these beds rhynchonellids and *Schellwienella,* an orthotetoid, form the principal elements of the brachiopod fauna. They were presumably able to withstand increased current velocity and to utilise the different substrate. Marine incursions in the form of the Archerbeck Ochre bed and higher horizons contain examples of the brachiopod *Latiproductus latissimus*, the fine spines of which provided support on the calcareous muds which formed the sea bed where they lived.

In the Thornhill Basin, Coal Measures of Westphalian age occur. Mudstones and siltstones with varied nonmarine bivalve faunas form distinct horizons. Some of the valves of the shells lie oblique to the bedding of the strata, so may occupy positions of growth. The Westphalian 'mussels' may have lived in fresh water, though the actual salinity is unknown. What is clear, however, is that during the deposition of the beds containing these fossils there was no direct connection with the sea.

Few, if any, of the fossils that may be found are stratigraphically significant as individuals, but assemblages of forms can be used to provide a faunal framework for the subdivision of the Carboniferous rocks of the region.

Excursion 1

LANGHOLM AND CANONBIE:
the evolution of a sedimentary basin

OS 1:50 000 sheets 79 Hawick & Eskdale,
85 Carlisle & The Solway Firth
BGS 1:63 360 sheets 10 E Ecclefechan,
11 Langholm
Route map: Figure 10

Main points of interest Silurian turbidite sedimentology, Caledonian folding, the Permo-Carboniferous stratigraphy and evolution of the Northumberland Trough, Carboniferous lavas.

Logistics This excursion will look at geological outcrops over a relatively wide area so is best done in a full day by car, working upwards through the geological succession. Localities 1 and 2 are right by the road, but the rest include stream or river sections where wellington boots will be needed if the sections are to be examined closely.

Introduction Langholm lies on the north margin of a Permo-Carboniferous sedimentary basin, the Northumberland Trough. The objective of this excursion is to look at the rocks filling the basin, to determine their characteristics and the environment in which they formed, and to piece these observations together into a model for the evolution of the northern margin of the Northumberland Trough through time. The Northumberland Trough contains rocks which range in age from early Carboniferous to Permian (Tables 1 and 2); they were deposited under changing environmental conditions which started as a shallow tropical sea and ended as a desert. The trough itself resulted from the stretching and down-faulting of sedimentary rocks of Silurian age, which had already been extensively folded and faulted during the Caledonian Orogeny. The range of rocks of differing lithology and age makes Langholm an exciting area in which to investigate how a sedimentary basin starts, how it evolves and how sediments fill it through time. The area is described in detail by Lumsden et al. (1967).

1 Peden's View Quarry: Hawick Group greywackes

From Langholm turn NW off the A7 and follow the B709 up the valley of the River Esk. Peden's View Quarry [NY 345 862] is 5 km from Langholm on the right.

The rocks here belong to the Hawick Group (Carghidown Formation) of Wenlock age and form part of the old basement of the Northumberland Trough. Beds of greywacke are dominant, a poorly sorted and immature sandstone, interbedded with shales. They were deposited by turbidity currents which flowed across the sea bed, mostly from the NE along the axis of the Silurian sedimentary basin. Each bed of greywacke represents an event when a turbidity current, charged with sediment, deposited its load. The base of the greywacke bed is generally coarse grained but as the current slackened progressively finer sediment was deposited (see Figure 6) to produce graded bedding. The effects of a turbidity current on the soft, fine-grained sediment deposited during a previous flow can be seen in the erosional sedimentary structures. In Peden's View Quarry large bedding planes are exposed along which groove casts are seen to have bifurcated, and grooves within grooves have developed. These features give a real impression of the direction of flow of the turbidity current and some idea of its erosive power. Prod marks can also be seen. These result when debris carried in the current scores the underlying unconsolidated mud before being plucked back into the current. Load casts can also be seen where the denser greywacke, once deposited, has sunk into the soft mud below. Ripple marks are less common but may also be seen here.

These sedimentary structures are useful in determining the environment of deposition but they can also tell which way up the strata are resting. From the steeply inclined orientation of the bedding planes

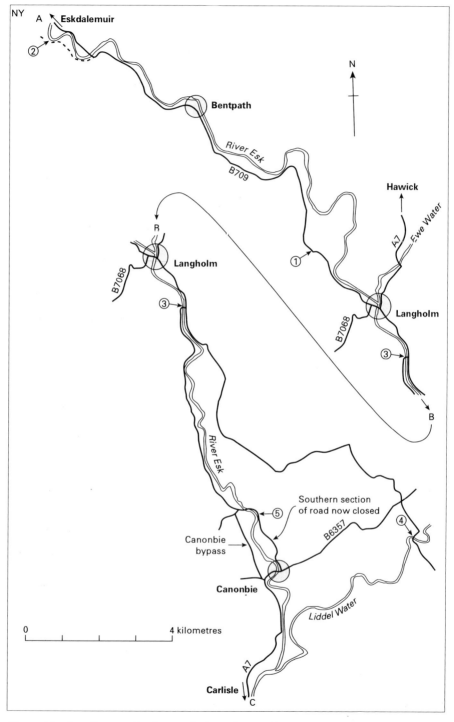

Figure 10   Locality map for the Langholm and Canonbie excursion.

it is clear that the strata have been compressed and folded, but to determine the nature of the folding in terms of anticlines or synclines it is necessary to know the way up of the strata. Groove casts, prod marks and load casts are features only found on the *bottom* of a greywacke bed. Using this knowledge it can be seen that the beds here are upside down, with the beds getting younger downwards. This conclusion may be tested by looking for other sedimentary structures: graded bedding and ripple marking should confirm it.

The rocks have been folded and the orientation of the bedding here can be determined by measuring the dip and strike of the bedding planes. However, other planar surfaces are also present in these rocks. The process of folding has produced new platy minerals which have grown with the plates perpendicular to the principal direction of stress. These planes are cleavage planes and they are often orientated approximately parallel to the axial plane of the folds. Measuring the orientation (dip and strike) of the cleavage plane thus allows you also to determine the orientation of the axial plane of the folds. The next locality will develop this concept further.

2 White Birren Quarry: folding in Hawick Group greywacke

Continue NW on the B709 through Bentpath. About 3.5 km beyond Bentpath the B709 turns abruptly right to cross the River Esk. Immediately before the bridge, a minor road continues straight on towards Lockerbie. Follow this for a short distance; White Birren Quarry [274 918] is a small disused quarry by the roadside on the left. Fine-grained greywackes are interbedded with thin beds of red mudstone. The strata are part of the Hawick Group (Carghidown Formation) as at Locality 1, but here show tight folds with subhorizontal hinges. The orientation of these hinge lines and that of the axial planes of the folds, particularly the smaller ones, can be measured using a compass clinometer. Slaty cleavage has formed by the growth of new platy minerals parallel to the axial plane of the folds. The orientation of the cleavage planes can again be measured and these data compared with

the orientations of the axial planes of the folds. Both the axial planes and the cleavage surfaces dip steeply to the SE. In the SE of the quarry (left as you view the rock face) the folds are fairly open but on the NW side become tight to isoclinal. Sedimentary structures are abundant and flute casts are particularly well developed on the bases of thicker greywacke beds. They confirm the direction of younging on the fold limbs.

The quarry also shows an example of an igneous intrusion, a dolerite dyke. This is a dark coloured rock, rich in ferromagnesian minerals (usually pyroxene) and appears to be highly altered. The dyke cuts across the folded bedding of the sedimentary strata and is therefore younger than these rocks; it is probably of early Devonian age. The NW side of the dyke is marked by a strike-parallel fault with slickensided surfaces at the dyke margin. The absence of red mudstone interbeds from the strata to the SE of the dyke suggests that movement on the fault was at least several metres. The geological features to be seen in the quarry are summarised in the sketch cross-section, Figure 11.

3 Skipper's Bridge: Birrenswark lavas

Return to Langholm and head south on the A7 for 3 km. At Skipper's Bridge continue south on to the B6318 immediately before the A7 turns right on to the bridge. Park on the roadside [371 833]. Access to the rocks is by a gate on the west side of the bridge. The section can be examined for about 1.5 km downstream from the bridge. **Extreme care should be taken if the river is in flood.**

The Birrenswark lavas can be seen on the riverside at Skipper's Bridge. The main lava lithology is olivine-rich microporphyritic basalt, with olivines or pyroxenes less than 2 mm in size. The lavas are rarely fresh and often the olivine or pyroxene is replaced by reddish brown iron oxides. The upper parts of individual lava flows are commonly amygdaloidal, with former gas bubbles in the lava now filled by secondary minerals, usually calcite. The thickness of lavas here is at least 50 m. At Skipper's Pool [3703 8328], sedimentary rocks can be seen

24

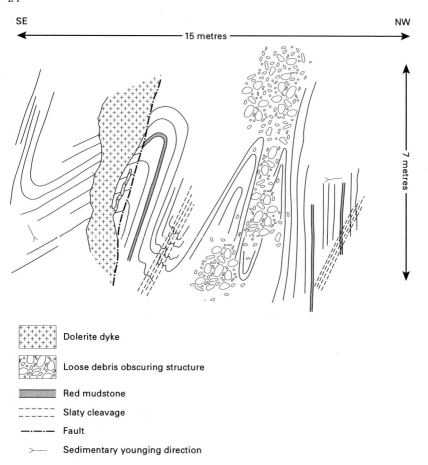

SE ◄──────── 15 metres ────────► NW

7 metres

⊞	Dolerite dyke
▥	Loose debris obscuring structure
▨	Red mudstone
- - - - -	Slaty cleavage
—·—·—	Fault
>—	Sedimentary younging direction

Figure 11 Tight, gently plunging folds exposed in the SW face of White Birren Quarry (Locality 2). After Gallagher et al. (1983).

interbedded with the basaltic lavas. These are iron-rich, water-laid deposits formed by reworking the weathered rubbly tops of the lavas. Angular blocks of basalt, probably locally derived, can also be seen in these strata.

This volcanic episode marks a period of crustal extension and the initiation of the Northumberland Trough. Extension of this sort produces rifting, where normal faults, principally at the basin margins, move to form a graben structure. Crustal thinning associated with these processes results in increased heat flow and the generation of basaltic magmas.

4 Liddel Water: Upper Liddesdale Group, Penton Anticline

From Skipper's Bridge, continue on the B6318 south for 18 km until the Liddel Water is reached at Penton Bridge [433 775]. Cars can be parked in the small car park by the bridge and access to the downstream section is by a footpath along the northern bank of the river. The section in Liddel Water at Penton Linns demonstrates a sequence of changing environments in the Upper Liddesdale Group of Carboniferous (Brigantian) age. The sequence and the structure are both best examined in the section downstream from Penton Bridge. The oldest rocks occur in the core of the prominent Penton Anticline.

On the east limb of the anticline a succession can be followed upwards from the Penton Limestone, found in the core of the anticline, to the Bridge Limestone, found close to the foundations of Penton Bridge. The sequence of lithologies on the west limb of the fold is shown in graphical form in Figure 12, and a brief description of the sequence is given below.

Section in the Liddel Water at Penton Linns

	Thickness (m)
Upper Liddesdale Group	
sandstone	7.32
siltstone	1.83
silty mudstone with ironstone nodules	4.58
mudstone, calcareous	0.61
Harelawhill Limestone	
limestone with beds of calcareous mudstone; beds of chert near top	9.59
Coal	0.18
sandstone, rooty	3.74
siltstone, coaly streak at base	0.30
sandstone, rooty	0.38
Gastropod Limestone	
limestone with thin beds of calcareous mudstone	5.13
mudstone	1.42
sandstone with coal fragments	0.13
Coal	0.51
sandstone, rooty	3.20
Coal	0.08
sandstone with beds of seatearth and siltstone	3.20
mudstone	0.31
Coal	0.13
seatearth	0.64
mudstone, calcareous at base	1.66
limestone, red and irony at top	1.22
sandstone and siltstone, flaggy	3.69
mudstone with ironstone nodules, calcareous at base	7.07
Tombstone Limestone	
limestone with thin beds of calcareous mudstone, argillaceous limestone at base	4.22
Coal	0.20
seatearth, pale grey and black	0.76
Coal	0.08

sandstone	1.73
mudstone and siltstone with ironstone nodule	2.98
Linns Limestone	
limestone, red, irony and nodular at top, sandy at base	4.30
Rhynchonellid Sandstone	
sandstone, rooty	0.81
sandstone and siltstone, thinly bedded	2.98
mudstone	0.92
sandstone, calcareous, rooty	0.76
Coal	0.05
seatclay	0.69
sandstone with thin beds of seatearth, rooty throughout	1.42
sandstone with thin beds of siltstone	8.47
mudstone, calcareous, with ironstone nodules	1.98
Bridge Limestone	
limestone with thin beds of calcareous mudstone	3.66
mudstone, calcareous, with thin beds of limestone	1.53
Coal	0.08
sandstone, rooty at top	4.07
sandstone, silty, with beds of siltstone and coarser sandstone	6.25
mudstone, silty, with beds of irony siltstone	0.92
mudstone with ironstone nodules	1.68
Penton Limestone	
limestone with calcareous mudstone beds	6.69

The graphic log shows a sequence of marine limestones interbedded with clastic strata which commonly coarsen upwards from mudstone to sandstone, with seatearth and coal at the top. The pattern is repeated many times, each unit being termed a cyclothem. The graphic log also shows that the change from mudstone to sandstone is not always steady; there are oscillations between mudstone, siltstone and sandstone but the overall upward-coarsening pattern is maintained. The lithological variation in this sequence can be interpreted in terms of cycles of changing depositional environment.

The limestones were deposited in a shallow-marine environment and are made up of organic fragments, some large and recognisable and others broken down to fine-grained carbonate sediment. Large productoid brachiopods, *Gigantoproductus* sp., and large solitary corals are common in the

Figure 12 The Carboniferous section in the Liddel Water at Penton Linns (Locality 4).

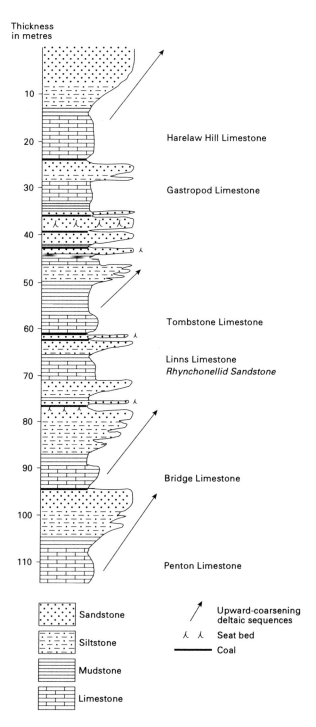

Thickness in metres

Harelaw Hill Limestone

Gastropod Limestone

Tombstone Limestone

Linns Limestone
Rhynchonellid Sandstone

Bridge Limestone

Penton Limestone

- Sandstone
- Siltstone
- Mudstone
- Limestone

- Upward-coarsening deltaic sequences
- Seat bed
- Coal

Penton Limestone. Near the top of this bed occur algal patches, *Girvanella,* and a trace fossil, *Zoophycos cauda-galli.* The Bridge Limestone is only sparsely fossiliferous but near the top *Zoophycos cauda-galli* occurs together with large crinoid stems and the colonial coral *Siphonodendron pauciradiale.* The Linns Limestone is sandy at its base and has the characteristic ochreous colour of a dolomitic limestone. The top of the Linns Limestone is red, iron-rich and knobbly. The Tombstone Limestone is poorly fossiliferous but the mudstone immediately above contains a diverse marine fauna including corals, brachiopods, gastropods, bivalves and goniatites. In the Gastropod Limestone at Loup Pool [430 774] crinoid columnals, brachiopods, gastropods, bivalves and trilobite fragments can be found. The Harelawhill Limestone crops out on the prominent tree-covered island. This limestone is sparsely fossiliferous but crinoid columnals and corals including *Siphonodendron junceum* are present; near the top are several beds of nodular chert.

The faunas in the limestones and overlying mudstones indicate that the depositional environment of these strata was a warm, shallow sea, probably close to a shoreline supplying fine-grained detritus. The presence of corals is a good indicator of shallow-water conditions, as these organisms require sunlight to survive.

In many cyclothems a coal seam rests on the sandstone. Examination of the top of the sandstone units commonly reveals the presence of roots, either as the thicker root stalk, *Stigmaria,* or as fine hair roots. Prominent black roots are present in the sandstones at the top of the clastic sequence above the Linns Limestone. Here the internal structure of the sandstone has been destroyed and a hard massive rock, a ganister, has been formed. Roots are present beneath all the coals and, where these penetrate into fine-grained strata, the original bedding is obliterated, alteration of the minerals takes place and seatclay is formed. These rooty beds are the fossilised remnants of the soil on which the coal-forming plants grew and, together with the coal, indicate a terrestrial swamp environment.

The pattern of coarsening-upwards sedimentation shows how the change from marine conditions with deposition of limestone, to terrestrial conditions with accumulation of coal, took place. Broadly speaking, the mudstones were deposited in front of an advancing delta where the water was still mostly marine, the lower siltstones and sandstones were deposited on the delta front as it prograded into the marine environment, and the higher ones were deposited with coals and seatclays in the fluvial and swamp environments of the delta top. A return to a marine environment and the deposition of limestone comes about by a combination of delta switching, basin subsidence, and worldwide changes in sea level. This cyclical pattern is typical of sedimentation in the Lower Carboniferous over much of northern Britain.

On the western limb of the anticline, the sequence of strata stops abruptly downstream against a fault downthrowing to the south and bringing the younger Catsbit Limestone (earliest Namurian) to outcrop in the bed of the river. The fault trend is approximately east–west, at right angles to the trend of the fold axis, and the strata south of the fault dip gently to the SW. If the sense of movement on the fault were vertical then the axial plane of the Penton Anticline should still be discernable on the south side of the fault. As it is not, it must be assumed that there is an element of lateral displacement in addition to downthrow to the south.

5 Gilnockie Bridge: mid-Carboniferous unconformity

Return north from Penton Bridge on the B6318 for 2 km, turn left on to the B6357 and continue to the village of Canonbie. Through Canonbie turn right on to the A7 heading north; note that this is a new bypass replacing the former A7 on the east side of the River Esk. About 4 km north of Canonbie turn right on to the old A7 (now closed) and park at Gilnockie Bridge [385 781]. The section can be best viewed from the south side of the bridge but direct access is via the north bank through the Mill.

At Gilnockie Bridge, Lower Coal Measures strata can be seen resting unconformably on beds of Namurian age (formerly called Millstone Grit Series, now named Stainmore Group). The central pillar of the bridge rests on coarse gritty sandstone beds, gently inclined towards the SE. These are rocks of the Lower Coal Measures. Beneath these strata are medium-grained sandstones of the Stainmore Group dipping at 30° NW. The plane of unconformity which separates the two sequences dips at about 10° to the east and can be traced for about 50 m along the north bank of the river. The unconformity displayed here has also been identified in boreholes in the area. The difference in dip between the beds above and below the unconformity suggests that it represents a period of compression, uplift and erosion during mid-Carboniferous time.

The closure of the old A7 in the area south of Gilnockie Bridge is due to the collapse of old workings in the Lower Coal Measures. Adits into these workings are recorded downstream at Byreburnfoot.

6 Canonbie: Permian to Triassic

From Gilnockie Bridge, return to Canonbie via the new bypass and at its junction with the old A7, turn left, heading north. Continue through the village and, immediately after crossing the bridge over the River Esk, turn right and park at the churchyard [395 763]. Access to the riverbank is by a public footpath.

Walking along the eastern bank of the River Esk affords views of the red sandstones, thought to be of Permian to Triassic age, on the opposite bank between Dead Neuk [3923 7621] and Prior Linn [3927 7615]. Large-scale dune cross-bedding can be seen with individual foresets in the order of 3 m high. Note that the tops of the foresets are truncated by bounding surfaces and each group of foresets represents the migration of an individual sand dune. The nature and significance of these bounding surfaces and the detailed sedimentary structures and grain characteristics of wind-blown sedimentary rocks in general, are described in Excursion 9. For a closer examination of these rocks at Canonbie, the opposite river bank must be accessed at Prior Linn on the A7 at the south edge of the village [394 759]. Like those at Locharbriggs (Excursion 9, locality 1), the sandstones at Canonbie are coarse grained and well sorted with well-rounded 'millet-seed' grains. These characteristics are typical of wind-transported sands.

The red sandstones are the last evidence for the filling of the Northumberland Trough which had become completely terrestrial, with desert conditions prevailing. However, these Permian strata were deposited in basins, like the Dumfries Basin and the Vale of Eden, which are elongated NNW–SSE and opened up in response to a new extensional regime. There is some evidence that this transition was preceded by a tectonic inversion, probably towards the end of the Carboniferous, when compression of the strata of the Northumberland Trough took place prior to the extension which established the new Permian basins.

S K Monro

Excursion 2

THORNHILL:
a small Permo-Carboniferous basin

*OS 1:50 000 Sheet 78 Nithsdale &
Annandale
BGS 1:50 000 sheets 9E Thornhill,
15E Leadhills
Route map: Figure 13*

Main points of interest Permian and
Carboniferous stratigraphy; desert sand-
stones and breccias; Coal Measures and
Lower Carboniferous strata; sandstones,
siltstones and mudstones; marine fossils;
Permian basalt lavas.

Logistics A whole day should be assigned
to this excursion if all the localities are
visited. Alternatively it may be possible to
combine part of the excursion with some
localities around Dumfries (Excursion 9). A
good starting point is the town of Thornhill
where there are shops and public conveniences. A coach can be driven to all the localities mentioned but some roads are single
track and turning space is limited. Most
localities involve relatively easy walks of
2–3 km on tracks. Locality 4 involves a steep
valley side descent and re-ascent. Wellingtons
or boots are advised since some of the best
exposures are stream sections.

Introduction At Thornhill (Figure 13)
rocks of Permian and Carboniferous age
occupy a fault-bounded basin orientated
north–south and 18 km long (Pringle and
Richey, 1931). Smaller outliers, which once
formed part of a larger basin, are present to
the east. The highest of these (presumed to
be Coal Measures) lies some 350 m above
sea level. The basin forms an important link
between the Solway and Midland Valley
basins (Figure 8). A particularly interesting
transition is seen within the Lower
Carboniferous sequence, where lithological
variation at the northern and southern margins of the Thornhill basin may indicate
differences in sedimentation imposed by
local barriers to marine transgression. Other
interesting features include a recognisable

Coal Measures sequence, comparable with
that in the adjacent Sanquhar Basin to the
north, but thinner and without the coals.
Excellent examples of Permian desert dune
sandstones, basalt lavas and alluvial channel
deposits can also be seen.

1 Park Quarry, Croalchapel: Closeburn Limestone Formation

From Closeburn take the Loch Ettrick road
as far as Croalchapel and park at the
entrance to the old Park Quarry [NX 907
913] (Figure 14). There is room here for
several cars or a coach. The quarry is one of
several in the area which formerly worked
the Closeburn Limestone. Sir James
Kirkpatrick established the Closeburn Lime-
works in 1772 for the purpose of providing
lime for land improvement, and for some
years he had to overcome a widely held prej-
udice that liming was actually bad for the
ground. As described many years later
(1828) by James Stuart Menteath:
'... so general was the opinion of the
injurious consequences of lime laid on the
ground for agricultural purposes, that the
proprietor, in order to introduce its use,
obliged his tenants in their leases, to lime a
certain quantity of land yearly, he
furnishing the lime, and even paying for
the carriage; and the tenants for their parts,
were bound to pay 5s. additional rent for
every 80 measures of lime, the quantity
considered sufficient for an acre.'
Unfortunately the limestones are no
longer visible but the upper part of the
Closeburn Limestone Formation, of Lower
Carboniferous (Brigantian) age, can be
examined in Park Quarry. On accessing the
quarry, **proceed carefully** to the degraded
quarry faces near the remains of the old
water wheel. Note also that **the deep,
steep-sided quarry hole is water-filled so
stay well clear**. The exposed strata comprise thinly bedded micaceous sandstone

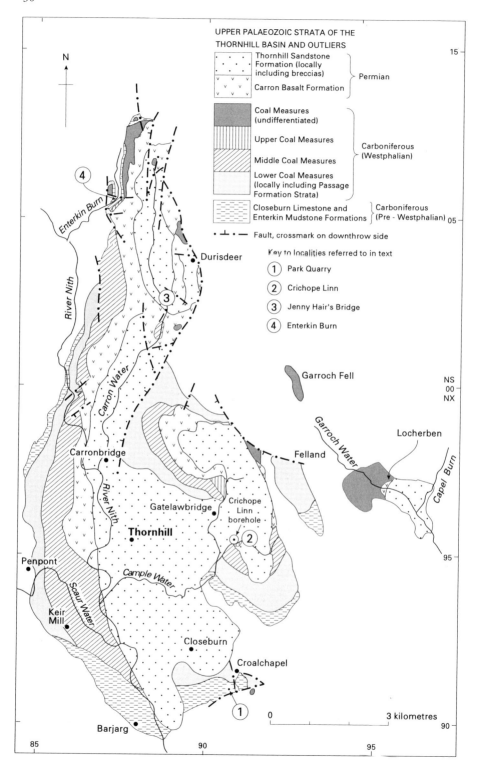

UPPER PALAEOZOIC STRATA OF THE
THORNHILL BASIN AND OUTLIERS

Thornhill Sandstone Formation (locally including breccias) — Permian

Carron Basalt Formation — Permian

Coal Measures (undifferentiated)

Upper Coal Measures — Carboniferous (Westphalian)

Middle Coal Measures

Lower Coal Measures (locally including Passage Formation Strata)

Closeburn Limestone and Enterkin Mudstone Formations — Carboniferous (Pre - Westphalian)

— · — Fault, crossmark on downthrow side

Key to localities referred to in text

① Park Quarry

② Crichope Linn

③ Jenny Hair's Bridge

④ Enterkin Burn

N

River Nith

Enterkin Burn

Durisdeer

Carron Water

Carronbridge

River Nith

Gatelawbridge

Thornhill

Penpont

Cample Water

Scaur Water

Keir Mill

Closeburn

Croalchapel

Barjarg

Garroch Fell

Garroch Water

Locherben

Capel Burn

Felland

Crichope Linn borehole

NS
00
NX

15

05

00

95

90

85   90   95

0   3 kilometres

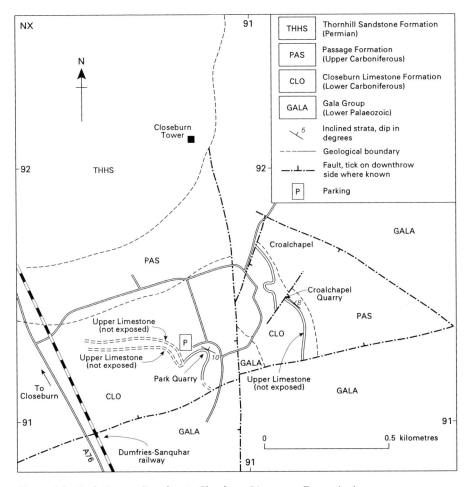

Figure 14 Park Quarry (Locality 1: Closeburn Limestone Formation).

and siltstone overlying red and fossiliferous, micaceous silty mudstone. The strata dip gently east into the quarry face.

The mudstone has yielded the following marine fauna (after Brand, 1990):
brachiopods: *Buxtonia* sp., *Pleuropugnoides* sp., *Productus* sp. *Schellwienella* sp.
bivalves: *Donaldina* sp. *Retispira*?, *Leiopteria thomsoni*, *Modiolus* sp., *Polidevcia attenuata*, *Schizodus* sp., *Wilkingia* cf. *elliptica*

Figure 13 Locality map and outline geology for the Upper Palaeozoic succession of the Thornhill basin.

echinoid: *Archaeocidaris* spines and fragments.

The underlying strata, no longer exposed, include two limestones originally worked. These appear to be present only at the south margin of the Thornhill Basin. The upper limestone was magnesian and poorly fossiliferous; the lower was so compact that it could only be worked with the aid of gunpowder. It was this limestone which yielded spectacular large fossils, several specimens of which are curated in the Royal Museum of Scotland. The fauna includes nautiloids, orthocones, gastropods, brachiopods and corals indicating a marine environment in which the sea was relatively free of terrigenous material. These rocks represent an incursion of the Lower Carboniferous sea across the Southern Uplands and perhaps indicate the first occasion when the Midland Valley was linked by a seaway with the Solway Basin.

The limestone was worked at both Croalchapel and Park Quarries and also at Barjarg and Porterstown, west of the River Nith. When the thickness of overburden became too great for quarry development, underground mining took place. Menteath (1828) reported that at the Closeburn mine:
'... strong pillars of nearly 6 square yards are left standing, as supports for the roof of the mine, which is high enough to admit the miner to stand erect at his work; and between the pillars the space of 30 feet is excavated.'

The remains of the great water wheel can still be seen at Park Quarry. Waggons laden with limestone were raised by the water wheel up an inclined iron railway from the excavation to the top of the kiln. The water was then channelled down a clay bed to a lower level where it fell on another wheel that put in motion the pump which drained the mine and at the same time drove a mill for sawing timber. Menteath noted:
'... The water after these useful applications, is next conveyed away for irrigation.'

Coal had to be brought for the kilns from Sanquhar or further afield for, although the Thornhill Basin contains Coal Measures, no coal is present.

2 Crichope Linn: Coal Measures and Permian strata

Crichope Linn lies 3 km east of Thornhill and about 4 km north of Croalchapel. The Linn is approached by a well-marked path from the narrow road linking Gatelawbridge with Closeburnmill. An area nearby at the back of Newton Quarry [907 955] (Figure 15), one of several old sandstone quarries at Gatelawbridge, serves as a parking place for several cars. It is also possible to take a coach to this locality but note that the roads are narrow and single tracked.

Situated near the eastern margin of the Thornhill Basin, Crichope Linn is a narrow gorge cut by the Crichope Burn in the Thornhill Sandstone Formation of Permian age. The Permian strata rest unconformably upon Coal Measures rocks which are seen downstream of the gorge.

Follow the path upstream on the north bank of Crichope Burn. Several stream sections in Coal Measures strata demonstrate some of the lithological characteristics of the sequence, which is best known from the core of the Crichope Linn Borehole put down by the BGS in 1962 (Davies, 1964; McMillan and Brand, 1995). Biostratigraphical evidence from fossil nonmarine 'mussels' identifies most of the exposed sequence as Middle Coal Measures. The top few metres may be Upper Coal Measures if a *Lingula*-bearing mudstone discovered in a tributary burn is equivalent to the *Aegiranum* Marine Band.

The strata consist of interbedded reddened mudstone, seatearth, siltstone and fine-grained sandstone. The mudstones are reddish purple to lilac with green-grey reduction spots. They contain plant stems, layers of nodular ironstone and occasional ribs of gypsum. Listric surfaces are common. The siltstones are also lilac or greenish grey and are commonly micaceous. They contain sandy laminae and plant fragments. Seatearths are typically mottled lilac, green and red and, despite alteration, contain roots. Former coal seams may now be represented by thin deep red, iron-rich mudstones above the seatearths. The sandstones are mostly greyish white with red staining; they are fine grained, thinly bedded and micaceous with small-scale ripple lamination. The deep weathering which has affected these strata (and possibly caused alteration of original thin coals) may be attributed to circulating groundwaters beneath an arid early Permian land surface (see Bailey, 1926; Mykura, 1960).

Continuing upstream, Permian red sandstone is best seen beside the path leading to the narrow Crichope Linn gorge. The unconformity between Coal Measures and Permian strata is not currently exposed but was proved in the nearby borehole, where the lowest Permian bed was a coarse-grained sandstone 1.4 m thick, with rounded pebbles of quartz and flakes of red mudstone indicating fluviatile origin. This was overlain by brick-red, medium-grained, cross-bedded

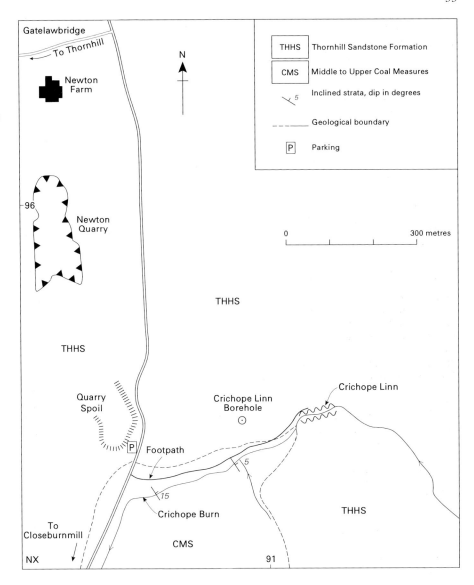

Figure 15   Crichope Linn (Locality 2: Coal Measures and Thornhill Sandstone Formation).

aeolian sandstone. The walls of the 30 m deep gorge are cut in the sandstone; Brookfield (1978, pp.132–134) used this locality as his type section for the Thornhill Sandstone Formation, which he interpreted as a desert dune deposit. The formation is characterised by well-sorted, well-rounded,

fine- to coarse-grained quartz sandstone in tabular to wedge-shaped cross-stratified sets.

Visitors may **proceed with care** further upstream past the spectacular narrow gorge; **the path can be wet and slippery** in places. The gorge has a number of historical associations, in particular with the Covenanters, and was the scene of the famous confrontation between Burley and Morton in Sir Walter Scott's Waverley Novel *Old Mortality*. The theme of Scott's novel was influenced by the career of Robert Paterson (1715–1801), 'Old Mortality', a stonemason and stone carver who held a lease on one of the Gatelawbridge red sandstone quarries which were worked for building stone from the 17th century until after the First World War. Gatelawbridge stone was used extensively both locally and in cities including Glasgow and Edinburgh. Recently Scottish Natural Stones Ltd extracted stone from the same lithological unit in Newton Quarry for use in Edinburgh at the new Financial Centre, Castle Terrace and the Edinburgh Solicitors Property Centre, 81 George Street.

Retrace the path to the Gatelawbridge–Closeburnmill road.

3   Jenny Hair's Bridge, Durisdeer: Permian lavas, breccias and sandstones

Some 7 km north of Thornhill near the north margin of the Thornhill Basin, sections at Jenny Hair's Bridge provide a good

opportunity to see some of the basal Permian sedimentary rocks and lavas. Limited car parking is possible at Jenny Hair's Bridge [NS 886 024] on the road leading from the A702 to Durisdeer (Figure 16). From the bridge a short round trip of 0.5 km downstream along the Carron Water enables the principal lithologies to be examined. This and several other localities are described in a field guide by Brookfield (1981). In this northern part of the basin and in the small outlier of Locherben to the east (Figure 13) the basal Permian strata comprise streamflood breccias interbedded with thin olivine-basalt lava flows of the Carron Basalt Formation. The overlying breccias, fluviatile sandstones and siltstones of the Durisdeer and Locherben Breccia formations (Brookfield, 1978, pp.132–134; 1980, p.191, figs. 5 and 7) are interpreted as sheetflood desert floor deposits. These pass up into aeolian dune sandstones, the Thornhill Sandstone Formation, as seen previously at Locality 2.

Under Jenny Hair's Bridge, when the water is low, it is possible to examine flat-lying coarse- and fine-grained red sandstones with fragments of basalt lava. Sand grain

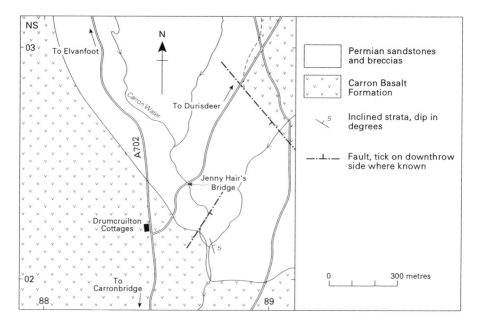

Figure 16   Jenny Hair's Bridge (Locality 3: Permian sandstone, breccia and basalt).

shapes vary from subangular to subrounded; rare rounded grains are present. The strata are interpreted as shallow-water stream channel deposits derived from local sources.

Some 250 m downstream on the east bank, stream channel deposits and interbedded sand dune deposits overlie lavas. The deposits comprise mainly coarse-grained, subangular to angular, red-stained quartz sand interbedded with sandy breccia, and include a few well-rounded grains. They also incorporate large blocks of amygdaloidal basalt which have been picked up locally. A few metres downstream, a small gorge is cut in the underlying amygdaloidal basalt. The lavas were erupted during small-scale rifting which took place in late Carboniferous to early Permian times. Similar volcanic rocks are present in the Permian basins at Mauchline (Mykura, 1967), Ballantrae and Loch Ryan (Stone, 1988) and in the Lochmaben basin.

At the junction of a small tributary, some 50 m farther downstream, there is a well-exposed, thin sequence of gently dipping breccia interbedded with coarse-grained red sandstone. The clasts in the breccia appear to be dominantly angular greywacke with a small proportion of basalt.

Evidence from all these localities indicates a local source for the sediment. At that stage there was only limited input from the desert dune sands which later came to dominate the sequence.

4   Enterkin Burn: early Namurian marine mudstone

Enterkin Burn, about 3 km NNW of Jenny Hair's Bridge, exposes fossiliferous Carboniferous strata resting unconformably on Ordovician turbidites at the northern extremity of the Thornhill Basin. Limited car parking is available at the junction [NS 874 046] between the farm track to Inglestone and the footpath to Wanlockhead (Figure 17). From here visitors should proceed north on the Wanlockhead track for about 0.5 km before descending westwards

down the steep valley side of the Enterkin Burn.

The valley side comprises a scarp of weathered basalt lava flows resting on poorly exposed Coal Measures. The base of the Coal Measures is best seen on the SE bank of the Enterkin Burn [8726 0542] where it is marked by a coarse-grained sandstone with quartz pebbles. This lies unconformably on about 2.5 m of sandstone, which rests on fossiliferous mudstone (Simpson and Richey, 1936). The beds below the unconformity belong to the Enterkin Mudstone Formation, which is exposed in several places in the Enterkin Burn. This formation consists of a thin, gently dipping sequence of purplish red sandstone and seatearth interbedded with deep purple-red, fossiliferous siltstone and mudstone. On biostratigraphical grounds, these strata could be as young as early Namurian, although a Brigantian age is also possible. A few metres downstream, sandstone underlying the fossiliferous beds rests unconformably upon steeply dipping Ordovician greywacke turbidites and shales.

The fossiliferous Enterkin Mudstone Formation beds contain a rich and varied fauna (Brand, 1990) including:
brachiopods: *Buxtonia* sp., *Composita* sp., latissimoid productoids, *Pleuropugnoides* sp., *Productus* sp., *Pugilis* sp., *Retispira decussata*
bivalves: *Aviculopecten* cf. *interstitialis*, *Edmondia* sp., *Leiopteria* cf. *thompsoni*, *Limipecten* sp., *Parallelodon* cf. *semicostatus*, *Pernopecten* sp., *Polidevcia attenuata*, *Schizodus?*, *Wilkingia?*
Nautiloids, orthocones and trilobite pygidia have also been found.

Aspects of the fauna are common to the north margin of the Thornhill Basin and the Sanquhar Basin to the north (Davies, 1970), suggesting that in the late Carboniferous the marine influence of the Midland Valley was being felt as far south as Thornhill.

A A McMillan

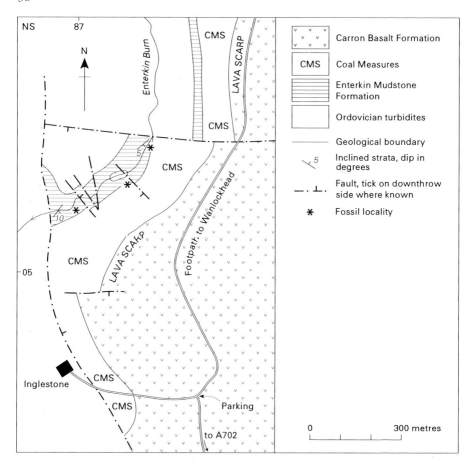

Figure 17   Enterkin Burn (Locality 4: Enterkin Mudstone Formation).

Excursion 3

ROCKCLIFFE to GUTCHER'S ISLE:
Criffell Granodiorite, Silurian and Carboniferous stratigraphy, structure of the Solway Basin margin

OS 1:50 000 Sheet 84 Dumfries, Castle Douglas & surrounding area
BGS 1:50 000 Sheet 5E Dalbeattie
Route map: Figure 18

Main points of interest Criffell–Dalbeattie Granodioritic complex; Ross Formation greywacke turbidites; Lower Palaeozoic structure; North Solway Fault; Lower Carboniferous basin-margin stratigraphy with conglomerates, sandstones, siltstones, marine fossils.

Logistics A large car park suitable for cars and coaches is situated on the left side of the road leading from the A710 to Rockcliffe village, near the top of a short steep hill [NX 851 536]. A short walk from here on the road around Rockcliffe Bay leads to public conveniences at the north side of the bay, near Port Donnel [848 538]. If the excursion between Rockcliffe and Gutcher's Isle (Localities 1–4, Figure 18) is to be attempted as a round trip the total return walking distance is approximately 6 km, partly on coastal paths and partly over shore sections where the rocks can be wet and slippery. From Gutcher's Isle the excursion can be extended using the coastal path to Port o' Warren and Portling Bay (Locality 5). There is no parking space at these places so arrangements should be made for transport to be available at the junction of the single track Port o' Warren road and the A710 (Figure 19). Total walking distance from Gutcher's Isle to the A710 junction is 3 km. Walking boots are the best footwear for the excursion. Although some of the localities can be inspected when the tide is in, the Carboniferous rocks on the shore at Castlehill and Gutcher's Isle can be seen only at low tide.

Introduction During a day's excursion many aspects of Southern Uplands geology can be seen in the well-exposed coast sections around Rockcliffe on the Solway shore. North of Rockcliffe there are good outcrops of the granodiorite margin of the Criffell–Dalbeattie plutonic complex (Phillips, 1956). These lie near the steeply dipping contact between the pluton and hornfelsed Lower Palaeozoic strata of the Ross Formation (Hawick Group), which are Wenlock in age (Figure 2). South of Rockcliffe Bay, a coastal path can be followed across turbidites of the Ross Formation to Castlehill Point. There, one of the finest exposures of the North Solway Fault is to be seen in the cliffs. The fault plane marks the north boundary of the Upper Palaeozoic Solway Basin and, at this locality, Lower Carboniferous sedimentary rocks (Rascarrel Formation) crop out on the shore. They are downthrown against a mass of porphyritic andesite which had intruded Ross Formation strata prior to fault development. On a clear day, Castlehill Point forms a fine viewpoint along the northern margin of the Solway Basin and across to the Lake District hills and St Bees Head.

1 Port Donnel: granodiorite and porphyritic andesite

From the car park walk westwards on the road around Rockcliffe Bay, noting the use of the local grey Criffell granodiorite in some of the stone-built cottages. Large blocks of the rock with fresh surfaces, probably from Dalbeattie, have been used on the foreshore as sea defence. The rock is coarse grained and composed of white plagioclase feldspar accompanied by dark biotite and amphibole. There are numerous dark rounded xenoliths, of a few centimetres diameter; some are hornfelsed country rock (greywacke sandstone) and some are partially assimilated more basic igneous rocks such as quartz diorite. The granodiorite is cut by pale aplite veins, up to 3 cm wide, made of fine-grained quartz, orthoclase and plagioclase feldspar.

The sharp contact between hornfelsed sedimentary rocks and the granodiorite of the Criffell–Dalbeattie Pluton may be seen on the shore at Port Donnel [847 537]. Pods of foliated porphyritic andesite (porphyrite) are present within the sedimentary rocks and crop out on the foreshore in the centre of the bay (Figure 18). The porphyrites form part of a suite of dykes formed during crystallisation stages of the Criffell granodiorite magma (Phillips, 1956).

The granodiorite at Port Donnel is much reddened by haematite staining. It is coarse grained and locally exhibits a foliation picked out by the alignment of plagioclase crystals. Careful inspection of the outcrop reveals small, round dark grey xenoliths of country rock, best seen on wave-washed surfaces. Several small NW-trending faults form shattered and veined zones in the otherwise blocky granodiorite. Small movements on faults of this trend may have occurred intermittently over a long period stretching from early Devonian into Carboniferous times. Prominent joints, produced during the cooling of the pluton, are another feature of the rock.

2 Portobeagle Shore: Ross Formation

Walk back round Rockcliffe Bay and take the signposted coastal track which leads south to Castlehill Point. Between the village and the point there is almost continuous coastal exposure of greywacke turbidites of the Ross Formation. Shore sec-

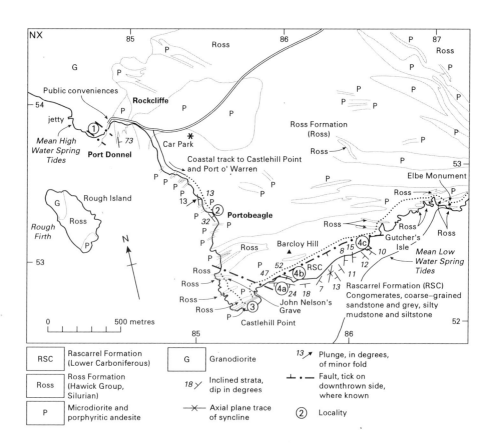

Figure 18 Locality map and outline geology for the Rockcliffe to Gutcher's Isle coastal section.

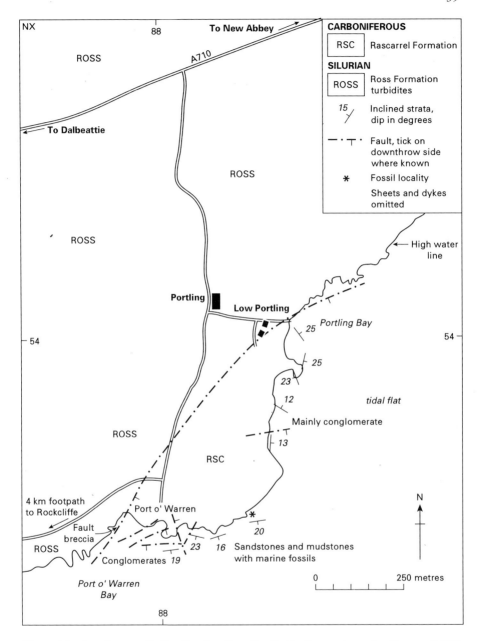

Figure 19   Locality map for Portling Bay (Locality 5). Outline geology after Deegan (1973).

tions at Portobeagle [853 530] are easily accessible.

The greywackes are generally medium to thickly bedded and are calcareous. Typically they are medium- to fine-grained sandstones and are interbedded with grey silty mudstone. Elsewhere, biostratigraphical evidence from graptolites in interbedded shales places the Ross Formation within the early Wenlock (see Excursions 5 and 11).

In contrast to the regional NE strike of Lower Palaeozoic strata, many bedding planes at this locality dip at low angles to the NE. This is because the beds have been folded about fold hinges plunging gently to the NW or SE. There is plenty of evidence for the strata being the right way up; prominent graded bedding and superb examples of ripple crests on upper surfaces of the turbidite units are notable features.

Zones of brecciation and shearing are common, as are numerous east- and NE-trending porphyritic andesite dykes which cut the sedimentary rocks. Some of the dykes are also brecciated.

3 Castlehill Point: viewpoint

From Portobeagle ascend the coastal path past John Nelson's grave, skirting the grazing field to Castlehill Point. Castlehill is the site of an ancient Fort, thought to have been occupied intermittently from about 400 BC until early mediaeval times. Pottery of mediaeval date found here is curated in Dumfries Museum. The viewpoint indicator highlights some of the places visible on a clear day and it is worth spending a few minutes attaching some geology to the scene. To the north, some 5 miles (8 km) away, lies Screel Hill (343 m), composed of hornfelsed, and therefore durable, greywackes. The hill lies within the aureole of the Bengairn quartz diorite intrusion, a part of the Criffell–Dalbeattie complex. To the west, Rough Island, Almorness Point and Heston Isle all comprise Ross Formation strata at the margin of the main Criffell granodiorite. To the NE is the village of Southerness, situated on Lower Carboniferous shallow-marine strata at the northern edge of the Solway Basin. Southwards some 24 miles (38 km) across the Solway Firth, St Bees Head is formed of Triassic St Bees Sandstone. Thirty miles (48 km) away to the SE Skiddaw (930 m), composed of Ordovician Skiddaw Group siltstones, lies south of the Iapetus Suture in the Lower Palaeozoic massif of the English Lake District.

The spectacular cliff immediately to the NE of Castlehill Point is the fault scarp of the North Solway Fault. This forms the abrupt northern boundary of the Upper Palaeozoic Solway Basin, separating Lower Carboniferous strata on the shore from Lower Palaeozoic turbidites intruded by Silurian–Devonian porphyritic andesites in the cliff.

4 Shore section from Castlehill Point to Gutcher's Isle: Rascarrel Formation

Locality 4a Walk down the steep path to the shore and across the shingle to the fault scarp. It represents a faulted unconformity and is formed of a carbonate-cemented fault breccia; the blocks and fragments are mainly of reddened porphyritic andesite, with some greywacke and mudstone. From here, Lower Carboniferous strata are exposed for 1.2 km eastwards along the shore. The section is rocky and can be properly examined only at low tide. The dip is generally to the south and decreases from about 50° within 10 m of the fault to less than 15° over a distance of 30 m seawards. The basal strata are conglomerates, rich in clasts of porphyritic andesite and granite. These pass into arkosic sandstones and dark grey laminated siltstones and mudstones (Deegan, 1973; Craig and Nairn, 1956). Some of the sandstones and finer-grained rocks contain marine fossils. All these beds have been assigned to the Rascarrel Formation (BGS, 1993a). Deegan (1973) interpreted the conglomerates and coarse-grained sandstones as the deposits of alluvial fans which passed laterally and upwards into shallow-marine sediments. Rapid lithological variations of this nature may be attributed to intermittent movement on the basin-margin fault and/or external factors affecting sea level. Some of the steeply dipping strata nearest the fault contain liquefaction structures and extensional faults interpreted by Ord et al. (1988) as the effects of seismicity on unlithified or semi-lithified sandstones.

Locality 4b On the shore between Barcloy Hill and Gutcher's Isle, at the east end of the Carboniferous outcrop, there are a number of fossiliferous horizons. In the intertidal zone [860 525] on the east limb of a gently NNE-plunging syncline, dark grey micaceous silty mudstones and siltstones have yielded a marine fauna including the bryozoan *Fenestella*, gastropods and crinoid columnals. The strata are locally full of terrestrial plant remains testifying to the presence of a well-vegetated land surface nearby. There is also evidence of extensive bioturbation, with *Chondrites* burrows particularly plentiful.

At the east end of the sandy bay at Gutcher's Isle [863 526], the faulted margin of the Carboniferous strata extends offshore. Here, Craig and Nairn (1956, p.252) recorded a carbonate-cemented fault breccia with fragments of porphyritic andesite, greywacke and mudstone, overlain by arkosic conglomerate fining upwards into a sequence of interbedded sandstones and black mudstones. The faunas from two of the sandstone horizons comprise the brachiopod *Punctospirifer scabricosta*, bivalves including *Modiola megaloba* and *Myalina* cf. *redesdalensis*, and other molluscs. Macrofossil evidence from these and other small outliers of the Rascarrel Formation is rather equivocal but suggests that the rocks equate with the Powillimount Sandstone Formation (Table 1) of the Southerness–Borron Point area (Excursion 10).

5 Portling Bay: Rascarrel Formation

The excursion can be completed at Gutcher's Isle and the route retraced to Rockcliffe, using the coastal path around the south side of Barcloy Hill. However, the excursion may be extended eastwards via the coastal path which eventually leads to Port o' Warren (Figure 19). Care should be taken when traversing this part of the coast; in places the path runs close to vertical cliffs. Those wishing to walk the coastal path should arrange for transport to meet them at the junction of the single track Port o' Warren road and the A710. No parking is available at Port o' Warren or Portling. Walking distance from Gutcher's Isle to the A710 junction is 3 km.

Seaward of the path are good exposures of Ross Formation turbidites which have been intruded by dykes and irregular lenticular bodies of porphyritic andesite; the petrography of these was described by King (1937). Good exposures can be found near the Elbe Monument [8684 5276] (Figure 18). The turbidites are locally brecciated. A thin veneer of green secondary copper minerals coats many of the joint surfaces.

Walk to Port o' Warren and take the narrow road to Portling. If time and tide permit, the shore section at Portling Bay, accessed by the lane leading from Portling to Low Portling, is worth a visit. Strata of the Rascarrel Formation are exposed between Portling Bay and Port o' Warren Bay. The strata were described by Deegan (1973). As in the Castlehill Point–Gutcher's Isle section, a lower sequence of conglomeratic alluvial fan deposits passes up into fossiliferous dark grey shales and sandstones. Thin limestones, cornstones and cementstones are also present. Craig and Nairn (1956) recorded the following marine fauna, dominated by nautiloids, from a shale near the top of the sequence (position shown by asterisk on Figure 19): *Lithophaga* cf. *lingualis* (bivalve), nauticoid gastropod, *Cycloceras* and *Loxoceras*? (nautiloids), *Spirorbis* (worm) and fish remains. Lower in the sequence thin impure limestones within a 9 m-thick arkose have yielded the calcareous blue-green alga *Bevocastria*, bellerophontid gastropods and ostracods.

A A McMillan

Excursion 4

SHAWHEAD, CROCKETFORD:
Gala and Hawick groups, sculptures and monuments

OS 1:50 000 Sheet 84 Dumfries, Castle Douglas & surrounding area
BGS 1:50 000 Sheet 9E Thornhill
Route map: Figure 20

Main points of interest This excursion considers the tract-defining fault between the Gala and Hawick groups and the lithologies to either side. Localities visited allow comparisons to be made between the Gala Group and Hawick Group turbidites, which contrast greatly in their depositional style. Moffat Shale Group strata are also examined. The area is notable for the presence of works by renowned sculptors, including Rodin and Henry Moore, placed near public roads on the Glenkiln estate by the local landowner. Monuments of historical interest are also a feature of the area.

Logistics There is no public transport. The use of a private car or minibus is advised as local roads are too narrow for a large coach. The excursion localities are at distances of 100 m to 1 km from the roadside. With the exception of the first locality, which is up a steep hillside, walking is of an easy nature. However, boots are advised as there are wet and muddy patches. A full day will be needed if all suggested localities are visited; a half day will be sufficient if only the stops close to the road are considered. Access in the area around the sculptures is not a problem, but these are **very popular** with visitors, and in summer the roads in their vicinity are often lined with cars. Permission to visit Localites 6 and 7 should be requested at Glen Farm, part of the Glenkiln estate. Permission for access to Localities 8 and 9 should be requested at Larghill Farm. Localities 11 and 12 are part of Crofts Farm (Figure 20).

Introduction Major faults, components of an imbricate thrust stack, divide the Southern Uplands sequence of steeply dipping turbidites and pelagic shales into a series of tectonostratigraphical tracts (Figure

1). The fine-grained sedimentary rocks of the Moffat Shale Group are relatively soft and the tract-defining faults formed preferentially within them. Thus the line of faulting is often marked by a series of Moffat Shale inliers and in areas of poor exposure, may be expressed as a topographic low across the landscape where the softer Moffat Shales have been preferentially eroded. Where sequences of turbidites are faulted against each other, without intervening shales, the line of the fault is very much more difficult to trace.

The Laurieston Fault, which defines the boundary between the Silurian Gala and Hawick groups of the Southern Uplands' Central Belt (Figures 1 and 2), can be traced across the area around Glenkiln Reservoir (Figure 20). (This is **not** the locality after which the Glenkiln Shale of Llandeilo–Caradoc age is named; that locality is included in Excursion 18). NW of the Laurieston Fault lies the Moffat Shale Group (Ordovician to Silurian) overlain by greywackes of the Gala 7 unit (Silurian). SE of the fault is exposed the Cairnharrow Formation (Silurian), the oldest unit of the Hawick Group.

Gala 7 turbidites in this area are typically thickly bedded and dominated by apparently structureless, medium- to coarse-grained or pebbly, non-calcareous sandstones. Bedding is often difficult to distinguish and sole structures and ripple cross-bedding are rare. In contrast, bedding in the Cairnharrow Formation is readily recognised and sole structures and ripple cross-bedding are common. Cairnharrow Formation greywackes are generally finer grained than those of the Gala Group, with fewer pebbles, and red detrital mica flakes may be present as a distinctive component. Cairnharrow Formation turbidites may also be calcareous, which is a general characteristic of the Hawick Group. Despite their differences, both formations were deposited on submarine fans in a mid-fan setting

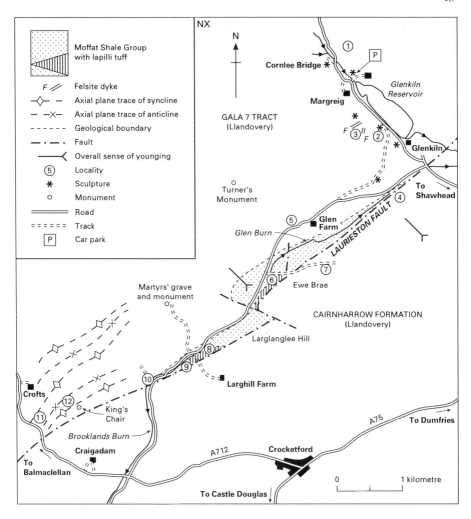

Figure 20   Locality map and outline geology for the Shawhead excursion in the Crocketford area.

(Figure 7). Gala 7 turbidites, however, were deposited from more highly concentrated, channelled flows.

1   Cornlee Bridge: Gala 7 coarse-grained turbidites

Take the A75 west from Dumfries. The right turn to Shawhead is on a straight stretch of the road, approximately 8 km from the end of the Dumfries bypass, and is clearly marked by a signpost. In the centre of

Shawhead village turn right, almost immediately left, out of the village, and left again towards Glenkiln. After a distance of 3 km the road follows the bank of the Glenkiln Reservoir. At the head of the reservoir leave the vehicle in a small parking place [NX 829 785], adjacent to a statue by Rodin known as 'Moses'.

From the parking place follow the Marglolly Burn 400 m upstream to Cornlee Bridge. An abstract bronze sculpture is positioned nearby. Cross the bridge, leave the road and ascend a rough path for approximately 250 m NE to the first prominent knoll [839 790]. Around you are many exposures typical of the Gala 7 unit in this area. Although no bedding surfaces are exposed, the way up of the beds and the direction of dip can be inferred by observing variations in grain size within a bed; bedding dips steeply towards the NW but may be locally overturned. Some of the turbidite beds have pebbly erosive bases which, together with grading, demonstrates younging to the NW. Return to parking place.

2 King and Queen: Gala 7 turbidites and sculptures

Drive back along the road towards the dam and park near a small gate into a field on the SW side of the reservoir [844 778]. This gate gives access to a farm track and the best known of the sculptures, a pair of crowned, seated figures known as the 'King and Queen', reputed to be by Henry Moore. Sadly, the statues were vandalised in early 1995. Small outcrops near the statues reveal turbidites which are finer-grained and more thinly bedded than those seen previously. They are characteristic of the lower part of Gala 7. Bedding, grading, way up and ripple cross-bedding are easily seen.

3 Margreig Hill: Gala 7 turbidites, dykes and sculptures

A sculpture like a totem pole is situated to the NW on Margreig Hill. This can be reached by continuing for 300 m along the farm track over a stream, then turning right off the track near a red sandstone plinth bearing the name of the sculptor Henry Moore. Walk NW towards the sculpture, to a gate in the wall. Beyond the gate and a stream crossing, porphyritic felsite dykes form prominent outcrops [840 778]. One has been used as a vantage point for a row of shooting butts. Near this dyke, bedding in the host Gala 7 sedimentary rocks dips gently to the north. Walk on up to the foot of the statue [840 779] where bedding resumes its regional steep north-westerly dip. Walk back to the farm track. Note the inscribed granite block with depictions of

elephants near the pheasant pens at the foot of the hill [846 775]. There is another sculpture, a bronze figure known as 'Madonna', in a stand of trees [843 770] 500 m further along the farm track. To continue the geological excursion return to the road and drive back towards Shawhead but at Glen Bridge take the first turning right up the valley of the Glen Burn.

4 Glen Burn: Moffat Shale Group, Laurieston Fault, Cairnharrow Formation and sculpture

An abstract sculpture on the roadside adjacent to Glen Burn marks the next stop [845 768]. The statue is a copy after a bronze original by Henry Moore. Park without blocking passing places.

The Glen Burn valley lies along the line of the Laurieston Fault. Turbidites of the Cairnharrow Formation lie SE of the fault; Moffat Shale Group and Gala 7 strata are present to the NW. Dark and greenish grey mudstones of the Moffat Shale Group are exposed in the burn, and in its bank can be seen a small north–south dioritic dyke. Graptolites from the Ordovician *linearis* Biozone have been collected nearby, and other graptolite faunas identified in this Moffat Shale inlier range up to the Silurian *sedgwickii* Biozone. A mudstone at the top of a Gala 7 turbidite in this area has yielded a graptolite fauna of the *turriculatus* Biozone. The transition from hemipelagic sedimentation (Moffat Shale Group) to turbidite accumulation therefore occurred during Llandovery times, (late *sedgwickii* to early *turriculatus* biozones: Figure 21).

On the far (south) side of the burn, deeply weathered sandstone of the Cairnharrow Formation forms the bank. Sole structures mark the base of the bed and clearly demonstrate younging to the SE. Cross the stream and walk NE across the hillside to an old wall. Thickly bedded turbidites of the Cairnharrow Formation are exposed in a small quarry once used as a sheep pen [849 769]. The sandstones contain distinctive reddish mica flakes, and the bases have large groove casts, accentuated by loading. Younging is to the NW; a synclinal fold axis has been crossed in the hangingwall of the Laurieston Fault. Cleavage is well

Figure 21
Graptolite
biostratigraphy
for the Moffat Shale,
Gala and Hawick
groups in the
Shawhead area.

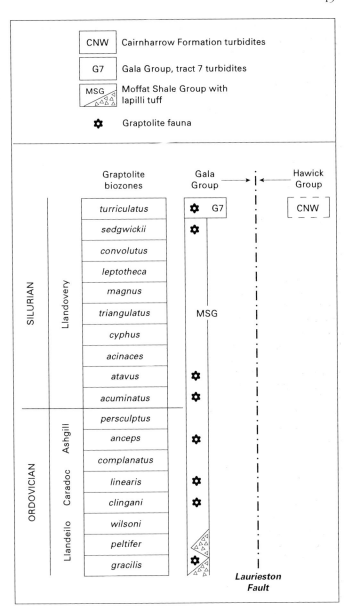

developed in the mudstone component of the turbidites.

5   Glen: Laurieston Fault

Drive SW past Glen Farm. Pause beyond the farm [829 762] to view the topographic expression of the Laurieston Fault. The valley floor is underlain by Moffat Shale, as exposed in the stream bed, but there is generally a cover of Quaternary deposits. A break of slope on the far hillside marks the fault between Moffat Shale Group and Cairnharrow Formation. The feature is most easily distinguished toward the SW, beside a plantation of conifers.

6 Ewe Brae: Moffat Shale Group tuffs and mudstones

Drive on and park near the entrance to a farm track that ascends Ewe Brae [826 756]. Where the track crosses the Glen Burn, mudstones of the Moffat Shale Group are exposed in the stream bed and trackside. All other exposures, forming knolls to the south of the track, are of lapilli tuff. The lapilli, pyroclastic grains of 1 mm or less, are readily distinguished on weathered surfaces as white or pale pink spheres that form a grain-supported texture in a dark matrix. A slight flattening of the lapilli defines bedding. Ordovician graptolites from the *gracilis, clingani, linearis* and *anceps* biozones have been collected from mudstones above the tuffs in this inlier. The tuffs therefore indicate eruptive volcanic activity in the Iapetus Ocean region during the Ordovician, but location and affinity of the volcanic centres is not known. Volcaniclastic grains interpreted to be from a volcanic island arc are known from Ordovician turbidite sequences within the Northern Belt (Stone et al., 1987; Styles et al., 1989), and the Moffat Shale tuffs may have come from the same source. Alternatively, they may be related to basalts in the Moffat Shale Group, which are inferred to have been generated by back arc spreading marginal to the Iapetus Ocean or by within-plate volcanism in the Iapetus Ocean (Lambert et al., 1981; Stone et al., 1987).

7 Ewe Brae: folding, Cairnharrow Formation and Turner's Monument

Follow the farm track to a quarry at the crest of Ewe Brae [835 758] where medium- to thick-bedded turbidites of the Cairnharrow Formation were worked. Steeply dipping strata, with beds grading from sandstone through siltstone to mudstone clearly young to the NW. Cleavage is well developed in the mudstones, where it is steeply inclined, and is also evident, though refracted, in the finer-grained sandstones. Both cleavage and bedding have been affected by shallow open folds with gently inclined axial planes and hinges that plunge a few degrees toward the SW; fold wavelength is about 4 cm and amplitude is about 2 cm. The folds are obvious on the quarry faces as open crenulations of the first cleavage. This folding is evidence for a second deformation episode (D2) imposed on the thrust-related deformation (D1) that produced the main cleavage. Slickensides on bedding plunge steeply to the SW and are probably associated with movement on the Laurieston Fault.

From this locality Turner's Monument can be seen to the NW, at the summit of Bennan. Johnny Turner was a previous resident of Glen Farm. During his lifetime he built this grand memorial to himself, having sought assurances that he would be interred there after his death. He reputedly chose the isolated hill top so that his grave would not be defiled by visitors. Return via the farm track to the metalled road and parked vehicles.

8 Larghill: Moffat Shale Group, Laurieston Fault, Cairnharrow Formation and Martyrs' Monument

Continue SW for 1.5 km to Larghill Bridge [817 745]. To avoid blocking the entrance to Larghill Farm, park with care on the right a little further on, at the entrance to a private forestry track.

Lapilli tuff within the Moffat Shale Group is exposed in the trackside at Larghill Bridge. One hundred metres further to the NE is a hillside exposure of graptolitic black shale. Peach and Horne (1899) described a graptolite fauna from here but fossil specimens are not abundant. More lapilli tuff can be seen beside the ruined wall farther up the hillside. The line of the Laurieston Fault is marked by the change to a steeper gradient; a spring issues at the fault line.

Approximately 150 m due east of the spring, towards the crest of Larglanglee Hill, turbidites of the Cairnharrow Formation exposed in a small quarry [820 745] comprise thickly bedded, sandstone-dominated units interbedded with thinly bedded mudstone-dominated units. There has been some tectonic disturbance and cleavage is very well developed, perhaps due to the proximity of the Laurieston Fault.

From the quarry walk south to the cluster of trees on the crest of Larglanglee Hill [819 744]. In the SW corner of the plantation, turbidites of the Cairnharrow Formation can be seen in a series of exposures. Younging is towards the NW. The lowest beds comprise a thinning- and fining-upward sequence, over an interval of approximately 8 m. Thickly bedded turbidite units dominated by sandstone form the base and are overlain by medium to thinly bedded units of slightly finer-grained sandstone. The top of the sequence is of thinly bedded units of fine-grained sandstone grading into siltstone and mudstone. Such thinning- and fining-upward sequences in submarine fan deposits are thought to record the gradual abandonment of a distributary channel in a mid-fan setting (Walker and Mutti, 1973). Cleavage is only weakly developed in the mudstone tops of the turbidite units but is non-axial planar to the S1 fold stuctures. The strike of cleavage is rotated about 10° clockwise from the strike of bedding typical of the incongruent relationship between bedding and first cleavage seen in many Southern Uplands turbidite sequences. Cleavage formation may well have postdated the initial phase of folding; if so the relationship between cleavage and bedding cannot reliably be used to determine fold geometry or the way up of the bedding. A futher complexity here is the folding of bedding about small, open subhorizontal D2 hinges.

From Larglanglee Hill a Martyrs' Monument and walled Martyrs' Grave can be seen to the NW across Brooklands Burn.

9 Brooklands Burn: graptolitic Moffat Shale Group and Martyrs' Monument

The course of Brooklands Burn can be reached by walking 430 m SW to the foot of Larglanglee Hill and through a gate in the wall adjacent to the farm track [817 743]. An exposure of Moffat Shale excavated in 1991 in the Brooklands Burn [812 742] contained abundant graptolites. Faunas typical of the top *clingani* and low *linearis* biozones (late Ordovician) were collected. The shales are relatively undeformed, although the effects of small-scale faulting, folding and imbrication of bedding can be seen. From this locality return to the parking place at the entrance to the forestry track.

The Martyrs' Monument and walled Martyrs' Grave [810 751] that were seen

from the summit of Larglanglee Hill can be reached by walking for approximately 1 km along the private forestry track which is part of Craigadam Farm. The granitic monument is unweathered and the inscriptions, describing the death of Covenanters by shooting, can be easily read. The red sandstone gravestone and wall, which includes a stepped stile, have not withstood the effects of the elements so well.

10 Brooklands Bridge: view of Laurieston Fault

Drive approximately 1 km SW from Larghill Farm. The road runs approximately parallel to the Laurieston Fault. Stop at the entrance to a second forestry track near Brooklands Bridge [809 740] to view the topographic expression of the Laurieston Fault. Looking WSW the fault is seen as a dry valley. This is a fine example of a tract-defining fault associated with outcrops of the Moffat Shale Group; erosion of the soft lithologies has produced this surface expression of the structure. South of the fault are the turbidites of the Cairnharrow Formation (localities 4, 5, 7 and 8). The sequence to the north comprises very thickly bedded, sandstones of the Gala 7 unit (Localities 11 and 12).

11 Crofts Hill Quarry: deformation, Gala 7 turbidites

Drive south for 1.5 km from Brooklands Bridge to the crossroads with the A712 and turn right towards Balmaclellan. Continue on 1.7 km and park in a small lay-by on the right-hand side of the road, at a sharp left-hand bend [792 734]. A gateway leads from the lay-by into a field which has been recently planted with trees (1994) and contains a disused quarry [792 735].

In this area (Figure 20) Gala 7 turbidite beds have been folded into large-scale, NW verging folds. Very thickly bedded turbidites of Gala 7 are well exposed in the quarry, which has been worked within a fold limb that dips and youngs SE, as demonstrated by the well-exposed rippled top of a sandstone bed. The palaeocurrent direction, inferred from the asymmetry of the ripples, was also towards the SE.

Mudstone comprises only a small proportion of the turbidite units. In Crofts Hill Quarry these fine-grained lithologies have been imbricated into a narrow duplex structure between the massive sandstone beds by bedding-parallel shear, probably induced by folding. Reddening of the rocks is attributed to uplift and subaerial weathering in a desert environment during the Upper Palaeozoic.

12 Crofts Hill and Kings Chair: folding of Gala 7 turbidites

From the quarry walk NE along the crest of the hill to the summit cairn of Crofts Hill [793 737]. Many gently dipping beds are exposed; in fact, unusually for the Southern Uplands, most of the flat or rounded rock surfaces on Crofts Hill are bedding planes. The direct route to the hilltop is along strike within the SE-dipping and SE-younging fold limb. From the summit walk due east. As you approach a boundary wall a synclinal fold axis is crossed and bedding resumes the regional strike and dip, steeply inclined and younging to the NW. However, looking over the wall, large exposures of thickly bedded sandstone dipping and younging SE can be seen between newly planted trees. These form the next gently dipping fold limb

beyond an anticlinal hinge. The anticlinal fold axis can be traced as far as a small memorial (to a previous landowner) on Kings Chair and thence across the boundary wall. The south-easterly dip increases from about 30° to 70° towards the Laurieston Fault.

From here northwards to Lochenkit Loch the landscape is very much influenced by large-scale D1 folds. Steeply dipping, NW-younging fold limbs form the high ground, the lower ground being underlain by gently inclined south- and SE-dipping limbs. The effects of a later phase of folding, D2, are much more modest than D1 and can be seen in a small quarry near the boundary wall [795 737]. There the steeply dipping bedding youngs to the NW, as is evident from grading, sole structures and ripple lamination. In the east corner of the quarry, on a north-facing surface, a siltstone bed has been folded into second phase folds with an amplitude of less than 10 cm. The axial planes are horizontal. In this quarry, D2 crenulation of S1 cleavage can also be seen within the mudstone tops of the sandstone-dominated turbidites. From the quarry return to the lay-by. To join the A75 drive back along the A712 towards Crocketford.

M C Akhurst

Excursion 5

a volcanic vent, Hawick Group turbidites, graptolites

OS 1:50 000 Sheet 83 Newton Stewart &
Kirkcudbright
BGS 1:50 000 Sheet 5W Kirkcudbright
Route map: Figure 22

Main points of interest A Siluro-Devonian volcanic vent, Silurian turbidite greywackes and Wenlock graptolites, complex Caledonian folding.

Logistics All the localities lie SW from Kirkcudbright and involve relatively easy coastal walking: about 1.5 km at Locality 1, about 3.5 km at Locality 2, and about 7 km for Localities 3 and 4 if the coastal path is walked in both directions. A shorter return route from Locality 4 requires prior permission from Ross Farm. A low tide is advantageous but much can be seen under all but the highest tidal conditions. Vehicle access is good for Locality 1, where there is ample car or coach parking. However, as access for the other localities is via minor roads and parking space is limited, the full excursion should not be attempted in any vehicle larger than a minibus. Total driving distance from and back to Kirkcudbright is about 25 km.

Introduction Kirkcudbright is an attractive small town with a picturesque harbour situated on the estuary of the River Dee. Maclellan's Castle, a ruined tower house dating from about 1580, may be seen in the town centre. Close by the Tollbooth dates from 1627 and the old Merkat Cross still features the jougs (a form of pillory) 'for the public humiliation of offenders'. About 3 km north of the town, on the A711, the Tongland dam and hydro-electric power station may be visited and a guided tour could form an appropriate adjunct to the geological excursion (for booking details phone 01557 330114).

The Kirkcudbright area is underlain by Carghidown Formation (Hawick Group) greywackes, and siltstones. These were deposited during the Silurian period about 430 million years ago. The coastal sections to the SW of the town provide splendid outcrops, illustrating turbidite sedimentology and complex Caledonian structure, and it is these that provide the focus for the excursion. Examples of igneous intrusive rocks will also be seen and graptolites of Wenlock age may be found in the Ross Formation beds, a Hawick Group component slightly younger than the Carghidown Formation and exposed farther south. Still younger strata of the Riccarton Group crop out to the SE of Kirkcudbright and are examined in detail by Excursion 11. It would be possible to include some elements of that excursion as an extension of the itinerary described here. The complex fold structure may be further examined in the excellent coastal exposures slightly farther NW at Barlocco [NX 585 486] which are described in detail by Treagus (1992).

1 Shoulder O'Craig: volcanic vent

The excursion is best begun at the car park and picnic area adjacent to The Doon and Gull Craig beside Nun Mill Bay [NX 658 487]. This is situated about 5 km from Kirkcudbright and is reached via the A755 and B727. About 600 m NE from the parking area an agglomerate-filled volcanic vent (Figure 23) cuts Silurian greywacke and siltstone (Carghidown Formation). The sedimentary rocks are exposed on the foreshore in Clinking Haven as steeply inclined beds striking NE and locally folded into tight, upright structures. A good array of turbidite features can be seen on the wave-smoothed surfaces and includes graded bedding and loaded bed bases. A penetrative cleavage is developed subparallel to bedding in the finer-grained lithologies but does not continue into the vent agglomerate which was therefore a post-tectonic intrusion. The agglomerate, believed to have been intruded in latest Silurian or

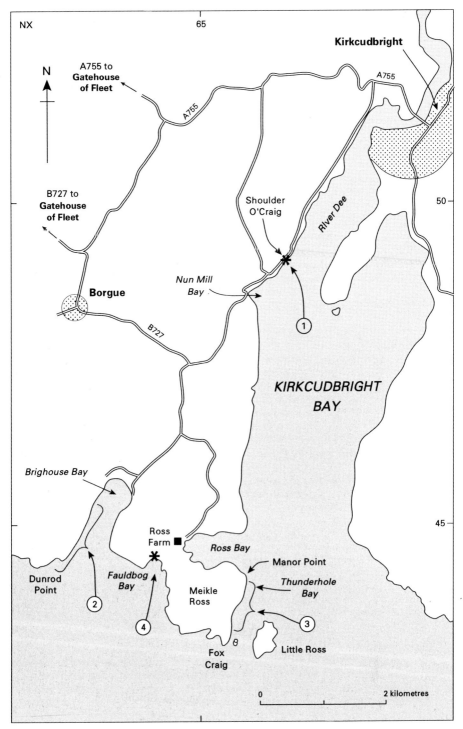

Figure 22 Locality map and outline geology for the Kirkcudbright excursion.

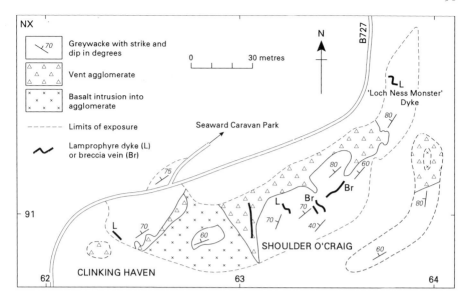

Figure 23 Outline geology of the Shoulder O'Craig volcanic vent (Locality 1).

early Devonian times, is one of a number of such vent features scattered across SW Scotland. A fresh kersantite (biotite-plagioclase lamprophyre) phase of the vent intrusion has given a K-Ar age of 410 ± 10 Ma (Rock et al., 1986a). The vent occupies the northern side of Clinking Haven forming the Shoulder O'Craig cliffs [663 491] and probably extends for a short distance inland. Lamprophyre dykes cut both the vent agglomerate and the turbidite country rock. Detailed petrographical and geochemical data for the intrusive rocks are given by Rock et al. (1986a).

The texture of the vent agglomerate is best seen on the wave-polished surfaces on the NW side of Clinking Haven. The cliff sections provide more extensive outcrop in three dimensions and confirm that the agglomerate consists principally of variably rounded greywacke, siltstone and sporadic microdiorite or basaltic clasts set in a fine-grained matrix; the latter is largely altered to carbonate and chlorite. Clast size is very variable and ranges up to rafts of country rock a few metres in length. The preponderance of sedimentary clasts in the vent suggests that initially it emitted steam and gases for the most part and did not directly

tap a source of magma. Thus the vent agglomerate should more accurately — but less descriptively — be termed an intrusion breccia. It is cut by a number of basalt bodies and lamprophyre dykes the larger of which are shown in Figure 23. Note the irregular and fractured biotite-olivine basalt mass which intrudes the agglomerate in the western end of the vent. It is generally clast-free and its contact with the surrounding agglomerate varies from sharp to diffuse and gradational. Oval, pillow-like textures and possible flow fractures may suggest that the intrusion was emplaced in a semi-solid state (Rock et al., 1986a). However, it does imply that the vent developed from a steam and gas escape route to a conduit for magma.

Other dykes cut the greywacke country rock and a noteworthy example occurs about 20 m beyond the NE extremity of the vent. This has been dubbed the 'Loch Ness Monster' dyke on account of its bizarre outcrop pattern. It is a kersantitic lamprophyre consisting of biotite phenocrysts set in a dark grey feldspathic matrix. The highly irregular form is thought to reflect high volatile pressure during emplacement.

2 Brighouse Bay: Carghidown Formation greywackes and structure

From Locality 1 follow the B727 Kirkcudbright to Borgue road for about 2 km SW towards Borgue before turning left towards Brighouse Bay. About 2 km of unclassified road leads to the head of the bay where parking is available on the raised beach. The west side of the bay (Figure 24) provides extensive exposures of well-bedded greywackes of the Carghidown Formation (Hawick Group, Figure 2), but the structural complexity is considerable. The greywacke beds are repeatedly folded and sheared out, with remarkable variability in the attitude and orientation of the fold hinges. The relationships are best examined between Point of Green and Dunrod Point [628 445] on the SW corner of the bay, reached by a coastal walk of about 1.5 km. This is the recommended starting point for a traverse back along the coastal section. Fold structures are abundant but one of particular interest can be seen on the west side of Point of Green (**2a** in Figure 24). This fold is downward-facing or inverted: the apparent antiform is in fact synclinal. The antiform plunges moderately to the NE and the curved upper surface is covered with well-developed flute casts and load structures, marking it out as an inverted bed base. A non-axial planar slaty cleavage is also clearly seen to transect the axial surface and both limbs of the fold by a few degrees clockwise. Traversing eastwards across Point of Green several other steeply plunging folds are separated by shear planes which on a large scale merge to form an anastomosing zone. At Point of Green some thick greywacke beds appear in the sequence and large flute casts are preserved on the base of the thickest (**2b**). This bed can be seen to cut down through the underlying more thinly bedded greywackes, an example of channelling. Eastward towards Dunrod Point steeply plunging fold hinges are contained within the anastomosing shear system (**2c**). Their inter-relationship may be conveniently examined in detail at the NE corner of Dunrod Point [6286 4459], a structural summary of which is shown in Figure 25. From this locality the coastal section continues NE towards the head of

Brighouse Bay. Near-continuous exposure reveals much folding of the greywacke strata with variably but often steeply plunging hinges separated by sinuous shear zones. Thicker greywacke beds often show a good array of bottom structures and there is a strong, ubiquitous slaty cleavage. Note that the cleavage is axial planar to some of the folds but clockwise transecting in other examples; hinge plunge variation commonly occurs within the axial plane. These folds are believed to have formed in a transpressive stress regime when a variable component of sinistral shear was imposed on the overall NW–SE regional shortening. A detailed discussion of this phenomenon was given by Stringer and Treagus (1980). The incidence of folding decreases, and the frequency with which the section is cut by shear zones increases, towards the NE as the route leads back to the parking area at the head of the bay.

3 Meikle Ross: Ross Formation greywackes and siltstones

This small peninsula forms the southern extremity of the west side of Kirkcudbright Bay. It is reached by means of unclassified roads which link Brighouse Bay with Ross Farm [646 447]. Manor Point forms the headland on the south side of Ross Bay (about 1.5 km SE along the footpath from Ross Farm) and from the Point about a kilometre of well-exposed coastal section extends south. It is most readily accessible if the path is followed to the southernmost point of Meikle Ross and the coastal section then traversed northwards.

The strata are well-bedded greywackes and siltstones with sporadic interbedded grey-green shale and belong to the Ross Formation (Hawick Group, Figure 2). Restricted graptolite faunas (Figure 26) of the *M. riccartonensis* Biozone (early Wenlock) have been found in rare hemipelagite horizons (localities 52–55 of White et al., 1992).

Bedding is fairly regular with a general dip of about 60–70° to the SE; beds are commonly inverted and young towards the NW. Bottom structures are abundant, and ripple marks and sand volcanoes can be seen on the top surfaces of some beds. Fold

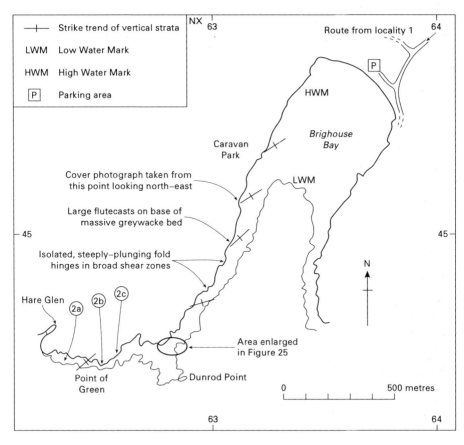

Figure 24   Locality map and geological notes for the west side of Brighouse Bay (Locality 2).

hinges are far less evident than was the case at Brighouse Bay; the best examples are seen around Thunderhole Bay (Figure 22). However, the evidence for variable plunge of fold hinges is merely more subtle in this locality and can be demonstrated by a systematic examination of the lineation formed by the intersection between bedding and cleavage. The cleavage is axial-planar to the folds, as can be demonstrated along strike on the island of Little Ross (beyond the scope of this excursion) and so the lineation can be taken as parallel to local fold hinge orientation. Overall there is a smooth variation in the plunge of the lineation, from 47° to the ENE at the north end of the section to 38° to the WSW in the south passing through a maximum plunge of 64° where

the lineation is parallel to the dip of the cleavage. Diachronous formation of the cleavage under a varying stress regime seems the most likely explanation for these relationships, a similar mechanism to that proposed at Brighouse Bay. Further discussion of the tectonic implications of the Meikle Ross section is given by Kemp (1986; 1987a).

4   Fauldbog Bay: graptolitic hemipelagites

Well-developed fold structures can be seen on the west side of Meikle Ross at Fauldbog Bay [642 444], a locality which is also notable for the abundance of graptolites in the interbedded hemipelagite horizons. The west-facing coast of the bay exposes strata

54

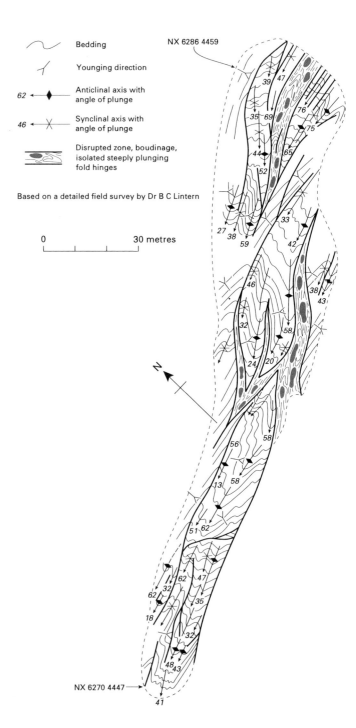

Figure 25 Detail of structure near Dunrod Point (Locality 2).

Bedding

Younging direction

62 Anticlinal axis with angle of plunge

46 Synclinal axis with angle of plunge

Disrupted zone, boudinage, isolated steeply plunging fold hinges

Based on a detailed field survey by Dr B C Lintern

0   30 metres

NX 6286 4459

NX 6270 4447

Figure 26 Examples of graptolites from the Ross Formation; all × 5, except for a and b, × 10.

(a, b) *Barrandeograptus? bornholmensis* (Laursen), *centrifugus* Biozone.
(c) *Monoclimacis* cf. *vomerina vomerina* (Nicholson), *centrifugus* to *riccartonensis* biozones.
(d) *Monoclimacis vomerina basilica* (Lapworth), *centrifugus* to *riccartonensis* biozones. (e) *Monoclimacis vomerina* s.l. (Nicholson), *centrifugus* to *riccartonensis* biozones.
(f, g) *Monograptus riccartonensis* Lapworth, *riccartonensis* Biozone.

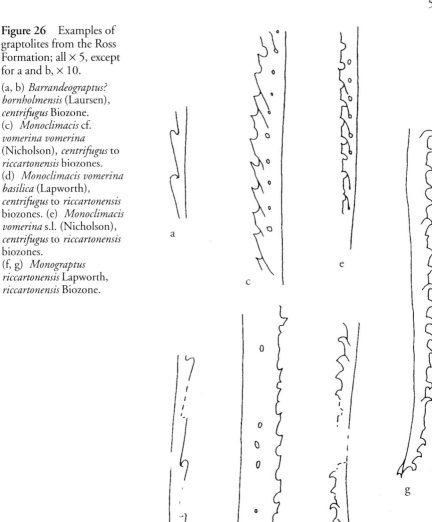

lithologically similar to the Ross Formation but containing some thin red mudstones characteristic of the Carghidown Formation. The boundary between the two formations is taken at a fault in the northern extremity of the bay, the strata on the east side are assigned to the Ross Formation and those on the west to the Carghidown Formation. Variable and complex folding may be seen in many parts of the shore section. Sheared zones separate the folded areas from units of more uniformly bedded strata.

To reach Fauldbog Bay continue along the coastal path around the headland and up the west coast of Meikle Ross. Good exposures of graptolitic hemipelagites of the *Cyrtograptus centrifugus* Biozone (basal Wenlock) can be examined in intertidal reefs at the northern end of Fauldbog Bay [642 445 to 644 443] (localities 61–63 of White et al., 1992). Graptolites collected here include *Barrandeograptus? bornholmensis* (Laursen), *C.* cf. *centrifugus* Boucek, cf. *C. grayi* Lapworth, *Monoclimacis vomerina basilica* (Lapworth), *Mcl. vomerina vomerina* (Nicholson), *Mcl. vomerina* c.l., *Monograptus priodon* (Bronn), *M.* aff. *priodon*, M. *remotus* Elles & Wood, *Retiolites geinitzianus angustidens* Elles & Wood and *R. geinitzianus geinitzianus* Barrande. Approximately 750 m to the south, [around 644 437] (localities 57–60 of White et al., 1992) hemipelagites in the intertidal reefs contain a restricted fauna of the *Monograptus riccartonenis* Biozone, mainly *M. riccartonensis*. A selection of graptolites recovered from these localities is shown in Figure 26. They are of Wenlock age (Figures 2 and 5).

Both sides of Fauldbog Bay expose abundant minor folding but the NW side is of particular interest. Many of the folds there are inverted (downward-facing) and enclosed within shear zones reminiscent of the Brighouse Bay section; a similar origin seems likely.

From Fauldbog Bay it is possible to cross the fields eastwards towards Ross Farm if prior permission has been obtained. Otherwise the coastal route should be retraced.

P Stone, R F Cheeney and D E White

Excursion 6

AFTON WATER, HARE HILL and BAIL HILL:
Ordovician submarine fans, antimony and a seamount volcano

OS 1:50 000 Sheet 71 Lanark & Upper Nithsdale
BGS 1:50 000 Sheet 15W New Cumnock
Route maps: Figures 27 and 28

Main points of interest Thick Ordovician turbidite fan sequence with greywackes, conglomerate, red chert; antimony mineralisation; volcanic rocks and possible olistoliths.

Logistics Access to Glen Afton (Localities 1–3) and Bail Hill (Localities 5–9) involves the use of single-track roads unsuitable for vehicles larger than a minibus. Roadside parking is usually adequate for 3–4 cars. A visit to the Hare Hill antimony mine (Locality 4) involves a 5 km round-trip hike over rough ground with a climb of about 300 m.

Introduction Just south of New Cumnock, the glaciated valley of the Afton Water (the *Sweet Afton* eulogised by Robert Burns) affords one of the best and most accessible inland cross-strike sections in the Ordovician Northern Belt of the Southern Uplands. The section displayed in the vicinity of the Afton Dam is one of the best exposures of conglomerate in the region.

The antimony mine at Hare Hill is one of only two localities in Scotland where stibnite has been found in significant amounts. The other is at Glendinning, near Langholm (Appendix 1).

Around Bail Hill on the NE side of the River Nith near Sanquhar is the most extensive area of volcanic rocks in the Northern Belt of the Southern Uplands. It includes unusual Ordovician lavas containing remarkable, large euhedral phenocrysts of clinopyroxene. An extensive series of basaltic lavas, agglomerates and trachytic intrusions can be seen around Bail Hill itself, while several outlying tuff members are interbedded with the surrounding greywacke succession. The volcanic and sedimentary rocks of the Bail Hill area have

been intensively studied by McMurtry (1980a, b, c) and this part of the excursion is largely based on his work.

THE AFTON WATER SECTION
(Figure 27)

Glen Afton is approached from New Cumnock, which lies on the A76. Take the B741 (Dalmellington) road and after about 100 m turn south towards Craigdarroch along the unclassified road on the west side of the Afton Water.

1 Afton Water, Laight: Marchburn Formation greywacke and chert

Park at the memorial to Robert Burns about 400 m south of Laight [NS 614 114]. After paying due homage to Scotland's National Bard, scramble down the west bank of the Afton Water where, if the water level is sufficiently low, interbedded red chert, cherty mudstone, laminated siltstone and greywacke of the Marchburn Formation can be examined in the river. At this locality, close to the Southern Upland Fault, the attitude of the strata is anomalous in regional terms; the beds dip generally east at 20–40°. The greywackes are dull greenish purple, rich in feldspar and contain obvious red grains of chert and acid lavas. They are the finer-grained equivalents of the 'Haggis Rock' microconglomerates which can be traced from Glen Afton NE to Leadburn near Edinburgh.

This locality must be only a few hundred metres south of the Southern Upland Fault (SUF), though in this area the fault itself is overstepped by the Carboniferous rocks of the New Cumnock Coalfield, which cross the fault to rest unconformably on Ordovician strata. A 6 m-wide Tertiary tholeite dyke trending 070°, parallel to the SUF, can also be examined here.

58

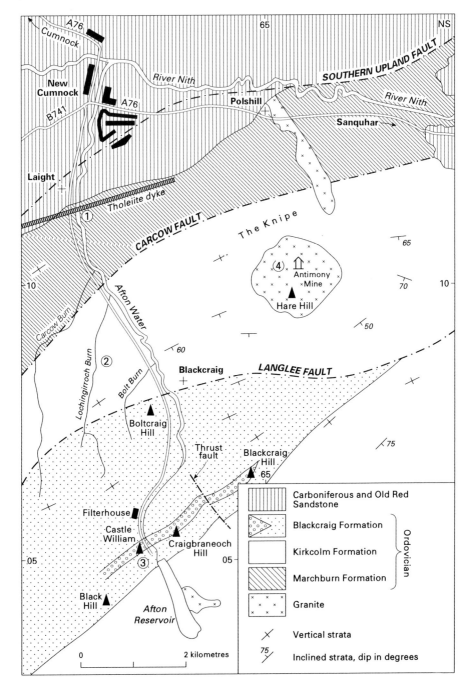

Figure 27 Locality map and outline geology for the Afton Water section and Hare Hill (after Floyd, 1982).

2 Lochingirroch Burn and Bolt Burn: Kirkcolm Formation greywackes

Continue south on the public road for a further 2 km and park near Lochingirroch Farm [622 094]. Walk up Lochingirroch Burn where thick sequences of rhythmic, parallel-bedded 'flysch' sandstone and hemipelagic mudstone can be examined. These are classical turbidites of the quartz-rich Kirkcolm Formation and display many good examples of internal Bouma sequences (Figure 6) including graded bedding and parallel and cross-lamination. External sedimentary structures such as flute and groove casts, flame structures and loaded bedding can also be seen. In areas where fold hinges may not be visible, sedimentary structures can often be used to show reversals of younging direction and thus provide evidence of folding. Happily, however, the flaggy type of lithology in Lochingirroch Burn appears to fold particularly well and the hinges of numerous small-scale steeply plunging folds (probably D3) can be seen.

After about 800 m exposure becomes poor. Return to the road and drive south for a further 1 km to Bolt Burn Bridge [629 085]. Walk up Bolt Burn to examine another good section in quartzose turbidite sandstones of the Kirkcolm Formation, with further examples of D3 folding. The prominent Boltcraig Hill, immediately to the south, consists of massive greywackes of the Blackcraig Formation. These are best examined at the next locality.

3 Afton Dam: Blackcraig Formation greywackes and conglomerates

From Bolt Burn Bridge, continue south along the public road as far as the entrance to Afton Waterworks, where, with the permission of the superintendent, it should be possible to park at the filterhouse [627 056]. Walk south from here for about 600 m along the private road towards the dam, to examine the rocks in the spillway and the bed of the Afton Water downstream. This 1 km-long section is one of the best exposures of massive greywackes and associated boulder conglomerates in the entire Southern Uplands. It forms part of the type section of the Blackcraig Formation (Floyd, 1982), a 1500 m-thick sequence of thickly bedded greywacke-turbidites and conglomerates with a distinctive petrography. The greywackes and the matrix of the conglomerates contain large amounts of epidote, pyroxene and amphibole, which are often abundant enough to impart a distinct dark green colour to freshly broken rock surfaces.

The prominent crags of Craigbraneoch Hill, Castle William and Black Hill are formed by the base of the formation, whose massive greywackes resist erosion better than those of the Kirkcolm Formation to the south, and effectively form the natural barrier across Glen Afton now utilised by the dam. Downstream, in the distance, the steep western flank of Blackcraig Hill displays excellent large-scale bedding features dipping steeply towards the north, with an obvious low-angle thrust dipping gently northwards and visibly displacing some particularly massive beds.

In the vicinity of the dam, the beds strike generally 065° and both dip and young towards the NW. The lower part of the succession consists of 300 m of massive, thickly bedded coarse-grained greywackes with sporadic pebbly patches. These are succeeded by about 170 m of coarse-grained greywackes and boulder conglomerates in units up to 7 m thick. Some of these thick beds effectively form large-scale 'mega-Bouma' units, with an internal sequence of grading, parallel lamination and trough cross-stratification. The latter feature, together with basal scours and cobble imbrication, consistently indicates sediment transport from the NW, across the structural trend of the Southern Uplands.

Most of the conglomerates contain well-rounded boulders of extra-basinal origin, up to 1.5 m in diameter, including granite, gabbro, porphyry, basalt, vein quartz, quartzite, chert and siltstone. The presence of rare boulders of conglomerate suggests that much of the extra-basinal material may be polycyclic, derived from older conglomerates, and this may account for the variety of clasts and their high degree of rounding. Channelling at the base of rudite units gives a good indication of the erosional potential of the fast-moving, powerful and boulder-charged turbidity currents and debris flows which must have transported these sediments.

A few of the conglomeratic units contain only intrabasinal clasts, angular blocks of greywacke and dark siltstone. The greywacke clasts are petrographically identical to the enclosing greywacke, suggesting that they were eroded from the walls of channels cut into partly lithified units of the Blackcraig Formation on the submarine fan itself, rather than from the walls of the feeder canyon. Clasts which preserve bedding sometimes show differential rounding or erosion of their sandstone/siltstone layers, again suggesting that they were only partly lithified during their brief clastic existence.

The granite boulders in the Blackcraig conglomerate were studied by Elders (1987), who identified at least three distinct petrographical suites which were dated by the Rb/Sr method. In Glen Afton, the oldest suite consists of weakly foliated biotite-bearing granites which gave an age of 1231 ± 120 Ma. A suite of muscovite-bearing granites gave an age of 702 ± 86 Ma while a group of hornblende-biotite granites yielded an age of 491 ± 14 Ma. Elders investigated possible source areas for these rocks in Newfoundland, where granites of similar composition and age patterns are found, and used this to suggest a sinistral strike-slip fault movement of the order of 1500 km between the Southern Uplands and Newfoundland.

Traced both laterally (along-strike) and downstream (across-strike and up-sequence), the proportion of conglomerate gradually declines until the succession consists only of the coarse-grained sandstone which forms the matrix of the conglomerates. At the top of the succession, in the vicinity of Blackcraig Farm [637 080], the formation becomes quite thinly bedded and consists of fine-grained flaggy greywackes which still, however, retain the distinctive petrographical character of the underlying more massive beds.

A detailed sedimentological study of the Blackcraig Formation was carried out by Holroyd (1978) who compared the conglomerates with those at Corsewall Point (Excursion 15, Locality 2) and Craighit (Excursion 7, Locality 5). Overall, the Blackcraig Formation was interpreted as a mid-fan facies deposit, with the lower conglomeratic portion deposited within major channels, up to 2.5 km wide, in the proximal mid-fan region.

HARE HILL (Figure 27)

4 The Knipe: antimony mineralisation

From Glen Afton, drive back to New Cumnock and take the A76 east towards Kirkconnel and Dumfries. About 3 km beyond New Cumnock, park in one of the roadside lay-bys near Polshill Farm and walk south up the Garepool Burn. At the sharp bend where the general course of the burn changes from east to north, walk SW away from the burn for about 300 m across a peaty plateau towards the old trial workings [658 105] on the hill slope beyond.

The stibnite (Sb_2S_3) vein on Hare Hill has been known since the 1840s when a small trial mine was driven along it. The vein is located within the small granite intrusion of The Knipe (Dewey et al., 1920). This late-Caledonian pluton is about 1.5 km in diameter and consists of a fine- to medium-grained, slightly porphyritic biotite-hornblende granite. It is intruded into Ordovician greywackes of the Kirkcolm Formation, which have been baked to form a thermal aureole of hard purple hornfels.

Mine abandonment plans (held by the BGS) show that the adit was 55 m long, with an initial trend of N035° near the entrance, swinging to about 020° after some 30 m. A raise was driven up to the surface about 18 m inside the tunnel, and the vein exposed and worked down from the surface. The vein was vertical and said to range from 30 to 55 cm wide, though was reportedly lost after about 37 m into the hillside. Some roof falls have occurred and the mine is now silted up and inaccessible. Water is drained off via an iron pipe and used as a water supply.

There is a heap of mine spoil including vein material lying at the tunnel entrance. Mineral specimens show needles of metallic grey stibnite in a white vein-quartz matrix, though in places the stibnite has weathered to a yellow ochreous crust, probably the antimony oxide, cervanite ($Sb_2O_3.Sb_2O_5$).

A second stibnite vein, which had been reported in estate papers from the 1840s, was relocated by the author in 1971, some 750 m west of the trial mine. The second locality [6507 1032] lies on the east bank of the Blackdams Burn and is marked by obvious signs of earlier trenching and small overgrown spoil heaps. The vein material consists of grey stibnite needles set in white chert-like quartz; blocks can be found in the burn.

The Hare Hill area was intensively prospected between 1982 and 1988 by BP Minerals (Boast et al., 1990) who found indications, both within the granite and at the intrusive contact, of gold mineralisation associated with a zoned As-Sb-Cu-Pb-Zn hydrothermal assemblage. Disseminated and vein-type mineralisation both occur, the latter thought to be controlled by the intersection of north–south and ENE (Caledonoid) trending fractures.

BAIL HILL (Figure 28)

From Hare Hill, return to the A76 and continue south towards Dumfries. About

4 km beyond Kirkconnel, at the large bridge over the Crawick Water just before the town of Sanquhar, turn left on to the B740 towards Crawfordjohn. After about 200 m, and just before the railway bridge, turn left on to the single-track road which gives access to the Bail Hill area [760 143]. Roadside parking for cars/minibuses is possible in the vicinity of Bail Hill and Localities 5–8 can all be reached by walking from there. Locality 9 is best approached from the B740.

The Bail Hill Volcanic Group consists of an extensive pile of highly porphyritic autobrecciated lavas and pyroclastic rocks of Ordovician age (McMurtry, 1980a, b, c; Hepworth et al., 1982) whose early basaltic stages (Cat Cleugh Formation) were erupted on to black graptolitic shales (Locality 7). Later lavas and agglomerates of hawaiite and mugearite composition (Peat Rig Formation and Grain Burn Member —Locality 5) make up the bulk of the volcanic succession and the whole pile was finally intruded by a volcanic neck, now infilled with lava (Bught Craig Member — Locality 6).

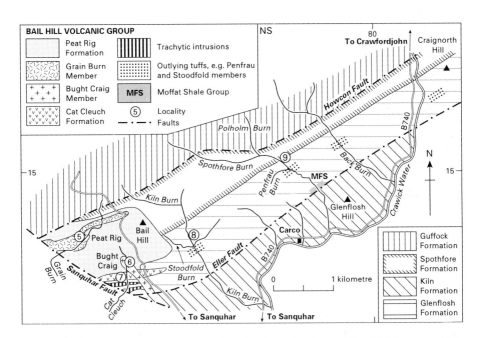

Figure 28   Locality map and outline geology for the Bail Hill area (after McMurtry, 1980a).

Outlying pyroclastic members crop out in a series of burns NE of Bail Hill. They consist of crystal and lithic tuffs and agglomerates which interfinger with greywackes and siltstones of the Kiln Formation (Localities 8 and 9). The Bail Hill volcano may be envisaged as a seamount, initially extruded on to a sea floor of black shales, whose magma evolved on the basalt–hawaiite–mugearite–trachyte mildly alkaline trend. As the lava and pyroclastic pile built up, the volcano was gradually swamped by submarine fan sediments until the volcano finally became extinct and was buried under coarse-grained proximal terrigenous deposits.

5 Grain Burn: lavas and agglomerates

From the road near Bail Hill, walk west about 100 m into the headwaters of Grain Burn [753 142] and traverse downstream. In this area hawaiite/mugearite lavas and agglomerates of the Peat Rig Formation can be examined. The lavas contain phenocrysts of feldspar (oligoclase/andesine), amphibole (pargasite), apatite and biotite/ phlogopite. Hawaiite lavas of the Grain Burn Member also crop out hereabouts in the burn.

6 Bught Craig: infilled volcanic neck

From Grain Burn, walk about 1 km SE across the moor towards Bught Craig [757 135], near the head of the west branch of Cat Cleugh, in which the Bught Craig Member is exposed. This volcanic unit is thought to represent an infilled volcanic neck which had previously fed the Bail Hill volcano but then became choked with blocks of igneous material and lava. At its type locality, the rock consists of a hawaiite lava matrix containing fragments of coarse- and fine-grained igneous rocks including gabbro, diorite and a variety of lava and dyke lithologies. Some of the clasts cannot be matched with rock types presently exposed at Bail Hill, suggesting that the volcanic edifice was formerly more diverse and extensive than at present.

7 Cat Cleugh: euhedral clinopyroxenes

Continue downstream in Cat Cleugh [757 134] for about 100 m to examine basaltic lavas of the Cat Cleugh Formation. The lavas are autobrecciated and contain large euhedral black clinopyroxene (salite) phenocrysts up to 16 mm long. The pyroxene crystals are beautifully twinned, commonly visibly curved and display 'hourglass' zoning under the microscope. They are set in a green fine-grained lava matrix which also contains small phenocrysts of altered plagioclase and zeolite-filled amygdales. The lava matrix is soft and the pyroxenes can often be extracted without difficulty, leaving perfect casts of the crystals in the matrix.

Proceed downstream for another 150 m to examine the base of the Bail Hill volcanic succession, where weakly porphyritic basalt lavas can be seen resting conformably on black shales. These contain a *Nemagraptus gracilis* Biozone fauna (mid Ordovician) and correlate with the lower part of the Glenkiln Shales of the Moffat Shale Group. Downstream from the black shales, two trachytic intrusions can be seen in the next 150 m before the Ordovician section ends near the junction of the two branches of Cat Cleugh. Exposures of sandstone with plant fragments, grey mudstone and coal at this point belong to the Carboniferous sequence in the Sanquhar Coalfield. Although the basin has the overall structure of a NW-trending half-graben, the Sanquhar Fault forming its NE boundary appears to have been overstepped here by Carboniferous strata, with no evidence seen in Cat Cleugh for any large-scale faulting.

From Cat Cleugh, return to the road at Bail Hill. This forms a convenient break in the excursion; the next locality involves a 2.5 km hike across rough moorland.

8 Stoodfold Burn: lithic tuffs and siltstones

Starting from the road 500 m south of the summit of Bail Hill, walk about 600 m east to Stoodfold Burn [767 138] and traverse downstream. In Stoodfold Burn, close to its confluence with Kiln Burn, the outlying hawaiite/mugearite lithic tuffs and agglomerates of the Stoodfold Member can be examined. The tuffs interfinger with siltstones of the Kiln Formation and were derived by submarine grain-flow during pyroclastic activity on the adjacent Bail Hill volcano. Lithic fragments include lavas containing phenocrysts of amphibole, plagioclase, biotite/phlogopite and apatite. Similar lithic and crystal tuffs together with agglomerate and volcaniclastic mudstone are interbedded with fine-grained sandstone and siltstone of the Kiln Formation at its type section in the adjacent Kiln Burn [769 138]. Return to the vehicles and drive back down to the B740. At the junction, turn left (NE) under the railway towards Crawfordjohn and continue for about 4 km to just beyond Carco Farm.

9 Spothfore Burn: Glenflosh, Kiln and Spothfore formations; greywackes, conglomerates and tuffs

On the B740 Crawick to Crawfordjohn road, park a short distance east of Carco Farm and walk up Spothfore Burn from the bridge near its confluence with the Crawick Water [792 141].

The lower 800 m of the burn traverses quartz-rich greywackes of the Glenflosh Formation before crossing the Eller Fault into the black shales and chert (Moffat Shale Group) which underlie the Kiln Formation (Figure 28). Continuing upstream, hawaiite/mugearite tuff and agglomerate of the Stoodfold Member are seen interbedded with the fine-grained strata of the Kiln Formation. Close by in the Penfrau Burn tributary, interbedded tuffs of the Penfrau Member are of basaltic composition.

About 200 m upstream from Penfrau Burn, the thin-bedded sandstones and silt-stones of the Kiln Formation are succeeded conformably by the much coarser-grained Spothfore Formation. Lithologies include boulder conglomerate, pebble breccia, granule sandstone and siltstone. Clasts range in size up to several metres diameter and are entirely of intra-basinal origin: about 95 per cent of them are of sedimentary material such as greywacke, siltstone or chert, with volcanic rocks making up the balance. The rather disorganised nature of many of the conglomerate beds suggests emplacement by a debris-flow mechanism, with occasional imbrication evidence indicating flow towards the SE.

In Spothfore Burn, several large chert bodies (tens of metres in size) can be seen for about 200 m downstream from the junction with Polholm Burn. Features such as bedding oblique to the regional trend, randomly orientated internal folds, and sharp irregular contacts with the surrounding greywacke, have led to these chert bodies being interpreted as large gravity-emplaced olistoliths which have slid downslope or been eroded from the walls of a submarine canyon.

Along strike to the NE, additional outlying hawaiite/mugearite tuffs and agglomerates of the Back Burn and Craignorth members are interbedded with siltstones of the Kiln Formation in Back Burn [794 155] and on Craignorth Hill [811 163] respectively (Figure 28), though these localities are not included in this excursion.

J D Floyd

Excursion 7

Loch Doon and Carsphairn: Ordovician turbidites, mineralisation and the Loch Doon Granite

OS 1:50 000 Sheet 77 Dalmellington to New Galloway
BGS 1:50 000 sheets 8E Loch Doon, 14E Cumnock
Route map: Figure 29

Main points of interest Contact between the Loch Doon Granite and surrounding greywackes; lead-zinc mineralisation and abandoned lead mines; haematite vein; Ordovician greywacke, conglomerate, black shale and chert; porphyrite (porphyritic microdiorite) dykes.

Logistics The excursion begins at Loch Doon Dam, about 3 km along the minor road (signposted to Loch Doon Castle) which leaves the A713 about 2 km south of Dalmellington. At some localities parking is at the side of single-track roads; participants should show consideration for other road users by not parking in designated passing places. Localities 1, 2, 4 and 7 are only a short distance from the roadside, Locality 3 involves a longer walk mostly along paths, while Localities 5 and 6 require several kilometres of cross-country walking.

Introduction This excursion examines the contact between the Loch Doon Granite and the surrounding greywackes (Figure 29) at Locality 2. Localities 1, 4, 5 and 7 deal with the Ordovician sedimentary succession and associated minor intrusions in the Carsphairn area. The general tectonostratigraphical relationships of the sedimentary formations are illustrated in Figure 2 (Leadhills Group). The lead mines at Woodhead (Locality 3) and the haematite vein at Coran of Portmark (Locality 6) are of interest both to mineral collectors and to students of industrial archaeology.

The broad valley of the Glenkens, between Dalmellington and New Galloway, is also notable in containing several reservoirs for the original Galloway Water Power Scheme. This was built in the 1930s and

remains the only substantial hydroelectric scheme in Scotland outwith the Highlands.

1 Loch Doon Dam: Marchburn Formation greywacke

Park beside the tourist office/toilet block beside the dam at the north end of Loch Doon [NS 477 012]. Walk south for about 600 m along the wave-washed western shore of the reservoir to examine excellent *roches moutonnées* with good examples of glacial striae gouged into well-polished rock surfaces. The latter reveal good sections through medium- to thick-bedded, coarse-grained greywackes and laminated siltstones of the Marchburn Formation. Beds strike between 060° and 090° and dip south at 60–80°. However, excellent graded bedding and other sedimentary structures in the greywackes clearly demonstrate that the succession youngs towards the north and that the beds are therefore overturned. This bedding attitude is common across much of the Northern Belt, especially in the area immediately south of the Southern Upland Fault.

2 Loch Doon Castle: granite/greywacke contact

From the dam, continue south on the lochside road for a further 7 km to Loch Doon Castle [NX 485 950]. Park beside the castle and walk north along the loch shore to the rocky headland about 450 m NE of the castle and immediately below a roadside quarry. On the north side of the headland a sequence of dark hornfelsed greywackes exhibits well-developed sedimentary structures and strikes between NE and ENE.

Traversing south across the headland, north–south-trending fracture zones about 20 cm wide can be seen. Each is characterised by a series of individual fractures lying at a slight anticlockwise angle to the zone; individual bedding layers show sinis-

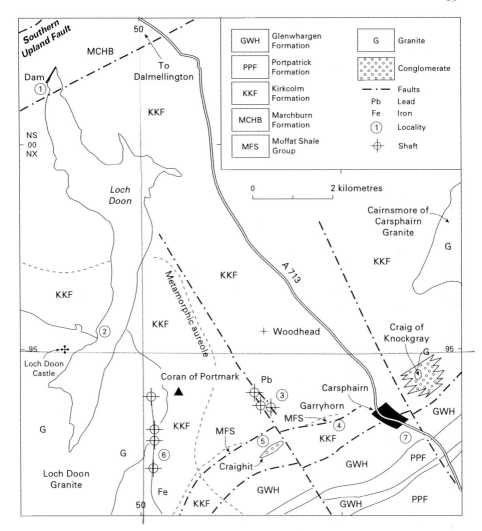

Figure 29 Locality map and outline geology for the Loch Doon–Carsphairn area.

tral displacement across the fractures. Locally these zones are crossed by a series of thin acidic veinlets which trend roughly ESE. The veinlets may have a stepped course caused by local diversions along the fracture planes.

On the south side of the headland, granodiorite veins become abundant as the margin of the Loch Doon pluton is approached. These veins cut the acidic veinlets described above and have a random orientation. The terminations of some of the larger veins

suggest that bedding has been forced apart on small brittle faults, though elsewhere the granodiorite veins contain xenoliths of greywacke which suggest some stoping during intrusion. The relationships between north–south fractures, acidic veinlets and granodiorite veins indicate an initial phase of brittle deformation with a sinistral displacement followed by a period of extension at right angles to the margin of the pluton.

To the south, the outcrop deteriorates but intermittent exposures of granodiorite indicate that the main contact lies immediately south of the headland. The overall trend of the contact in this area is ESE. Proceed along the foreshore to the next headland immediately south of the castle. Here the granodiorite contains abundant xenoliths of greywacke as well as autoliths of igneous material. The xenoliths are generally aligned parallel to the contact. Xenoliths may also be seen on a second headland about 100 m farther south. A particularly interesting example is a strip of greywacke several metres long which has been intruded by relatively fine-grained granitic material prior to incorporation in the main granodiorite.

The numerous ruins of brick buildings beside the road along the loch, and the concrete blocks in the loch itself, are the remains of a seaplane base which was established at Loch Doon during the First World War. Some curious embankments on the east shore at the head of the loch were also part of this project, which swallowed up large amounts of money and caused great controversy at the time. Loch Doon Castle itself originally stood on an adjacent small island in the loch, the top of which can still be seen when the water is low. During the 1930s, when the water level in the loch was raised as part of the hydroelectric scheme, the castle was dismantled stone by stone and re-erected at its present site.

3 Woodhead Lead Mines: lead and zinc mineralisation

Health and safety note: As with any former mining area, there may be hidden dangers involved from the presence of old shafts, adits, unsafe buildings etc. and special care is required, especially for younger (and elderly) participants. Visitors should also be aware of the insidious risk of heavy-metal poisoning (lead, zinc, copper etc.) both from mineral specimens and from the widespread contamination on the site. Precautions should therefore be taken with hygiene, especially during the consumption of packed lunches etc., both on site and afterwards.

From Loch Doon, drive back to the A713 and continue south towards Carsphairn.

About 1 km north of the village, turn west on to a farm road (gated) to Garryhorn Farm. With permission, park at the farm and proceed on foot, or drive west for about 1.5 km along the rough road to the mines.

The long-abandoned lead mines at Woodhead are situated on the north bank of the Garryhorn Burn [530 938]. The veins of galena, zinc-blende and minor chalcopyrite were discovered in 1838. Initially they were worked open cast before shafts were sunk and levels driven at depths of 16, 33 and 57 m. Lead production rose rapidly in the first few years, reaching a peak of 905 tons in 1842, before gradually dwindling to only 12 tons in 1873 (Wilson, 1921). However, even during its most productive period of 1840–1852, the Woodhead mines were never so important as the Leadhills/Wanlockhead operations.

There are several ruined cottages on the site together with the remains of the buildings and other works where the lead ore was dressed and smelted. As at Leadhills/Wanlockhead, there is evidence (in the headwaters of the Garryhorn Burn) of an elaborate system of contour-following channels which led water to the mines for powering pumps and other machinery. Again as at Wanlockhead, the highly poisonous fumes from the smelting hearths were led along flues in roofed-over trenches and eventually up the large stone chimneys which still dominate the site. **The trench flues are now largely grassed over and form dangerous pitfalls for the unwary.** Fumes from these primitive hearths contained a high proportion of lead and sulphur dioxide and, even in early times, lead poisoning was a well-known hazard for lead miners and smelters, as well as for local residents. This was often accepted as an unavoidable fact of life and diagnosed with the quaint term 'Lead Distemper'.

From the extensive physical evidence still remaining it is obvious that, in its heyday, Woodhead must have been a very busy little mining community. The isolation of the locality has contributed to its relatively well-preserved condition and it represents an important industrial archaeology site in south-west Scotland.

There are two main veins, named Woodhead and Garryhorn, both of which trend about 150°, hade NE at 62° and probably follow part of the extensive NW trending plexus of faults which delineates the valley of the Glenkens between New Galloway and Loch Doon. The vein infill consists mainly of broken country rock (greywacke of the Kirkcolm Formation) with strings and patches of calcite, dolomite and quartz in addition to the ore minerals. There is little sign of the halo of pervasive hydrothermal alteration of the country rock which forms such a notable feature at Leadhills/Wanlockhead. Good samples of ore minerals (particularly galena) and vein breccia can still be found on the various spoil dumps throughout the site. **The locations of several shafts are now marked by circular dry-stone dyke enclosures and should be treated with caution.**

In a small quarry at the north end of the site, beside an infilled shaft or collapsed stope, thick greywacke beds strike 090° and dip north at 85°. Gently pitching flute casts visible on the bases of several greywacke beds indicate currents from the NE and prove that the succession youngs northwards. The west wall of the quarry is defined by a slickensided fault plane, trending 150° and hading NE at 55°. This is probably a continuation, or a subparallel branch, of the fault which controls the Woodhead Vein. A vertical breccia vein trending 170° can also be seen on the north side of the quarry.

4   Garryhorn Burn: black shale and chert

While in the area, the opportunity should be taken to examine the thick hemipelagic shales exposed in the Garryhorn Burn [548 933] adjacent to and just upstream from Garryhorn Farm. A prominent microdiorite dyke forms the north bank of the burn for over 200 m whereas the south bank is formed by cherty black shales and grey bedded cherts, probably Moffat Shale Group strata brought up along a fault associated with the Leadhills Fault imbricate zone.

5   Craighit: Kirkcolm Formation conglomerates

The prominent hill of Craighit [534 926], is reached by a rough walk of about 1 km south across country from Garryhorn Farm. The summit is composed of thick beds of greywacke and boulder conglomerate. The most abundant clasts in the conglomerate are fairly angular pebbles of vein quartz up to 6 cm across but most of the larger blocks are intrabasinal clasts of dark calcareous siltstone and sandstone. These are more easily eroded than the greywacke matrix and therefore weather to form hollows in the conglomerate. There is also an abundance of well-rounded pebbles and boulders of fine-grained acid igneous rocks, including the largest block seen (38 cm × 20 cm).

Looking NE from Craighit, the rounded Craig of Knockgrey, 4 km distant, is also formed by greywackes and conglomerates of the Kirkcolm Formation, but the strata there are intruded and baked by a small granite cupola. Beyond and towering in the background is the large rounded mass of the Cairnsmore of Carsphairn Granite with its associated aureole of hornfelsed greywackes.

6   Coran of Portmark: haematite vein

While still in the Garryhorn area, the more energetic visitor may wish to visit a vein of haematite [505 911 to 503 938] situated in the hills west of the Woodhead Lead Mines and reached by a rough walk of 3 km and climb of 250 m from the mines. The vein was extensively prospected in 1869 and again in 1876 by the Dalmellington Iron Company via a series of cross-cuts and small shafts which reached a depth of 21 m. It is reported that about 400 tons of poor quality haematite were raised but abandoned on the ground as uneconomic to transport to Dalmellington (Macgregor et al., 1920). In 1901, Messrs Colvilles re-examined the vein by a series of trenches and bores but the prospect was again found to be uneconomic.

The 3 km-long haematite vein runs almost N–S and cuts the contact between the Loch Doon Granite and the Ordovician country rocks (greywackes of the Kirkcolm Formation). Extensive investigations proved the vein to consist of a fissure between 0.6 and 3 m wide, filled with brecciated and haematite-stained country rock and with only small masses of haematite ore.

The site of the vein is close to the north end of the Rhinns of Kells, a long ridge of hornfelsed greywackes forming an eastern wall to the Loch Doon Granite. A visit to the vein could thus provide additional geological interest to enhance the spectacular views on this very pleasant ridge-walk.

7 Liggat Bridge, Carsphairn: greywackes and dykes

From Garryhorn Farm, return to the A713 and drive south for 2 km through Carsphairn. Park at the War Memorial near the junction with the B729 at the south end of the village and walk down to the Water of Deugh below the nearby Liggat Bridge [569 929] on the A713 to examine medium-bedded coarse-grained quartzose greywackes of the Glenwhargen Formation. Bedding strikes 070° and dips 55° to the south though graded bedding in the greywackes clearly demonstrates that the succession youngs towards the north and is therefore overturned. Two prominent porphyrite (por-phyritic microdiorite) dykes, of late Silurian to early Devonian age, are also visible in the Water of Deugh at this locality. The northernmost dyke is grey, 3 m wide and trends 065° whereas the other is pale pink, 1 m wide, trends 078° and displays obvious internal banding parallel to its margins. The colour variation presumably reflects slight differences in composition and/or grain size between the two dykes.

About 200 m downstream from the bridge, medium- and thick-bedded greywackes of the andesite-rich Portpatrick Formation are exposed in the bed of the river close to the north bank, though the contact with the Glenwhargen Formation cannot be seen at this locality. Beds here strike 060° and dip south at 70°, though a paucity of way-up evidence precludes determination of younging direction. Abundant evidence from other parts of the Southern Uplands shows that the Portpatrick and Glenwhargen formations are interbedded.

J D Floyd and D J Fettes

Excursion 8

GIRVAN and BALLANTRAE: an obducted ophiolite

OS 1: 50 000 Sheet 76 Girvan
BGS 1: 50 000 Sheet 7 Girvan, 8W Carrick and 14W Ayr
BGS 1: 25 000 Sheet NX08, 18 and 19 (in part)
Route maps: Figures 30 and 31

Main points of interest Early Ordovician Ballantrae ophiolite Complex (pillow lavas, gabbro, serpentinite, chert and mélange), late Ordovician and early Silurian greywacke and conglomerate; late Ordovician reef limestone, Caledonian folding.

Logistics There is ample parking for cars and space for a coach near most localities. Most of the exposures are on the coast and require much scrambling over steep and sometimes slippery rocks. Maximum walk at any one locality is about 2.5 km along beach and cliff paths. The outcrops are best seen at low tide and ideally the excursion should be planned to coincide with low water at about 1pm; this should allow adequate access from 9am to 5pm. Most of the localities described have been designated Sites of Special Scientific Interest (Appendix 2).

Introduction The ophiolitic Ballantrae Complex and its sedimentary cover are well exposed between Girvan and Ballantrae. The area has been a focus of considerable geological research (summarised by Stone and Smellie, 1988). The geological complexity of the area is such that several days are required to examine all of the varied features exposed. Thus, previous excursion guides have included a three-day itinerary (Robertson et al., 1990) and the seven itineraries recently published by Bluck and Ingham (1992). The field excursion described below is intended to bring out the main features of the complex and its unconformable sedimentary cover in a single day. Those with more time available are referred particularly to Bluck and Ingham (1992).

The ophiolite complex consists of two main elements interleaved by faulting; ser-pentinised ultramafic rocks representing oceanic mantle and volcanic sequences representing the remains of island arc and ocean crust. The structure is dominated by NE–SW faults which divide the complex into discrete lithological zones such that northern and southern serpentinite belts separate three areas of mainly volcanic rock (Figure 30). A late Tremadoc to early Arenig age has been established for the eruption of the volcanic components (Balcreuchan Group); the interbedded sedimentary strata contain graptolite faunas of that age (Stone and Rushton, 1983; Rushton et al., 1986) and Sm-Nd radiometric dating of the basalts has given ages of 501 ± 12 and 476 ± 14 Ma (Thirlwall and Bluck, 1984). It is believed that the ophiolite was obducted on to the continental margin during the middle Arenig, since metamorphic rocks formed at this stage have been dated by the K-Ar method at 478 ± 8 Ma (Bluck et al., 1980). Some late Arenig sedimentary rocks, probably deposited during the final stages of obduction, are structurally included within the ophiolite (Smellie and Stone, 1992) and the oldest strata within the unconformably overlying cover sequence (Barr Group) are of Llanvirn age. Sedimentation above the ophiolite was controlled by a series of faults, downthrowing to the south and sequentially stepping back northwards. Thus the basal conglomeratic facies becomes progressively younger northwards; in the south the basal conglomerate is Llanvirn, in the north Caradoc (Williams, 1959; Ince, 1984). Above the basal conglomerate, which is commonly associated with shallow-marine limestone, facies become progressively more deep water upwards so that turbiditic greywackes and shales form much of the exposed sequence. This is more or less continuous up into the Silurian, with only a slight stratigraphical break and small angular discordance in bedding at the Ordovician–Silurian boun-

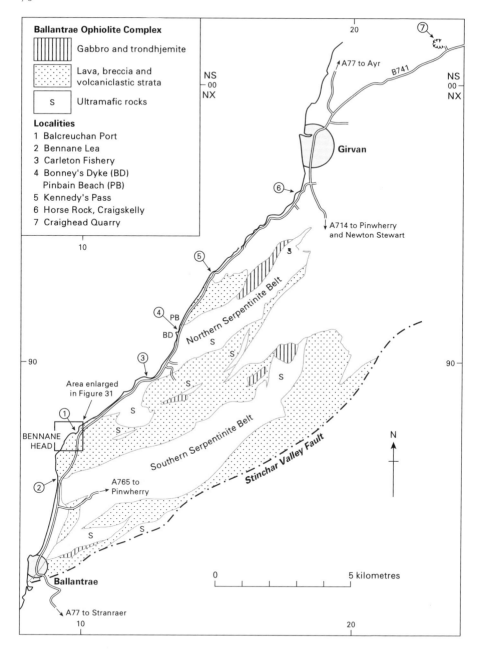

Figure 30 Locality map for the Girvan–Ballantrae excursion and outline geology of the Ballantrae ophiolite Complex.

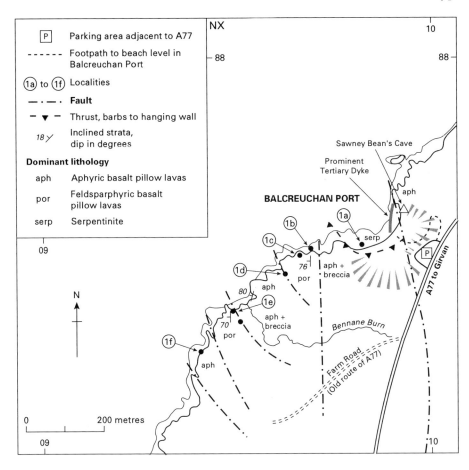

Figure 31 Locality map and outline geology for Balcreuchan Port (Locality 1) and the coastal section to the south-west.

dary. The main tectonism occurred late in the Silurian and produced folding and north-directed thrusts.

The ophiolite complex is examined at Localities 1 to 4, and the sedimentary cover at Localities 5 to 7. Locality 7 should be regarded as an alternative stop in a single day excursion but could be included in a more leisurely 2-day schedule. Since many of the coastal exposures are tide-dependent (local details given below) the order in which localities are visited may have to be varied to suit conditions. **Tide tables should be carefully checked** and the excursion planned accordingly.

1 Balcreuchan Port: structural imbrication in Arenig lavas and lava breccias

A convenient place to begin the excursion is the large lay-by overlooking Balcreuchan Port on the seaward side of the A77 (Figure 31) [NX100 876]. There is a fine view over the Firth of Clyde towards Arran and to Ailsa Craig, a spectacular Tertiary microgranite plug (Harrison et al., 1987).

From the car park descend into Balcreuchan Port by the steep footpath on the east side of the cove. **Take great care, the slopes are very steep** so do not leave the footpath. However, note the cliffs to the south and east; pillows of basalt lava can be seen on both sides.

At beach level there is extensive intertidal rock outcrop. Prominent here is a Tertiary basalt dyke, up to about 50 cm across and trending generally north across the foreshore. The dyke has resisted erosion and now stands proud of its host rock. Abundant amygdales are concentrated into zones parallel to the dyke margin and are normally restricted to only one side of the dyke.

The Tertiary dyke is intruded into highly altered ultramafic rock which at this locality consists largely of a mass of secondary quartz and carbonate veins. Such alteration is fairly common at the margins of serpentinised ultramafic bodies and is generally regarded as a side effect of the serpentinisation process. A north–south fault marks the east margin of Balcreuchan Port, beyond which the steep sea cliffs are formed by basalt lavas, both massive and pillowed. The petrographical and geochemical characteristics of the volcanic rocks are typical of lavas erupted in oceanic island arcs above subduction zones (Thirlwall and Bluck, 1984; Smellie and Stone, 1988 and references therein). Most of the sequence is tholeiitic but it includes some boninitic lavas with exceptionally high contents of Cr and Ni. This lava variety is relatively rare and modern examples are found exclusively in oceanic island arcs (Smellie and Stone, 1992). Within the lava sequence a cave, controlled by minor faulting, is reputed to have been the home of Sawney Bean and his family, the notorious 16th century cannibals.

From the cave and the adjacent boninitic lavas cross SW towards the opposite side of the bay. About two-thirds of the way across (**1a** on Figure 31), serpentinised ultramafic lithologies are exposed below mid-tide level: these are dunite (almost entirely olivine) and harzburgite containing both olivine and orthopyroxene. The pyroxene can be seen as bronze-coloured flecks in the background of dark green serpentinised olivine. A gently inclined contact, possibly thrust, separates the ultramafic rocks from the overlying lavas and lava breccias forming the SW headland of Balcreuchan Port. The route continues SW over the headland, an easy scramble at mid to low tide but quite diffi-cult at high tide, and across the next small bay to the cliffs on its far side. A prominent fault gully trends south (inland) from this point and its western side is formed by steeply dipping clastic sedimentary strata; note the marked swing in strike adjacent to the fault. Sandstones and mélange-like breccia (probably formed by slumping) make up most of the sequence, but an important intercalation of laminated red and cream fine-grained sandstone (**1b**) can be seen at the west end of the rock platform (just above low water mark). This laminated bed is important on several accounts, not least for the contained graptolite fauna which establishes an early Arenig age for this part of the sequence (Stone and Rushton, 1983). The lithology is distinctive, making it a readily identifiable marker horizon, and its sedimentological features allow the young-ing direction to be established. Check the layering carefully; it is cut out westward by a coarse feldspathic sandstone which is in turn overlain by a repeat of the red and cream striped lithology, but this time in a jumbled, chaotic form. A likely interpreta-tion is that a channel was eroded into the striped sandstone and partially filled by the coarse feldspathic sandstone; the channel walls then collapsed to give the chaotic deposit. The younging direction is clearly to the west.

Rejoin the footpath above these crags and continue west for a few metres to the next prominent outcrop. This is formed of reddened basaltic pillow lavas rich in feldspar phenocrysts and, at the east side of the outcrop, a conformable relationship can be established between the lava and fine-grained sandstone. Bearing in mind the younging direction established earlier, the lava almost certainly overlies the sand-stone. These lavas, and those to be exam-ined subsequently towards Port Vad and Bennane Head, have the geochemical char-acteristics of oceanic island or hot-spot lavas similar to the modern example of Hawaii. Such a major change in lava type emphasises the importance of the fault to the east of locality 1b.

For the next few tens of metres westward the feldsparphyric pillow lavas are well exposed, particularly on the flat surfaces overlooking the sea. An approximate north–south strike of steeply inclined bedding can be readily established, and a continuation of the westward younging confirmed, from the shape of the pillows. These have smooth convex upper surfaces but more irregular lower surfaces which bulge and drape into underlying cavities. Note the red chert filling spaces between some of the pillows. The feldsparphyric pillow lavas arc exposed on the next rocky headland (**1c**) but there they are cut by dykes of fine-grained basalt, best seen on the seaward end of the headland. The dykes are taken to be feeders for the next higher unit of pillow lavas because these have the same aphyric composition.

The contact between the two lava types is exposed in a fault gully about 15 m farther west (**1d**). A deep cleft is open to the sea but at the narrower, inland end the rock in the gully walls can be examined. **Take great care; the sea is a long way down and the exposure is precarious**. The eastern side of the gully is formed of feldsparphyric lava and the lowermost pillows in the western wall are also feldsparphyric. However, these are conformably overlain by aphyric pillow lavas, which then form the sequence continuing westward.

Continue west on the footpath, crossing faulted and brecciated aphyric lavas, towards the mouth of the Bennane Burn. Stratified, fine-grained clastic rocks overlying the brecciated lavas, are best examined beside a sea-water pool on the SW side of the burn (**1e**). Interbedded sandstone, chert and dark shale form a small cliff; the shale has yielded graptolites of middle Arenig age (Stone and Rushton, 1983). Thus, the traverse has passed from the lower to the middle Arenig, confirming the sedimentological evidence for westward younging.

From the sea-water pool climb inland for a short distance up a cattle track into a shallow NW–SE gully with rock forming low crags along its SW side. These crags expose a familiar sequence: reddened feldsparphyric pillow lavas conformably overlie fine-grained clastic strata including a red and cream striped sandstone remarkably similar to the early Arenig example seen at Locality 1b. The feldsparphyric lavas are well exposed to the SW and provide abundant evidence of continued and consistent steep dip and SW-younging. Chert and siliceous sandstone interbeds occur at intervals and from one of these an early Arenig graptolite fauna has been collected (Stone and Rushton, 1983). The comparison with the sequence traversed at Localities 1b to 1d is then further strengthened by the appearance of aphyric pillow lavas above and to the SW of the feldsparphyric pillows. The aphyric pillows are well exposed in landward-facing cliffs at the margin of a small embayment about 200 m SW from Bennane Burn (**1f**) but from there the coastal cliffs become impassable. A major fault repeating the succession seems probable and the most likely site is the NW–SE gully followed by the cattle track at Locality 1e above Bennane Burn.

Return to the car park above Balcreuchan Port and proceed to Locality 2, where the southward continuation of the section can be seen.

2   Bennane Lea: Balcreuchan Group (Arenig) conglomerate and chert

South from Balcreuchan Port the A77 has been re-routed inland for about 2 km to Bennane Lea. Some parking space is available on the seaward side of the road where it rejoins the coast and the extensive raised beach [092 858]. Vehicles should be left outside the cattle grid; access to the beach section is via a small sand pit. The old A77 road is now a private access route and should not be used. Further details and a full description of the sections are also provided by Bluck (1978) and in Bluck and Ingham (1992).

Exposures of Permian red sandstone beds, dipping gently south, can be examined at low tide. These lie at the edge of an extensive offshore Permian basin, the faulted eastern margin of which runs beneath the raised beach between Bennane Lea and Ballantrae. However, locally at Bennane Lea the Permian strata are unconformable on the Ballantrae Complex and the basal red sandstone contains clasts of spilitic lava (Stone, 1988).

There is a marked topographical change at Bennane Lea: steep sea cliffs to the north contrast with the raised beach, backed by relic sea cliffs cut in glacial till, to the south. The change takes place across a faulted junction between basaltic lava and breccia, to the north, and less-resistant ultramafic rock of the Southern Serpentinite Belt, to the south. The ultramafic rock exposed on the shore is altered and reddened, it also contains pods of gabbroic composition which are probably tectonic inclusions. The fault itself is exposed on the foreshore at Bennane Lea (subject to the vagaries of drifting sand) as a thin zone of silicification, north of which a massive tuff unit forms the first rocky outcrop. Traversing northwards a conformable contact between the tuff and underlying thinly bedded cherts can be seen. The cherts themselves contain altered radiolaria and are chaotically deformed into small-scale, disharmonic structures which seem most likely to be the result of soft sediment deformation through slumping. Slightly farther north, mass-flow conglomerates are interbedded with the cherts; the pebbles and cobbles present are mainly of spilitic lava and all can be related to lithologies exposed elsewhere in the Ballantrae Complex. Pale blocks, seemingly of limestone, at first appear out of place but contained chrome spinel grains suggest that they are likely to have originated as ultramafic rock. Alternations of bedded chert and conglomerate continue north for about 100 m, folded about several large, upright hinges which plunge steeply seawards. These are tectonic structures and can be correlated with the large anticlines and synclines clearly visible in the steep cliffs on the inland side of the old A77 road. The steep hinge plunges may bring down to the beach exposures the highest stratigraphical levels preserved, i.e. the mass flow conglomerates which are certainly not present in any of the inland outcrops.

Farther along, to the north of Bennane Cave, discontinuous layers of coarse feldspathic sandstone are interbedded with the chert. At one important exposure [0909 8627] such sandstone locally forms about 30 per cent of the sequence; close by and slightly north, black siliceous mudstone, locally stained green by secondary copper minerals, is exposed between large boulders. There is a marked change of strike in

this vicinity, and evidence for much minor faulting, but there is a consensus that the black mudstone stratigraphically underlies the chert and sandstone (Bluck and Ingham, 1992; Stone and Smellie, 1988, table 5). Slightly farther north, and lower in the sequence, similar siliceous mudstone layers are interbedded with basalt lava and breccia. A graptolite fauna recovered from these mudstones gave a middle Arenig age (Stone and Rushton, 1983), similar to that obtained at the sea-water pool (Locality 1e) in the Balcreuchan Port traverse. Fracture planes within the black mudstone may be coated with green, secondary copper minerals such as malachite.

North towards Bennane Head the rock exposed at sea level for the first few hundred metres is predominantly basalt lava but the cliffs inland of the old A77 consist mainly of basalt breccia which extends seaward to form the steep cliffs of Bennane Head itself. The breccia is believed to overlie the middle Arenig sequence seen at Locality 1e (Stone and Smellie, 1988, table 5). It can be most readily examined by continuing north for about 300 m to the southern flanks of Bennane Head [091 865] where it includes beds of coarse-grained sandstone. However, the general lithology can be examined in the abundant large loose blocks which surround the black siliceous mudstone exposures. This completes the section from Balcreuchan Port to Bennane Lea, a traverse from island arc lavas into and through an oceanic island volcano-sedimentary assemblage. Return along the beach to the parking area.

3 Carleton Fishery: ultramafic rock and altered dolerite

The next locality, Carleton Fishery, is about 5 km north along the A77. Ample parking is available in the well-signposted picnic site [123 894]. Walk east for about 100 m to the old black boathouse and descend to the beach on the NE side of the rock outcrop.

The outcrop is within the Northern Serpentinite Belt and ultramafic rock, mainly dunite, is exposed between the loose boulders and shingle. Locally, layered relationships on a centimetre scale are developed between the dunite and coarser-grained, pyroxene-rich harzburgite. The main mass of the outcrop is composed of dolerite, which was probably originally intrusive into the dunite. It has suffered extensive calcium-metasomatism and this has produced the fine-grained, flinty appearance of the marginal dolerite which is now composed of an assemblage of calcium-rich secondary minerals (e.g. prehnite, pectolite, hydrogrossular) known as rodingite. Large relict feldspar phenocrysts can be seen in some parts of the dolerite, and a large ultramafic enclave forms an eroded hollow on the top of the main rock mass. Another feature of interest is the network of thin (< 1.5 mm) chrysotile asbestos veins, seen in the ultramafic rock towards low water mark on the north side of the outcrop. The veins are mostly developed adjacent to the dolerite and parallel to its margins. Return to the parking area at the Carleton Fishery picnic site.

4 Bonney's Dyke and Pinbain Beach: gabbro pegmatite, Balcreuchan Group mélange and breccia

About 2.5 km north from Carleton Fishery is a locality known as 'Bonney's Dyke'. Parking is available in a rough lay-by on the seaward side of the A77 [136 910].

Bonney's Dyke is a term used in the geological literature for a mass of pegmatitic gabbro within the Northern Serpentinite Belt. The name derives from Professor T G Bonney, the eminent Victorian mineralogist who recognised the igneous origins of much of the Ballantrae Complex (Bonney, 1878). When approached from the south the gabbro stands out as a paler, more resistant body within the ultramafic rock. It is exposed just above high water mark and in the intertidal zone. The outcrop is slightly arcuate owing to the cumulative effect of minor sinistral wrench faults. The pegmatitic texture is spectacular, with plagioclase and altered clinopyroxene crystals up to 3 cm across within zones of marked grain-size variation. There is no sign of chilling against either the surrounding ultramafic rock or the numerous serpentinite xenoliths. Three types of marginal contact relationship are seen:

1 sharp gabbro-serpentinite contacts;
2 less well-defined margins where the gabbro is in contact with coarse pyroxenite veins;
3 sheared margins that are fine grained, flinty and particularly intensively Ca-metasomatised (rodingitised).

The south side of Bonney's Dyke shows a combination of types 1 and 2 whereas the north side is principally a sheared contact of type 3.

Pyroxenite veins occur intermittently throughout the ultramafic outcrop; they are pale green, coarse grained and up to about 50 cm across. The coarsest developments contain pyroxene crystals several centimetres across and can be seen slightly to the south of the gabbro towards low water mark.

From Bonney's Dyke walk north along the shore for about 350 m towards Pinbain Bridge. Several low intertidal outcrops expose fine-grained serpentinised harzburgite, although the movement of the beach sands may occasionally obscure them. Alternatively, drive up to a small lay-by on the seaward side of the road at Pinbain Bridge [137 913]. The Pinbain beach section, also described by Bluck (1978) and in Bluck and Ingham (1992), exposes the contact between the Northern Serpentinite Belt and the Pinbain volcano-sedimentary sequence. A Tertiary dyke trending approximately east–west is intruded along the contact and has baked the adjacent serpentinite so that it now stands out as the more resistant lithology, a reversal of the normal situation. North of the dyke, a mélange deposit is well exposed in the intertidal zone; within its foliated muddy matrix are clasts of basalt and rarer amphibolite and schist. Prominent large, pale grey, carbonate blocks are not of organic or even sedimentary origin; residual grains of chrome spinel within the carbonate reveal that they are altered ultramafic rocks. The origin of the mélange deposit was probably by mass flow but much of the foliation through the matrix may have been imparted by subsequent tectonic shearing.

The highest point within this sequence of rocky outcrops consists of brecciated spilitic pillow lavas. Many of the pillows retain their shape despite pervasive cracks but others have completely disaggregated. There is no fine-grained matrix with this deposit and it is uncertain whether it forms a discrete unit interbedded with the mélange or whether it is part of a very large clast contained within the mélange. The latter lithology is also exposed to the north of the breccia but there the proportion of clasts is higher, and the foliation less marked, than in the exposure to the south.

Farther north a complex fault zone reintroduces tectonic slivers of serpentinite into the section. These are not exposed at beach level but form the cliff behind the isolated raised beach inland of the A77 where some dunite contains large pods of chrome spinel. The main mass of steep cliffs and rocky coastal outcrop to the north is composed of volcaniclastic sandstone, the faulted contact with the serpentinite slivers being intruded by Tertiary dykes. These are exposed at beach level immediately south of the sandstones. The latter are at the base of a thick sequence of lavas and clastic sedimentary rock which is exposed continuously for some distance north along the coast. Graptolites have been recovered at the base of the sequence from siltstones which are exposed on the inland roadside of the A77 behind the crash barriers. An early Arenig age was deduced by Rushton et al. (1986) but the specimens are generally fragmentary, very scarce, and only recovered with much patient effort.

5   Kennedy's Pass: Caradocian Kilranny Conglomerate and Ardwell Formation

Drive about 2.5 km north from Pinbain to Kennedy's Pass. Ample parking is available in a lay-by on the seaward side of the road [149 932].

This locality allows examination of some of the late Ordovician strata which form an unconformable cover to the Ballantrae ophiolite. It is also described in an extensive field itinerary for the cover sequence given in Bluck and Ingham (1992). The full cover sequence records north-westward marine transgression, from the late Llanvirn onwards, across the obducted ophiolite. Sedimentation was controlled by a series of faults throwing down to the south but becoming sequentially younger to the north. The over-

all geometry is summarised in Figure 32, based largely on the work of Williams (1959; cf. Ingham, 1978 and Ince, 1984). The Barr Group rests unconformably on the ophiolitic rocks and continues up to the base of the Caradoc, whence the conformably succeeding Ardmillan Group ranges up to the high Ashgill.

At Kennedy's Pass the Kilranny Conglomerate is well exposed in the sea cliffs below the parking area. The Barr Group and the unconformable base of the sequence are here both faulted out and the Kilranny Conglomerate, low in the Ardmillan Group, is the lowest unit exposed. However, in lithology it is typical of the Barr Group conglomerates (e.g. Benan Conglomerate) which rest unconformably on the ophiolite elsewhere.

Overall the Kilranny Conglomerate is crudely stratified with both clast- and matrix-supported lithologies present. Some beds show clast imbrication and from this can be deduced a palaeocurrent flow from the north. Clasts range up to 1 m across and include red chert, basalt and gabbro (probably derived from the underlying ophiolite) and abundant felsitic and granitic rocks. Prominent amongst the latter are clasts of pink granite which have been dated by the Rb-Sr method at about 470 Ma (Longman et al., 1979). This suggests that intrusion occurred only a relatively short time before deposition (early Caradoc is approximately 455 Ma) and so rapid uplift and erosion of the source hinterland seem likely.

The conglomerate beds become younger northwards, and near the north end of the cliff exposure they are unconformably overlain by thinly bedded siltstones and greywackes of the Ardwell Formation. These are turbidites and appear to fill a channel eroded into the top of the underlying conglomerate. They are best examined about 100 m farther north where wave-polished surfaces reveal good examples of graded bedding and fine lamination. However, the most striking aspect of this section is the spectacular development of large and small chevron 'box' folds. Northwards from Kennedy's Pass the fold hinges trend approximately NE but plunge is variable; the southernmost examples plunge gently

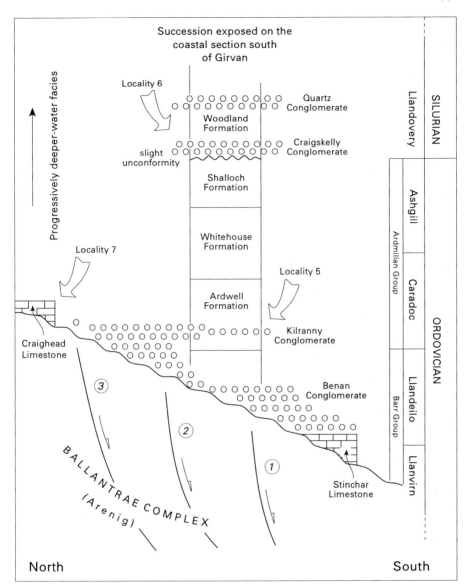

Figure 32 Schematic illustration of stratigraphical relationships above the Ballantrae Complex south of Girvan. Northwards marine transgression was controlled by a sequence of faults (developed in the order 1 to 3 etc.) throwing down to the south.

SW but, farther north, plunge passes through the horizontal and progressively steepens to about 45° NE. There is some controversy over the origin of these folds, which have been variously described as products of late Caledonian tectonism or as slump folds produced by the downslope movement of unconsolidated sediment: the former interpretation seems the most likely.

6 Cow Rock, Horse Rock and Craigskelly: contrasting early Llandovery conglomerates

Drive north from Kennedy's Pass for about 5 km to a large car park beside the beach on the southern outskirts of Girvan [182 964]. There is are toilet facilities here.

From the car park walk south along the beach on the seaward side of the Ainslie Manor Nursing Home (formerly the Haven Hotel). This section also forms part of an extensive itinerary in Bluck and Ingham (1992). Outcrops between the beach and the Nursing Home consist of a coarse, mainly matrix-supported conglomerate containing abundant quartz pebbles and siltstone clasts, many quite angular. A small proportion of metamorphic lithologies is also present. The bed is known informally as the 'quartz conglomerate' and is stratigraphically a part of the Scart Grit. Southwards the number and size of siltstone clasts increases and at Cow Rock, NW of the Nursing Home, the base of the conglomerate can be seen (at low tide) to channel into an underlying siltstone and fine greywacke sequence. This is the Woodland Formation, which contains a sparse shelly fauna of Llandovery age (Cocks and Toghill, 1973). The topmost few metres of the Woodland Formation, beneath the quartz conglomerate, are much disturbed by slumping.

The Woodland Formation underlies the small sandy beach extending for about 30 m SW towards the next rock outcrop, the Horse Rock. This is also formed of conglomerate but of a very different character to that previously seen. At the Horse Rock, and also on Craigskelly which can be reached at low tide, the Craigskelly Conglomerate is well exposed as a polymict and clast-supported lithology. It contains rounded pebbles of acid and basic igneous rock, some metamorphic fragments, jasper and clastic turbidite strata. The beds are quite thick, reaching about 8 m on Craigskelly, but at the Horse Rock the conglomerate is interbedded with turbidite greywacke units up to about 50 cm thick. The base of the Craigskelly Conglomerate is exposed on the SW side of the Horse Rock and may be seen at low tide subject to the vagaries of the shifting beach sand. An unconformable but sharp planar contact occurs between the conglomerate and the underlying thin greywacke and shale beds of the Shalloch Formation. The latter is of mid-Ashgill (Ordovician) age and the Craigskelly Conglomerate is taken to mark the base of the Silurian.

Palaeocurrent evidence, deduced from clast imbrication and bottom structures, indicates that the Craigskelly and quartz conglomerates were both derived from the NW. The cause of the abrupt change in character of the source terrane during the early Silurian is a matter of speculation.

Localities 1 to 6 will provide a full day's excursion and cover many points of interest within the Ballantrae Complex and its sedimentary cover. However, many of the exposures require examination at low tide and an inland site, Locality 7, is suggested as a partial alternative if the tides are unfavourable.

7 Craighead Quarry: Caradocian Reef Limestone

Craighead Quarry exposes Caradocian reef limestone overlying lavas of the Ballantrae Complex and is a Site of Special Scientific Interest for botanical as well as geological reasons. It is described as part of an extensive excursion itinerary for the Craighead Inlier in Bluck and Ingham (1992).

From Girvan drive north on the A77 towards Ayr and then turn right on to the B741 and continue for about 5 km. At Low Craighead Farm turn left; there is parking space for 3 or 4 cars in the entrance of the track leading to a disused quarry about 200 m beyond the farm on the left of the road [235 014]. Take care not to obstruct the adjacent farm track. Access to the quarry is via the track and thence by a footpath on the right which leads down on to the quarry floor. The footpath is frequently overgrown and may not be obvious.

The quarry walls expose parts of a late Ordovician limestone reef assemblage (Craighead Limestone) stratigraphically equivalent to a level within the Ardwell Formation (Figure 32). On the NW side of the quarry a dark mass of spilitic lava can be seen overlain by a limestone breccia containing much algal debris and algal-cemented basalt clasts. The lava is thought to be an inlier of the Ballantrae ophiolite seen at Localities 1–4. The stratigraphical relationships, with Caradocian reef limestone overlying Arenig ophiolite lava, continue the trend of north-westward transgression discussed earlier. The eastern walls of the quarry reveal a variety of reef-flank limestone types containing abundant, although mainly broken, fossils; corals and crinoids are the commonest groups. There is abundant evidence for slumping. The sequence within the quarry is much disrupted by faulting, probably related in the main to Carboniferous movement on the nearby Kerse Loch Fault.

P Stone

Excursion 9

Dumfries:
a Permian desert

OS 1:50 000 Sheet 84 Dumfries,
Castle Douglas & surrounding area
BGS 1:50 000 Sheet 9E Thornhill
Route map: Figure 33

Main points of interest   Aeolian dune
sandstones and flash-flood breccias of the
Dumfries Basin. The objective of this excursion is to build a picture of the varied desert
environment that existed in south-west
Scotland during the early Permian, around
270 million years ago.

Logistics   The Permian rocks of the
Dumfries Basin are examined at five localities in this itinerary, making up a full day's
excursion. There is good vehicle access, to
within a few hundred metres, at all localities. However, if a coach is used a little more
walking will be required at localities 2 and
4. Many more localities are detailed by
Brookfield (1981). Permission to visit the
Locharbriggs Sandstone Quarry, Locality 1,
must be obtained in advance from Baird
and Stevenson Ltd, Locharbriggs Quarry,
Locharbriggs. **This is a working quarry
and a hard hat should always be worn.**
Permission for access to the railway cutting
at Doweel Farm, Locality 2, must be
requested at the farmhouse. There is free
public access to Castledykes park in
Dumfries, Locality 3, during daylight
hours. At the time of writing access to the
disused Craigs Quarry, Locality 4, is unrestricted. Observation of the riverside outcrops near Glencaple, Locality 5, is most
easily undertaken at low tide; **extra care
should be taken when the river level is
high.**

Introduction   During the Carboniferous,
the Lower Palaeozoic rocks of the Southern
Uplands formed an uplifted massif. Fault-controlled depositional basins were filled
by deltaic and shallow marine sedimentary
rocks and lavas. Change from a coastal setting to a more arid, terrestrial environment
occurred at the end of the Carboniferous,
and rocks of Lower Palaeozoic to Carboniferous age were unconformably overlain by
a 'red-bed' sequence deposited in the desert
environment of early Permian times.

The Dumfries Basin is a synclinal half-graben structure bounded to the west by a
NNW-trending fault (Figure 33). Synsedimentary movement across the fault uplifted
the basement rocks to the west and influenced the depositional facies of the Permian strata. The sequence of Permian aeolian
sandstones and breccias within the basin is
up to 1600 m thick and unconformably
overlies Silurian turbidites and the early
Devonian Criffell granodiorite.

Many sedimentary processes are active in
a desert environment and produce rocks
with different characteristics. Nature and
thickness of bedding, grain size, grain shape
and roundness, the presence of clasts, the
clast lithology and sedimentary structures
are all used to infer the depositional processes. A hand lens will be needed to look at
specimens and a compass-clinometer to
measure the orientation of bedforms which
can reveal the direction of migration of the
Permian dunes. Comparison of the various
Permian rock types will demonstrate the
variety of sedimentary processes active in
the Dumfries Basin during the Permian.

1   Locharbriggs Quarry: dune-bedded desert sandstones

Locharbriggs Quarry is beside the A701,
4.5 km NE of Dumfries, to the north of
the village of Heathall. The entrance to the
quarry and workshops is on the west side of
the road [NX 994 810] and is marked by a
red sandstone wall bearing the name of the
quarry. There is a car park for visitors with
ample space for coaches.

Figure 33   Locality map and outline
geology for the Dumfries excursion.

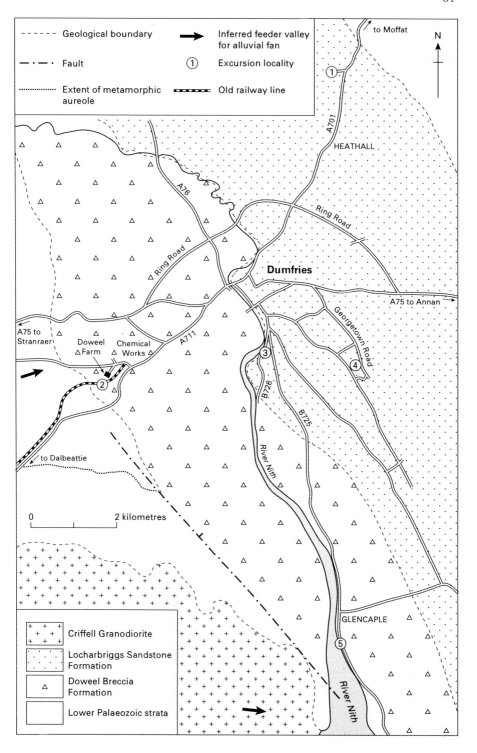

This is a working quarry which extracts blocks of stone for building and ornamental work. **Within the quarry a hard hat must always be worn.** Watch out for any machinery that may be around and note that **some of the faces will be steep so take care.** Because the stone is being continually quarried, the faces that can be seen will vary. Two quarries remain; the northern one is largely disused but the southern one is being actively worked. Go first to the northern quarry and take some time to look at the old face from a distance. Note that extensive curved and planar beds produced by large-scale dunes can be traced over about 5 m. The many cut blocks around provide an opportunity to look at the lithological characteristics of the rock using both the naked eye and a hand lens. It is red in colour due to a haematite coating on the individual grains. Close examination shows that it is a sandstone composed of grains varying in size from fine to coarse. Within any individual bed the grains appear to be well sorted but there is a considerable contrast in grain size between different beds. Grains in the beds of fine-grained sandstone are subrounded to subangular, whereas the grains in beds of coarser sandstone are usually well rounded, with individual grains having a frosted appearance. Most of the grains are glassy quartz but some highly altered; milky white feldspar is also present.

A closer look at the worked face in both quarries will allow a more detailed analysis of the dune bedforms. The orientation of the large-scale cross-beds can be recorded by measuring the strike and the amount of dip. These data are useful in reconstructing the environment and geometry of the features. An individual cross-bed, called a foreset, can have a dip of anything up to 35° but tracing this downwards the dip will decrease, curving into the underlying surface.

Individual foreset beds, usually up to 10 cm thick, have a wedge-shaped geometry with little internal structure. Tracing one of these beds laterally shows that it thins down the dip of the foreset. Finely laminated beds may be seen, usually where the dips are low. Small-scale cross-beds, similar to subaqueous ripples may also be found. These may be in areas of low dip or on top of larger foresets.

The cross-beds are commonly truncated by lower-angle planes, called bounding surfaces, which define cross-bedded units that may be 0.1 m to 10 m thick. A hierarchy of bounding surfaces can be built up, in which the first-order surfaces, those lying closest to horizontal, cut all other surfaces. These relationships are shown diagrammatically in Figure 34. The bounding surfaces are frequently associated with removal of the red colouration from the rock on either side. This may be due to the passage of groundwater leaching out the red haematite.

Environmental interpretation The characteristics of the individual sand grains, particularly the high degree of sorting, the roundness and the frosted appearance, suggest that these grains were transported by the action of wind. Transport by wind is highly selective, with grains being either removed or deposited depending on their size and the velocity of the wind. Individual beds are therefore well sorted but, with changing wind velocity, the size of the transported grains will be either coarser or finer, hence the successive beds of differing grain size. Wind transport is also responsible for the rounding of individual grains and for producing the characteristic frosted appearance.

The scale of the sedimentary structures suggests that these beds were deposited as large dunes. The gently dipping side of the dune (the stoss side) faces into the wind and grains are being continually moved upwards towards the crest. The steep side of the dune (the lee side) is the site of successive avalanche flows as the dune migrates down wind. The large-scale cross-beds are the preserved foresets on the lee side of the dune formed by this process. The wedge-shaped beds with no internal structure represent the individual avalanches, each formed as a single event. Each dune was stabilised then overtaken and eroded during the deposition of a subsequent dune, resulting in truncation at the top of the dune and the development of a first order bounding surface. Very large dunes will have smaller dunes migrating, piggy-back over them, creating second- and third-order bounding surfaces (Figure

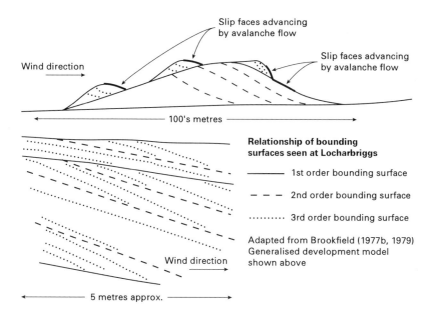

Figure 34 Cross-section through an idealised large dune structure illustrating formation of bounding surfaces (not to scale). Adapted from Brookfield (1977b, 1979).

34). These relationships will be seen again at Locality 4.

The geometry of the dunes can be deduced using the orientational data gathered by measuring the dips and strikes of the foresets. These represent the orientation of the lee slope of the dune, the most steeply dipping foresets giving the most accurate orientation. The stoss side of the dune is rarely preserved as this is where erosion takes place (Figure 34). Low depositional dips are typical of interdune areas, where sediment may accumulate by the accretion of particles stuck together by moisture from dew or from rising groundwater. Grainfall lamination will be present at the dune margins where avalanching is not present. Wind-blown ripples may be preserved on the dune surface sand and are commonly transverse to the dune crests. The tracks of any passing animal may be preserved in the interdune deposits. Footprints of an early reptile, a forerunner of the Jurassic and Cretaceous dinosaurs, have been found in these rocks (McKeever, 1994).

2 Doweel Farm railway cutting: alluvial fan breccias

Permian sedimentary rocks deposited on the west side of the Dumfries Basin are well exposed in an old railway cutting at Doweel Farm [NX 938 739]. From Locharbriggs Quarry turn right from the main entrance to the quarry on to the A701 and drive approximately 3 km SW to the junction with the Dumfries ring road. Turn right on to the ring road and travel 4 km west, following signs for A75 to Stranraer. At the end of the ring road turn right on to the A75 and, after only 500 m, turn left on to a minor road signed to Cargenbridge. Drive past the ICI chemical works to a T-junction with the A711 and turn right in the direction of Dalbeattie. Drive 1 km and turn off, to the right, on to a minor road. The entrance to Doweel Farm is a narrow driveway on the left. Park in the farmyard after arranging access permission. Coach parking is best on the roadside after the turn from the A711. Walk south through the farm to the line of the old railway, turn and walk west along the cutting.

The cutting is 500 m long with sedimentary breccias exposed in its vertical sides. The breccia clasts are angular and poorly sorted, from a few millimetres to about 30 cm across, and supported in a matrix of fine-grained, reddish coloured sandstone. The clasts are of turbidite sandstone and shale, thermally metamorphosed turbidite lithologies and finely crystalline intrusive acid igneous rocks. Breccias dominate the exposure but thin units of red sandstone can also be seen which are lenticular, usually less than 10 cm thick but many metres in lateral extent. The sandstones are thinly bedded, fine grained and mostly of red quartzose sand with small clasts of turbidite sandstone and shale. A hand lens reveals that a few of the quartz grains are very well rounded.

There is a crude alignment, or imbrication, of the breccia clasts; they 'dip' in a westerly direction. Bedding within the breccias is defined by the thin sandstone layers but within each thick breccia unit there is an upward decrease in grain size. Pockets of large cobbles may also be present between the breccia units.

Environmental interpretation   The breccias at Doweel Farm were not deposited by the same processes as the fine-grained aeolian sandstones at Locharbriggs Quarry. Transport of the coarse-grained breccia clasts and their deposition in thick beds indicates a very energetic sedimentary environment. The beds are tabular, with no evidence of channelling. The nature of each bed, grading up through breccia into fine-grained sandstone, demonstrates a single depositional event waning in strength, probably a sheetflood on an alluvial fan in a desert valley (wadi). The pockets of cobbles may have been concentrated by the first surge of each sheet flood event (Brookfield, 1980). Imbricated clasts 'dip' in an up-flow direction; flow at Doweel was, therefore, eastwards. The breccia clasts are of local derivation; Silurian turbidites are exposed 300 m further west in the next cutting and the Doweel cutting is only 1.5 km from the metamorphosed aureole of the Criffell granodiorite. Clasts of fine-grained, acidic, igneous rocks may have been eroded

from the many dykes that locally intrude the Silurian turbidites. The rare occurrence of well-rounded aeolian quartz grains in the sandstone tops of the sheetflood units indicates the existence of contemporary wind-blown sands.

Arid desert environments are subject to rare, heavy rainstorms. High runoff, in an area devoid of vegetation, causes flash floods. We can envisage that storms of this sort eroded rocks from the uplands west of the basin and swept the debris eastwards down a desert wadi. The breccias were deposited as the floods slowed and spread out over the wadi floor. Fault-controlled relative uplift of the Lower Palaeozoic basement at the western margin of the basin during the Permian ensured a constant supply of debris.

Alluvial breccias dominate the west side of the Dumfries Basin and are named the Doweel Breccia Formation after the type exposure in this railway cutting (Figure 33). A borehole drilled within the ICI chemical works at Cargenbridge recovered approximately 200 m of breccias; bedded mudrocks and sandstones are present only at the base of the core (Brookfield, 1978). Waterlain breccias and aeolian sandstones interfinger where sheetflood deposits from the west side of the Dumfries Basin periodically prograded into the dune fields in the centre of the basin. The relationship between the waterlain and aeolian deposits is examined at the next locality.

3   Castledykes Park, Dumfries: alluvial fan breccias and the relationship with the dune-bedded sandstones

Castledykes Park, Dumfries [976 746] is a public park in the town of Dumfries. From Doweel Farm, return to the A711, turn left and drive 3 km into Dumfries. In the town you will see many splendid buildings constructed of the red aeolian sandstone from Locharbriggs Quarry. Cross the River Nith over New Bridge and turn immediately right on to White Sands. Drive to the junction controlled by traffic lights at St Michael's Bridge, turn left on to St Michael's Bridge Road and almost immediately right on to St Michael Street. Drive 300 m along St Michael Street to a roundabout and turn right on to Nith Bank (B725), then fork right on to Kingholm Road (B726) down to the bank of the river Nith. Park on the right side of the road. Enter Castledykes Park by the south gate which is on the left side of the road. The rose garden has been developed within an old quarry in which aspects of the Permian environment can be studied. In particular, this quarry shows the relationship between aeolian dunes, of the type seen at Locharbriggs, and alluvial fan breccias like those in the railway cutting at Doweel Farm.

The north face of this old quarry demonstrates the relationship between the rocks deposited in different environments. At the east end of the north face (extreme right-hand side) the lithologies that were seen at Locharbriggs can be identified. These are red well-sorted sandstones with high-angle cross-bedding and with individual grains showing the diagnostic well-rounded and frosted characteristics of wind-blown sediments. Below this unit are less well-sorted sandstones with only small-scale cross-bedding. These sandstones also contain flecks of white mica (muscovite) and are interpreted as fluvial deposits.

Above the aeolian sandstone the rock has a different character entirely. Most of the face is made up of a coarse breccia with cobbles up to 0.30 m in diameter. The base of the breccia bed is erosive, cutting through both the aeolian and the fluvial sandstones. The conglomerate is poorly sorted, the clasts are mostly matrix-supported and finer-grained material surrounds each of the larger clasts. The breccia clasts are mostly turbidite sandstone but some felsite and distinctive blocks of granite are also present.

Environmental interpretation The interpretation of this quarry helps build a more complete picture of Permian sedimentation in south-west Scotland. Again, as at Locharbriggs, some aeolian dune-bedded sandstones are present. The contrasting micaceous sandstone was deposited under fluvial conditions in a river or stream indicating that streams did flow through the area at times. The coarse-grained conglomerate demonstrates a dramatic change in environment. For these rocks to be deposited, a high-energy environment is needed with rapid transportation and deposition to pre-

vent sorting of the clasts. In contrast to the environment inferred at Doweel, there is a well-defined channel filled with poorly sorted breccias and overlain by sheetflood deposits. These were most probably deposited by a flash flood flowing down a channel cut through the underlying sediments during a previous flood. Clasts within the breccia illustrate the lithologies that were at outcrop around Dumfries in Permian times. Most of the lithologies can be identified at the surface today (Figures 1 and 8) suggesting that the present landscape is not much different from the Permian one. Either there has been little erosion since Permian times, or the Permian landscape has been re-excavated by post-Permian erosion.

4 Craigs Quarry: cross-section through a Permian dune

A cross-section through a Permian dune is exposed at Craigs Quarry [998 743]. From Castledykes Park drive back (north) up Kingholm Road (B726), turn left at the junction with Nith Bank (B725) and return to the roundabout junction. Turn right on to Craigs Road and follow it for 700 m. The road bends round to the left and becomes Gillbrae Road. Continue for 800 m to a T-junction and turn right on to Georgetown Road. Follow this for 800 m through a residential area; beyond the junction with Calside Road, the road becomes much narrower. If you are travelling by coach, park on the roadside just before Calside Road and continue to Locality 4 on foot. Cars may continue a further 900 m along Georgetown Road, carrying straight on at the crossroads at Undercraigs. Craigs Quarry is to the west (right) of the road. There are two entrances; take the second entrance opposite the house named The Knowe [NY 000 743]. Turn right into the quarry entrance and drive or walk to the north corner of the quarry. Craigs Quarry has previously been used as a landfill site **so appropriate care should be taken.**

Dune sandstones are exposed in two faces, roughly at right angles, at the NW corner of the quarry. The faces are more than 10 m high and expose a cross-section through a dune. Curved chisel marks pit the surface of the face, a relict of previous quarrying techniques. Reptilian footprints have been recorded from the dune sandstones from this quarry (Harkness, 1850).

Examined closely, the red sandstones appear well sorted and either coarse or medium grained (about 0.5 to 1 mm). The sand grains are mostly quartz; they are well rounded and frosted, typical of wind-blown sands. The sandstone is thinly bedded, with beds defined by the grain size variation from coarse to medium. The two faces, at approximately 90°, not only give an insight into the considerable size of the dune bedforms but also reveal their three-dimensional geometry. A subhorizontal first-order bounding surface (Figure 34) is exposed in both faces just above the present-day floor of the quarry. In the north face, west-dipping cross-beds defined by variations in grain size are planar in their upper parts but curve down to meet the first-order bounding surface. In the strike-section of the west face this curvature is much exaggerated. A second, gently inclined first-order bounding surface is present at the top of the north face. Cross-beds beneath this surface are truncated.

In the corner between the faces, about 4 m above the quarry floor, a second-order bounding surface is exposed. It is marked by a thin horizon of more fine-grained rock. In the north face it dips to the west and truncates the underlying cross-beds. Traced round to the west face the second- order bounding surface becomes subhorizontal and the angular discordance with the underlying cross-bedding is.more marked. Note the contrast in dip of cross-bedding above and below the second-order bounding surface in the west quarry face. Another, parallel, second-order bounding surface extends from the eastern edge to the centre of the north face.

Environmental interpretation The exposures at Craigs Quarry demonstrate the large scale of dune structures developed during the Permian in the Dumfries Basin. The largest aeolian dunes, or draas, are estimated to have been 100–250 m in height (Brookfield, 1977a; 1980). Cross-beds above the first-order surfaces record the westward migration of a draa structure. Erosion of the draa and migration of smaller dune struc-

tures across it is evident from the second-order bounding surfaces and overlying cross-bedded sandstones. Migration of these dunes was oblique to the main draa structure as demonstrated by the change in orientation of cross-bedding below and above the upper second-order surface in the west face. The change in orientation of cross-bed foresets does not, necessarily, imply a change in the predominant wind direction. Dunes can be complex structures with cross-beds orientated at many angles to the predominant wind direction.

5 River bank, Glencaple: alluvial breccias of granitic clasts

The last locality is near Glencaple. From Craigs Quarry drive south along Georgetown Road for 400 m and turn right on to another minor road. Turn left where this road meets a T-junction and drive 3 km south then take a right turn to Glencaple. In Glencaple turn left on to the B725. This route follows narrow, minor roads suitable only for small vehicles. If you are travelling by coach, go back into Dumfries and take the B725 to Glencaple at the roundabout junction. From Glencaple drive south along the B725 and park by the road 300 m south of the village. Outcrops of Permian rocks lie to the west of the road, in the estuary, just above high water mark [995 681].

Now-familiar Permian sedimentary breccias are exposed in a small shore section in the east bank of the River Nith. Angular clasts of a granitic lithology, first noted in the exposures in Castledykes Park, are predominant. Clasts of metamorphosed turbidite sandstones and mudrocks are common, but fragments of unmetamorphosed turbidite lithologies are also a minor component (Brookfield, 1980).

Environmental interpretation The sheet-flood breccias exposed south of Glencaple differ from those at Doweel and Castledykes in the predominance of a single clast type. The clasts are granodiorite, derived from the Criffell intrusion, which is only 2 km to the west. The pluton underlies the high ground west of the Nith and the faulted eastern margin of the pluton is marked by the abrupt change in gradient at the foot of the hill. Palaeocurrent direction, inferred from breccias at Glencaple (Brookfield, 1978), was toward the NE directly away from the granodiorite.

Comparison of clast composition within the Doweel Breccia Formation demonstrates very local derivation from the fault-defined western margin of the Dumfries Basin. Only at the centre of the basin, near the eastern extent of the Doweel Breccia Formation, is there a more varied mixture of clast types. Deposition of alluvial-fan debris near the west side of the Dumfries Basin during the Permian was, therefore, confined within at least two separate alluvial fans (Figure 33) which overlapped only at the centre of the basin.

To return to Dumfries drive north along the B725.

M C Akhurst and S K Monro

Excursion 10

SOUTHERNESS to BORRON POINT:
Lower Carboniferous of the Solway Basin

OS 1:50 000 Sheet 84 Dumfries,
Castle Douglas & surrounding area
BGS 1:50 000 sheets 5E Dalbeattie, 6 (Annan)
Route maps: Figures 35 and 36

Main points of interest   Lower Carboniferous stratigraphy and structure; limestones, sandstones and siltstones. algal beds, shallow marine fossils and trace fossils.

Logistics   This coastal itinerary begins at Southerness, reached via a minor road from the A710 between New Abbey and Dalbeattie. Parking for large coaches is available only at Southerness, from which Localities 1–4 (Figure 35) can be visited. At low tide, it is possible to walk 2.5 km north-eastwards from Southerness across the sandy Gillfoot Bay to Powillimount to reach Localities 5–10, (Figure 36). Alternatively, cars and

minibuses only can be parked at the shore beyond Powillimount Farm for Localities 5–10. For the best appreciation of the sections, the shore should be walked at low tide. Total return walking distance (excluding the optional crossing of Gillfoot Bay) is about 1 km at Southerness and 5 km from Powillimount to Hogus Point. As with all coastal sections, the rocks may be wet and slippery.

Introduction   Lower Carboniferous rocks of Dinantian age are well exposed along the Southerness shore and between Powillimount and Borron Point. Unlike the strata which lie close to the North Solway Fault (as at Rockcliffe, Excursion 3) the sections at Southerness are representative of a wide range of depositional environments from fluviatile to open shallow marine conditions.

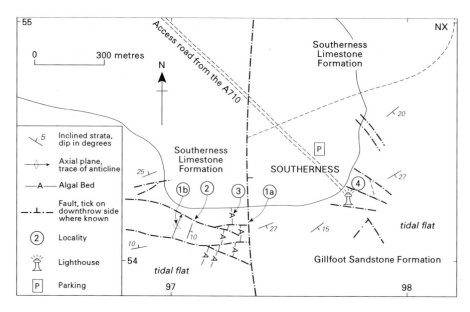

Figure 35   Locality map and outline geology for the Southerness shore section (Localities 1–4).

The rocks contain a rich macrofossil assemblage which enables them to be correlated with the equivalent Lower to Upper Border Group strata of the Langholm district, ranging in age from Courceyan to Asbian (Table 1). They have been described in detail by Craig (1956) and Deegan (1970).

The oldest strata, the Kirkbean Cementstone Formation, are found in scattered inland exposures on the south flanks of Criffell, notably in Kirkbean Glen [NX 975 591], where they rest partly on a thin development of basaltic lavas (Birrenswark Volcanic Formation) and partly on Upper Old Red Sandstone strata; this sequence rests with marked angular unconformity on Silurian turbidites. Access to the Kirkbean section is unfortunately restricted and this excursion concentrates on the younger rocks exposed at the coast.

1 Southerness shore: Southerness Limestone Formation

Cars and coaches may be parked at Southerness village [977 543]. From there proceed on to the foreshore by the old lighthouse and walk west for 0.4 km to the faulted eastern boundary of the Southerness Limestone Formation (Locality 1a, Figure 35). The type section (Craig 1956) of the Southerness Limestone Formation occupies a 0.3 km stretch of coast from here to a gently NNE-plunging anticline (Locality 1b). Localities 2 and 3 are specific points of interest within the type section which exposes some 135 m of fossiliferous, thinly bedded calcareous mudstones, siltstones and limestones. At least four prominent thick beds of sandstone are present. Easterly dips vary from 5 to 45°.

Although a number of east–west faults displace the strata, a reasonably complete section across the east limb of the anticline can be measured (Deegan, 1970). In the upper part of the formation Deegan identified three sedimentary cycles ranging in thickness from 8 to 15 m. Prominent algal horizons are developed at similar positions in two of the three cycles. An idealised cycle may be summarised as follows:

Flaggy sandstone with plant remains
Interbedded limestone and micaceous mudstone
Interbedded limestone and calcareous mudstone
Nodular algal band
Thin muddy limestone with calcareous mudstone
Fine-grained rippled sandstone
Flaggy micaceous sandstone with ripple marks and plant remains

The cyclicity reflects varying depositional environments and may be attributed to gradual subsidence combined with variations in terrigenous sediment input possibly related to periodic dip-slip movement on basinal bounding faults. Each cycle commences with sandstones, probably deposited in a littoral environment, which are succeeded by calcareous beds formed under shallow subtidal conditions. Sandy limestones containing ooliths indicate that the sediments were affected by wave action. However, the algal beds show little sign of reworking and probably represent slightly deeper water sedimentation below the wave base. A traverse of the shore section enables the cyclicity identified by Deegan to be followed. Specific highlights include the Syringothyris Limestone (Craig, 1956) and algal beds.

2 Syringothyris Limestone

A good exposure of the Syringothyris Limestone, estimated by Craig (1956) to be 16.7 m thick, is seen some 600 m west of the lighthouse (Locality 2, Figure 35). The limestone comprises several beds of argillaceous limestone and calcareous mudstone, and contains a varied marine fauna of brachiopods including Syringothyris cuspidata, bivalves, polyzoa and crinoid ossicles. Faunal similarities with the Harden Beds of Langholm were noted by Lumsden et al. (1967) and indicate that the Southerness Limestone Formation probably spans the boundary between the Lower and Middle Border Groups of Langholm (Table 1).

3 Algal stromatolite beds

Above the Syringothyris Limestone, about 550 m west of the lighthouse, two distinctive algal stromatolite bands, 1.2 m and 1 m thick, are present within the sequence. Craig (1956) and Frölicher (1977) referred the stromatolites to the genus *Somphospongia*. They resemble the dome type described by Leeder (1975) from the Lower Border Group of the Northumberland Basin. Individual domes are up to 30 cm in diameter with a relief of 10 to 15 cm and are set in a calcareous mudstone matrix. They are composed of alternating micritic and detrital laminae. Calcareous algal filaments commonly wrap fragments of shell including gastropods and ostracods. The irregular, nodular exterior of the algal growths indicates limited reworking. Basing his observations on studies of modern stromatolites, Leeder (1975) inferred that domed types formed in a low intertidal to shallow subtidal depositional environment.

4 Southerness Lighthouse: Gillfoot Sandstone Formation

Walk back towards Southerness, across the fault (Locality 1a) which downthrows east and brings the Gillfoot Sandstone Formation in against the Southerness Limestone Formation.

Between 120 and 150 m of strata assigned to the Gillfoot Sandstone Formation are exposed on the shore between here and a position south of Powillimount Farm [9880 5620]. The formation conformably overlies the Southerness Limestone Formation, and Craig (1956) placed the top of the formation at the base of a breccia forming the base of the succeeding Powillimount Sandstone Formation (Locality 5).

The Gillfoot Sandstone Formation comprises white and purplish, flaggy, quartzose sandstones; conglomerates with intraformational fragments; red flaggy siltstones; and mudstones. A few red to grey, thin-bedded, sandy limestones with scattered detrital fossil remains are also present. Conglomerates, which form about 20 per cent of the succession, have a calcareous matrix and contain intraformational fragments in addition to pebbles of vein quartz, greywacke and microdiorite derived from the Southern Uplands hinterland to the north. Some more feldspathic layers are dominated by microdiorite and felsic rock debris derived from Lower Palaeozoic minor intrusions.

The formation is sparsely fossiliferous. A derived fauna, collected by Craig from the

sandstone on which the lighthouse stands, suggests that the strata are of Arundian age and equivalent to part of the Middle Border Group of Langholm (Lumsden et al., 1967).

The lithologies indicate a more marginal depositional setting than that of the underlying formation. The conglomerates may have been transported from the hinterland and deposited by periodic sheetfloods flowing over low-lying supratidal areas. Textures in some of the sandstones indicate wave action and a littoral environment. Shallow subtidal environments may be indicated by the presence of thin fossiliferous, sandy limestones.

5 Powillimount Shore: Powillimount Sandstone Formation

Access to the Powillimount shore is via the road which links Powillimount Farm with the Kirkbean to Southerness road. A small car park at the shore beyond the farm (Figure 36) is suitable for cars and minibuses only. Immediately below the car park some 160 m of strata exposed on the shore between Powillimount Bay [9880 5610] and Thirlstane [9925 5690] are assigned to the Powillimount Sandstone Formation. The top 25 m are distinguished as the Thirlstane Sandstone Member, a prominent ridge of thick-bedded sandstone with spectacular penecontemporaneous deformation structures (Craig, 1956; Deegan, 1970; Ord et al., 1988).

The base of the Powillimount Sandstone Formation is drawn a short way SW of the car park, at the base of a grey calcareous breccia, above the highest bed of purple mudstone in the Gillfoot Sandstone Formation. The strata form part of the SE limb of a major NE-trending anticline and on the coast are further folded about a tight, gently plunging syncline–anticline pair, the axial planes of which trend NNE. Faunal assemblages are similar to those in

Figure 36 Locality map and outline geology for the shore section between Powillimount and Hogus Point (Localities 5–10).

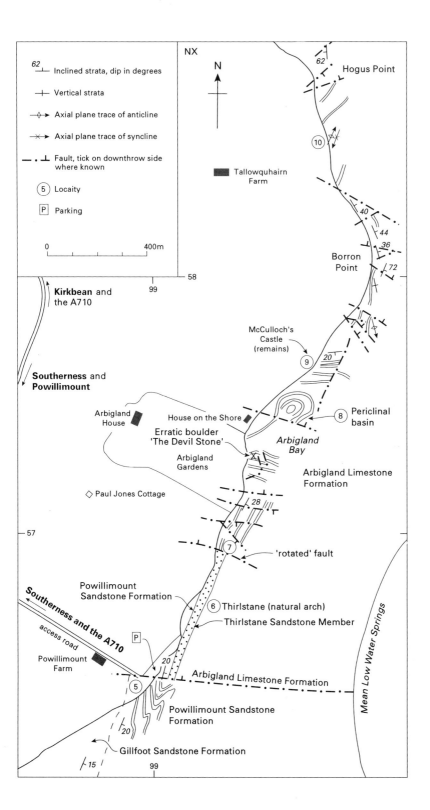

NX
N

62 — Inclined strata, dip in degrees

—+— Vertical strata

—◇→ Axial plane trace of anticline

—×→ Axial plane trace of syncline

—•⊥ Fault, tick on downthrow side where known

⑤ Locaity

P Parking

0   400m

Hogus Point

62

⑩

Tallowquhairn Farm

40

44

36

72

Borron Point

Kirkbean and the A710

58

99

Southerness and Powillimount

McCulloch's Castle (remains)

⑨

20

⑧ Periclinal basin

Arbigland House

House on the Shore

Erratic boulder 'The Devil Stone'

Arbigland Gardens

Arbigland Bay

Arbigland Limestone Formation

◇ Paul Jones Cottage

57

28

⑦

'rotated' fault

Powillimount Sandstone Formation

Southerness and the A710

access road

P

⑥ Thirlstane (natural arch)

Thirlstane Sandstone Member

Powillimount Farm

20

⑤

Arbigland Limestone Formation

Mean Low Water Springs

Powillimount Sandstone Formation

20

Gillfoot Sandstone Formation

15

99

the Middle Border Group of Langholm. Aspects of the fauna immediately below the Thirlstane Sandstone resemble those of the overlying Arbigland Limestone Formation.

Lithologies include calcareous and quartzose sandstone, sandy limestone with beds of dark grey fissile mudstone, and calcareous mudstone. Locally, thin coals and associated seatearths are present. Sandstone beds are laterally extensive, ranging in thickness from 0.3 to 3 m. They are well sorted and commonly exhibit ripple cross-lamination. Many contain abundant carbonaceous plant remains and are extensively burrowed, particularly by *Chondrites*. Limestones range from arenaceous to argillaceous and contain detrital fossil remains, ooliths and rolled algal nodules. One distinctive oncolite bed, 0.3 m thick, contains rounded algal-coated lithic and fossil fragments. The individual oncolites are generally spherical and up to 1 cm across. Oncolites are produced by the accretion of sediment on to mobile grains through the action of algae, and their presence indicates constant agitation of the sea floor by wave action.

The characteristic lithologies, especially rolled algal nodules and detrital fragments, point to a shallow-marine environment exposed to gentle wave action. Deegan (1970) proposed that the sediments were deposited in a tidal lagoon protected from the effects of severe storms by some form of offshore sand barrier. The presence of thin coals and seatearths indicates periodic shallowing of lagoonal waters and the development of vegetated low-lying supratidal flats.

6 Thirlstane natural arch: Thirlstane Sandstone Member

Walk about 50 m NE from the car park to a prominent sandstone ridge [991 565] which can be followed to beyond the Thirlstane natural arch. The ridge is formed by the 25 m-thick Thirlstane Sandstone Member. At the base of the Thirlstane Sandstone the contact with the underlying strata is irregular, and intraformational fragments and large plant remains are present in the lowest beds. The fine natural arch at Thirlstane and nearby exposures to seaward display various sedimentary structures in a pinkish grey, medium-grained, well-sorted,

quartzose sandstone. The rocks are characterised by large-scale trough cross-bedding and a spectacular development of liquefaction structures which increase in frequency and magnitude from south to north along the outcrop. It is worthwhile examining the extraordinary degree to which the original bedding has been disrupted. In a detailed study of these structures Ord et al. (1988) recognised different types of structure including oversteepened and recumbently folded cross-stratification, domes, sand volcanoes and zones of anastomosing, vertical cracks. They attributed the magnitude and frequency of the liquefaction structures to causes such as local seismicity, and deduced the presence of a syndepositionally active fault lying north of the present outcrop.

Deegan (1970) proposed that the Thirlstane Sandstone formed as an offshore sand barrier which initially enabled the inshore lagoonal environment of the Powillimount Sandstone Formation to develop. The evidence is equivocal, however and, as Ord et al. suggest, an alluvial origin is also a possibility.

7 Thirlstane to Arbigland Garden: Arbigland Limestone Formation

All the strata exposed between Thirlstane (Locality 7) and Hogus Point [997 589] (Locality 10) are assigned to the Arbigland Limestone Formation, estimated to be some 300 m thick (Craig, 1956). The conformable junction between the Thirlstane Sandstone Member and the Arbigland Limestone Formation (noted by Smith, 1910) is often obscured by shifting sands; the most obvious contact is a normal fault, (Locality 7) 200 m NE of the Thirlstane natural arch [993 569]. The fault plane appears to have a reverse throw and may have been rotated through vertical. Between this fault and an ESE-trending hinge fault opposite Arbigland Garden, the strata strike parallel to the coast. North of the second fault a narrow zone of disrupted bedding is succeeded by a series of beds striking ESE. Perched prominently on these is a huge erratic block of Criffell granodiorite known locally as the 'Devil Stone'. Tradition has it that the Devil bit off this chunk of Criffell and spat it out on the shore. Conventional glacial theory would suggest that the block was eroded and transported to its present position by a glacier during the last ice age.

The lithologies of the lower part of the Arbigland Limestone Formation resemble those of the Powillimount Sandstone Formation. Key features to look out for include thick-bedded, bioturbated, calcareous sandstones with coalified plant casts, thin sandy limestones locally with ooliths and algal debris, dark grey carbonaceous mudstones, and thin coal partings.

8 Arbigland Bay to Borron Point: Arbigland Limestone Formation and pericline

Walk from the Devil Stone across the sandy Arbigland Bay. Diversions from the geology here include the fine gardens of Arbigland House, built by William Craik in 1755, and Paul Jones Cottage, where John Paul Jones (1747–92), founder of the American Navy, was brought up. The gardens may be visited (vehicular access from the Kirkbean to Southerness road) on certain weekdays.

North of the bay a small, shallow, periclinal basin structure is present (Locality 8). North of here the strike of the strata swings from east–west through ENE to NE, to become subparallel with the line of the coast around Borron Point [995 580]. The strata are cut by numerous normal faults of ESE and SE orientation.

9 Arbigland Bay to Borron Point: faunal assemblages and sedimentary features of the Arbigland Limestone Formation

A traverse of the shore between Arbigland Bay and Borron Point is worthwhile for anyone with an interest in the sedimentology and faunal characteristics of shallow marine shelf sediments. The strata here were termed by Deegan (1970) the Middle Arbigland Beds. They are richly fossiliferous and contain a fine compound rugose coral fauna including spectacular massive hemispherical colonies of *Lithostrotion clavaticum*, first recorded by Smith (1910). Some are in life position with individual corallites visible on the upper surface. Overturned colonies show only the outer walls of the corallites radiating from the central columella. **Please do not hammer them out.**

Deegan (1970) described the strata below McCulloch's Castle [996 577] (Locality 9) as mainly thin argillaceous and sandy limestones interbedded with calcareous mudstones and several prominent thick beds of massive bioturbated sandstone. Many beds of sandstone and sandy limestone have been extensively and repeatedly reworked by sediment feeders, and burrow forms such as *Chondrites, Diplocraterion* and *Rhizocorallium* are commonly seen. The limestones and mudstones have an abundant and diverse fauna including corals, brachiopods, bivalves, gastropods, crinoids, bryozoa and orthocones. Faunal equivalence with the Upper Border Group of Langholm (Lumsden et al., 1967), of Asbian age, is considered most likely. In the Langholm district, the Glencartholm Volcanic Beds form the base of the Upper Border Group and these rocks have been equated with the Clattering Band of Bewcastle (Day 1970) which George et al. (1976) place at the base of the Asbian. It follows that if correlation of the Middle Arbigland Beds is extended to the Clattering Band then the lower part of the Arbigland Limestone Formation (Locality 7) is probably Holkerian (as noted by George et al.).

At Borron Point stratigraphically higher rocks are downthrown by two small faults. Here the strata are steeply inclined and locally overturned. The sequence is characterised by thick-bedded bioturbated sandstone, and ripple cross-laminated fine-grained sandstone interbedded with calcareous mudstone and a few argillaceous limestones. Shallow sandstone-filled scours and washouts are common.

10 Hogus Point: northernmost exposures of the Arbigland Limestone Formation

Those who wish to visit the northernmost exposures of the formation at Hogus Point [997 588] should continue along the shore north from Borron Point. Alternatively the excursion can be completed at Borron Point and the route retraced to Powillimount Farm.

The strata at Hogus Point are reasonably well exposed. They are disposed about a tight, gently NE-plunging anticline–syncline fold pair. The rocks comprise thick units of thin-bedded silty, calcareous mudstone, well-bedded sandstone and thin-bedded sandy limestone. Although Craig (1956) considered the strata at Hogus Point to be the highest in the sequence, a fauna collected more recently indicates a position no higher than the beds lying south of Borron Point. The indications are that the rocks lie on the upthrow side of a SE-orientated normal fault, the trace of which may lie north of Tallowquhairn Farm [993 584].

Lithological characteristics of the sequence between Thirlstane and Arbigland Garden together with the sparse, locally detrital, fauna are consistent with a restricted lagoonal environment in which there was limited reworking of sediment. Overall, however, the Arbigland Limestone Formation was probably deposited within the intertidal to subtidal zone. An open, shallow-marine environment is indicated by the abundant fauna in the Middle Arbigland Beds (Deegan, 1970).

A A McMillan

Excursion 11

Dundrennan Ranges, Gipsy Point:
Silurian submarine slump features

OS 1:50 000 Sheet 83 Newton Stewart & Kirkcudbright
BGS 1:50 000 Sheet 5W Kirkcudbright
Route maps: Figures 37 and 38

Main points of interest   Major slump structure, sand volcanoes and sedimentology of the Raeberry Castle Formation, Wenlock graptolites.

Logistics   The area lies within the Ministry of Defence Test and Evaluation Establishment near Dundrennan, a strip of coastline which has been **used as a firing range for many years**. Recently announced plans (1994) indicate that its future is uncertain. The MOD has no objection to people visiting the area, except **when firing is in progress**! At such times **red flags and explanatory notices are displayed**. Notification of firing times is held by the Harbour Master and Tourist Information Office in Kirkcudbright. Access on foot is feasible without special permission when the range is not in use, normally evenings, weekends and public holidays, although it is always best to inform the range authorities in advance. Large parties, or visitors wishing to take vehicles into the range area, should contact the Commanding Officer beforehand (Test and Evaluation Establishment, Dundrennan, Kirkcudbright DG6 4QZ). **Do not touch** any strange objects encountered during the excursion.

Introduction   The primary aim of this excursion is to examine a gigantic slump structure, lying within a channel in a sequence of Wenlock turbidites belonging to the Gipsy Point Unit of the Raeberry Castle Formation (Riccarton Group). A series of sand volcanoes, probably formed by dewatering of the slump, lies just above the disturbed beds. Other tectonostratigraphical units within the Raeberry Castle Formation, showing diverse facies associations, can be seen further east along the coast. These represent channels, lobes and fringes within a

submarine fan complex that built out from the north; the dominant transport direction was from the NE. From the entrance to the MOD establishment on the A 711 Kirkcudbright–Dundrennan road [NX 718 474] proceed south towards the shore, along the road leading to Little Balmae (Figure 37). About 1 km from the shore there is a small car park [692 449], to the left of which a track, with a sign marked 'Gipsy Point' leads down to the coast. A ten-minute walk brings the visitor to an area of numbered firing targets, and an old tank which forms a convenient landmark. From here proceed to the cliff top above Port Muddle. The localities of interest are indicated on Figure 38. Comprehensive details of the section are given by Kemp (1987b). For a longer excursion this itinerary could be extended to examine the stratigraphically adjacent Ross Formation at localities 3 and 4 of Excursion 5 (Kirkcudbright).

1   Port Muddle: Gipsy Point Unit

This bay is excavated at the seaward end of a fault trending NNE, which may be traced inland as a boggy depression. All the beds in this vicinity lie within the Raeberry Castle Formation, now known to be Wenlock in age. Four thin bands of graptolite-bearing hemipelagite, which crop out below the cliff on the east side of the bay ,provide confirmation.

According to Kemp (1987a and b), there are three definable tectonostratigraphical units within the Raeberry Castle Formation: the Gipsy Point Unit, the Raeberry Unit, and the Mullock Bay Unit. It is the Gipsy Point Unit (*riccartonensis* to *flexilis* biozones) that occurs here, on both sides of Port Muddle. All the beds are vertical and show quite diverse facies associations. Kemp described an A Member, of rather monotonous thin- to medium-bedded turbidites with some hemipelagic muds, and a B Member, with channelised arenites, rudites

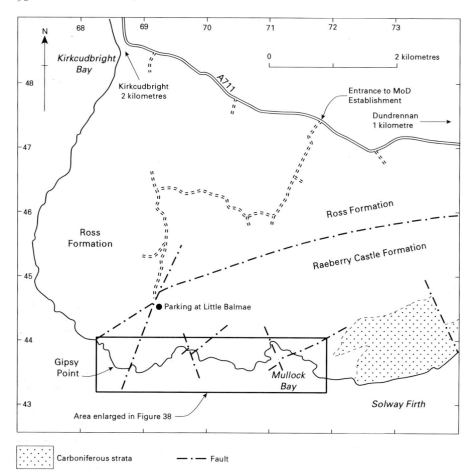

Figure 37 Locality map and outline geology for the Ministry of Defence Dundrennan Range.

and slumps, interbedded with thin-bedded sandstones, siltstones, and mudstones. Kemp interpreted these deposits as part of a meandering and laterally migrating channel-levee complex on a submarine fan, with the coarser deposits lying within the channels and the fine beds representing levees. All these sedimentary features are easily visible from the cliff top. It is possible to descend to the shore here, but the details are better seen at Gipsy Point.

2   Gipsy Point: slump

A walk of some 300 m in a WSW direction, keeping the old tank to the left and crossing a ruined wall, brings the visitor to the cliff top at Gipsy Point [685 436]. A new military earthwork lies just to the west. The slump, which lies within the B Member of the Gipsy Point Unit, is well seen from the cliff top. It is some 30 m thick and lies within a channel-fill sequence consisting of chaotic and dis-ordered thin-bedded sandstones. The sequence is vertical and youngs NW; above and below the slump the beds are undisturbed. One prominent horseshoe-shaped sedimentary fold within the slump sequence is particularly evident from this vantage point. It is clear that the sediment forming the slump must have slid down

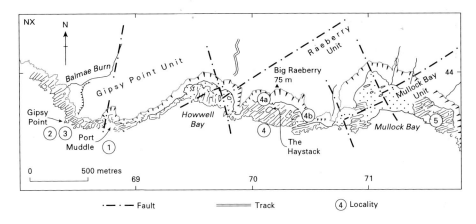

Figure 38 Shore section between Gipsy Point and Mullock Bay showing localities and outline geology.

into the channel in a semi-consolidated state, the bedding becoming chaotically folded in the process, but remaining cohesive.

It is possible, **with care**, to descend to the coast from here, to examine the slump more closely. The erosive base of the slump (SE side) can be seen cutting into the underlying beds, forming fossilised channels with flute casts; in some places rip-up clasts can be seen in the mudstone. The whole sequence has been folded by a large anticline–syncline pair which traverses part of the section and is clearly seen as a large box-fold on the vertical face near the point of descent from the cliff top.

3 Gipsy Point: sand volcanoes

Directly overlying the large slump is a single layer (now vertical) of spectacular sand volcanoes, originally described by Lovell (1974), who suggested that they formed as a result of dewatering of the underlying slump. Above lies a coarsening-upward sequence of thin sandstone–mudstone layers, interpreted as an interchannel or overbank sequence. The sharp junction between the top of the slump, with its attendant sand volcanoes, and the overlying beds is very well seen in the cliff face. This shows clearly that the original channel had been abandoned by the time renewed deposition began.

Lovell identified ten sand volcanoes, occurring in three groups, over 100 m of strike section. Five of these are easily accessible, even at mid-tide. The largest and most obvious is over 3 m across, and is almost completely preserved. It is about 1.5 m deep and has a depressed central crater nearly 0.5 m across. Several of the other volcanoes are cut across, showing laminated sandstone with complex internal structure, as if the water had escaped in a series of pulses. One small volcano directly overlies another smaller one. A thin sandstone bed connects the sand volcanoes of the landward and central groups, but does not extend to the seaward set. In this latter group, however, is a sand volcano, cut so as to display the central pipe, which in this case is filled with coarse sandstone. Stringers of gritty material have developed in the underlying sandstone, and penetrated upwards into the sediment overlying the volcano during the dewatering process. This example is the only one to show a direct connection between the beds above and below the volcano.

The thin sandstone beds of the overbank sequence directly overlying the sand-volcano horizon show some interesting sedimentary structures. Firstly there are ripple marks with slightly different orientations, seen on successive vertical faces near the cliff edge. Secondly there are other structures, well worth examining, on the lower surfaces of the thin sandstone units down on the shore, a few metres above the sand volcanoes. Some of these faces are smooth but show convolute lamination in cross-section; other surfaces display very fine load casts. In some instances an otherwise smooth surface has only one or two isolated load casts, of which some are simple, whereas others are grouped together like bunches of grapes. Many faces, however, are entirely covered with load casts. One surface, about a metre above the sand volcanoes, displays strings of clearly orientated load casts, suggestive of modified ripples.

Small dolomitised concretions can be seen within the slump close to the base of the cliff, and several small fault-planes within the vicinity are likewise dolomitised. These may possibly have been synsedimentary faults penetrated by the diagenetic fluids associated with the concretion-forming process.

4 Big Raeberry: Raeberry Unit

The section east from Gipsy Point to Mullock Bay shows many features of interest and should be visited if time permits. From the east side of Port Muddle, to the far side of Howwell Bay, underneath the prominent hill of Big Raeberry, the turbidites belong to the Raeberry Unit (*rigidus* to early *flexilis* biozones) of the Raeberry Castle Formation. Kemp (1987) who logged the whole section in detail, recognised three separate facies. The medium- to occasionally thick-bedded turbidites of the A Member were interpreted as deposits of the depositional lobe of a submarine fan. The very regular, thin-bedded turbidites of the B Member were considered to be a fringe facies of the fan lobe, whereas the alternating medium- and thin-bedded base-absent turbidites of the C Member were taken to represent a channel-mouth facies.

These distinctions are evident in the cliff section east of Big Raeberry, where the beds young to the NW. Just west of the prominent feature known as the Haystack [702 437], the alternating thick and thin beds of the C Member form spectacular Z-folds (Locality 4a in Figure 38). In the prominent north–south-trending cliff some 200 m to the east (Locality 4b) all three members are clearly seen. The seaward end is formed from the varied lithologies of the A Member, the top of which is marked by a thick bed forming a notch in the cliff top. Landward of this lie the strikingly regular, alternating sandstones and siltstones of the B Member, of which the top is marked by a prominent vertical band of structureless siltstone, known as the 'homogenite wall'. This bed may be at the same horizon as the Gipsy Point slump, marking some large-scale event within the depositional basin. The ragged-looking C Member, with its projecting sandstone bands, is distinct and forms the north end of the cliff. The bases of many of the sandstones throughout this sequence are marked with flute casts showing variable transport directions.

5 Mullock Bay: Mullock Bay Unit

About 1 km further east, excellent sections in the Mullock Bay Unit of the Raeberry Castle Formation are well exposed along the shore. The beds here yield graptolites of the *ellesae* and *lundgreni* biozones, and are distinguished by having more hemipelagite and less sandstone than any of the other units seen along this section. Kemp (1987) divided these into two members. Member A consists of thinly bedded fine sandstones, siltstones and mudstones, alternating with channelised arenites and rudites. They are quite like the B Member of the Gipsy Point Unit, and like them are interpreted as having formed in a channel-levee system on a submarine fan. The B Member consists of a complex of alternating thin- to medium-bedded sandstones and shales, with occasional coarser horizons considered to represent prograding depositional lobes.

Return to Port Muddle along the cliff top or the shore.

E N K Clarkson and C M Taylor

Excursion 12

GATEHOUSE of FLEET:
structural complexities of the Hawick Group

OS 1:50 000 Sheet 83 Newton Stewart &
Kirkcudbright
BGS 1:50 000 Sheet 4E Wigtown
Route map: Figure 39

Main points of interest Sedimentology
and structure in the late Llandovery Hawick
Group, polyphase deformation, late Caledonian porphyry and felsite dykes.

Logistics The area may be approached
either from Gatehouse in the east or from
Creetown in the west via the A75 road and
the excursion may be started or curtailed at
Ravenshall Point, Mossyard Farm or Low
Auchenlarie Farm. Note that account has
to be taken of the state of the tide at
Auchenlarie, Mossyard and the Newton
shore. The likelihood of congestion in the

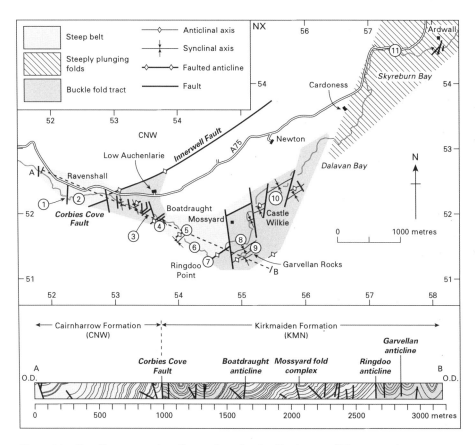

Figure 39   Locality map and outline geology for the Gatehouse of Fleet excursion.

Mossyard Farm car park during the holiday season may also have to be considered. Localities visited are situated along the coast between the Ardwall shore [NX 585 545], on the Fleet estuary 2 km west of Gatehouse, and Ravenshall Point [523 523] on the east side of Wigtown Bay. Exposures are in the wave-cut platform, intertidal skerries and cliffs. Nearby cuttings along the main A75 Carlisle–Dumfries–Stranraer road are informative but are not now recommended for examination due to the hazard of high-speed traffic. On a clear day the A75, which follows the coast a short distance inland, gives good views of the Cumbrian mountains and the Isle of Man.

Introduction The eastern coastline of Wigtown Bay provides good sections through the Cairnharrow and Kirkmaiden formations of the late Llandovery Hawick Group. The succession consists of greywackes which are typically poorly graded and bedded in units mostly less than 1 m thick. Fine arenite forms up to 90 per cent thickness of each unit and grades upwards into pelite; T_{abde} (Figure 6) cycles predominate. Grading is expressed mainly in the progressive upward intensification of cleavage into the finer-grained intervals. A high quartz content commonly imparts a vitreous lustre to fresh surfaces. Calcareous nodule trails parallel to the bedding are dispersed through many of the thicker arenite intervals, reflecting a general abundance of secondary carbonate within the Hawick Group as a whole. Sole markings are well developed in the Cairnharrow Formation, but are scarce in the Kirkmaiden Formation. They are predominantly non-directional drag marks, with small directional flute casts, longitudinal ridge casts and prod marks. Directional sole markings denote palaeoflow towards the WSW, the prevalent trend within the area and subparallel to the regional fold plunge. Deposition in an intermediate to distal trench, or lateral lobe of a submarine fan, is suggested (Weir, 1974).

The strata have been subjected to a continuity of deformation in which two stages, designated 'main' and 'late' (cf. Needham, 1993), are prominently developed. An 'early' soft-sediment deformation is sparingly represented. The main-stage folds are of two contrasting styles: NW-facing homoclinal zones of steeply inclined bedding up to 1 km and more wide ('steep belts'), which alternate with comparably wide tracts of dominantly open, upright buckle folds; where asymmetrical these latter structures are SE-verging. Adjacent structurally contrasting belts are separated by strike faults downthrowing SE (Weir, 1968; 1979). Evidence from elsewhere in the outcrop of the Hawick Group suggests that the strike faults, though now steep, originated as thrusts over-riding towards the SE, and were subsequently steepened and back-rotated. Anticlines are commonly faulted along their axial surfaces, suggesting that the folds grew ahead of the developing thrusts, ultimately to be cut by them. The SE-downthrow of the strike faults, in combination with the NW facing of the steep belts, has led to duplication of the succession, and there are no gross changes in stratigraphical horizon across the 10 km-wide outcrop of the Cairnharrow and Kirkmaiden formations (Craig and Walton, 1959). The main cleavage in the pelite intervals is steep, penetrative and slaty, with development of new sericite; an equally steep but irregular, non-penetrative and spaced cleavage occurs in the arenites. The cleavage is rotated by up to 15° clockwise relative to fold axial surfaces indicating continuous deformation under a sinistral transpressive regime. This also resulted in the reactivation of at least some of the rotated main strike faults with a sinistral strike-slip displacement (Stringer and Treagus, 1980).

Late-stage structures are more variable. Open folds with wavelengths of a few metres, asymmetrical with respect to dip though symmetrical in relation to limb lengths, verge NW and affect the steep belts. Minor NW-directed thrusts are associated with small recumbent folds which refold the main folds; an associated flat-lying crenulation cleavage displaces the main cleavage. This episode postdates the sinistral transpressive phase and is likely to relate to a period of back-thrusting (Stone et al., 1987). The late crenulation cleavage dips SSE at 45° or less. It is irregularly spaced, planar and weakly penetrative in pelites, and spaced, irregular, non-penetrative and strongly refracted to steeper inclinations in arenites.

A conjugate set of NNE sinistral and ESE dextral wrench faults displaces the main folds and succeeds the thrusting episode. Porphyry dykes of late Caledonian age are especially associated with axes of parasitic main-stage anticlines within the steep belts but also invade at least one late wrench fault.

1 and 2   Ravenshall Point: Cairnharrow Formation

Follow the A75 west from Gatehouse for 10 km to a lay-by on the south side of the road [525 524]. This can accommodate more than one coach. Follow the path to Ravenshall Point, which breaches the wall near the west end of the lay-by and turns sharply west for 300 m.

The Cairnharrow Formation as developed at Ravenshall consists of turbidite units characterised by abundance and variety of sole markings both directional and non-directional. Exposures around high water mark [522 522], across the small bay beyond the western headland (**Locality 1**), are reached through a natural arch which cuts the headland (**safety helmets advisable**). Bed bases display a comprehensive range of sole markings.

A thick breccia horizon in the western headland may have been formed by slumping of a thick turbidite bed, probably during the late deformation. In such circumstances brecciation may be caused by bed-parallel fluid escape in response to seismic pumping following shear failure on a basement fault (Murphy, 1984). The locality is within a steep belt which has been refolded by late asymmetrical folds. These include a medium-sized monoform in which the upper limb has dips varying around 30° and the lower steep limb is vertical.

On the north (landward) side of an isolated stack (**Locality 2**) at mid-tide level 100 m east of the eastern headland [524 522], one bedding surface displays current ripple marks denoting a SSE-directed palaeoflow. Another bedding plane exposed on the south side of the stack displays structures which mimic linguoid ripple marks with wavelengths comparable to those already

examined. Close examination reveals that these are small monoformal folds cut by minute, evenly spaced thrusts dipping NNW and with top-to-SE displacements. These are late structures, the 'pseudo-ripples' of Craig and Walton (1959).

3 and 4   Auchenlarie shore: Kirkmaiden Formation

Drive east on the A75 for 1.5 km to the caravan site at Low Auchenlarie Farm [536 521]. Transport may be parked by arrangement with the caravan site shop, which may charge a fee. Follow the metalled road on foot southwards to its eastward turn at the cliff top (250 m) and descend the steep gullied track for about 100 m to the shore (**Locality 3**). These exposures are also described in Excursion 16, Locality 1.

Along the Gatehouse coastal section the greywackes of the Kirkmaiden Formation (Rust, 1965) contrast with those of the Cairnharrow Formation in displaying a scarcity of sole markings and internal structures, though grading is more convincingly developed, principally as T_{ae} units. The turbidites of this formation are typified by a large thickness range. Packets of turbidite units reaching upwards of a metre thick, and including one succession of conspicuously thick beds, alternate with sequences of thinly bedded and pelite-dominated units a few metres thick at the most. Some thick packets constitute thinning- and fining-upward cycles, which may terminate in pelite-dominated sequences. The succession here crops out within a buckle fold belt 750 m wide.

Pelite partings, which are well exposed in fault gullies in the western headland of the small bay, carry a well-developed main cleavage which is penetrative with regular spacing and a near-vertical attitude. This cleavage carries crenulations on a scale of a few millimetres, related to a coarse, evenly spaced and weakly penetrative late cleavage with a shallow SSE dip. One conspicuously thick pelite interval near the mouth of the nearest gully clearly displays the intersecting relationship of the late and main cleavages. The crenulations are strongly asymmetrical, with long limbs facing upwards and short limbs facing downwards. This broadly reflects the style of the larger late asymmetrical folds which here have axial surfaces dipping at around 35° SSE. Hinges in the larger folds are rounded with no thickening and the axial traces are nearly horizontal. Limbs are roughly equidimensional, around 5 m in length and with amplitudes of less than 20 per cent of wavelength. Arenites carry a coarse, irregular and irregularly spaced fracture cleavage dipping 45° SSE.

Quartz veins in arenite immediately south of the cliff path carry slickenfibres and the associated pelites a stretching lineation, both of which are aligned parallel to the regional fold hinge plunge. About 100 m east of the cliff path, the most thickly bedded turbidite sequence on the Gatehouse coast displays a series of late folds having uncommonly large wavelengths of around 25 m and amplitudes of up to 15 m. Axial separation of the folds is here controlled by bed thicknesses. A detached exposure to seaward shows an isolated example of back-thrusting, in which the steep limb of a small recumbent fold is displaced by a minor thrust with an indeterminate top-to-NW displacement.

The wide and shallow gully (**Locality 4**) of the Boatdraught [537 518] follows the boundary fault between the Auchenlarie buckle fold belt and a steep belt 1.3 km wide to the SE. This gully, though lacking exposures, is likely to have been eroded out along a disruption zone generated by the fault (Needham, 1993).

A bedding plane 50 m east of Boatdraught is covered with small sand volcanoes related to dewatering during the early, soft-sediment deformation. These structures are around 60 mm long and are elongated parallel to the main cleavage. This denotes axial extension during the main deformation and confirms the evidence of the slickenfibres and the stretching lineation at the previous locality.

5 to 10 Mossyard shore: Kirkmaiden Formation and minor intrusions

Continue east along the A75 for a further 900 m to the junction with the Mossyard farm road [544 525]. Follow this road south for 1 km to the farm. The road beyond the farm is unmetalled and unsuitable for coaches; passengers should disembark at the farm and follow the road to the coast on foot, coaches returning to Auchenlarie to park. A parking charge is levied and to gain permission for access it is advisable to contact Mossyard Farm, Gatehouse of Fleet, Kirkcudbrightshire in advance.

The Kirkmaiden Formation here lies partly within the Auchenlarie–Mossyard steep belt (to the NW) and partly in a buckle fold belt characterised by upright, open to very tight main-stage folds with wavelengths of more than 100 m to less than 1 m. This belt continues past Mossyard at least as far as Gatehouse. From the car park, walk SW along the rocky shore for about 1 km; two parasitic main fold pairs within this steep belt can be examined at **Locality 5** [542 515]. The more northerly fold pair has been coaxially refolded into a SE-verging recumbent attitude such that the main cleavage is also nearly horizontal. The main structure, which deforms a more thickly bedded sequence, originated as a tight fold pair with an axial separation of 3 m and a rounded axis with little or no thickening. The core of the anticline is occupied by a pale, pinkish grey porphyry sheet about 1 m thick. This has a dense in-situ growth along each margin consisting of alkali feldspar phenocrysts about 2 cm long with their long axes aligned roughly normal to the dyke margins. The intrusion belongs to the late Caledonian acidic suite and is unsheared; it thus postdates the main folding and was deformed along with the main fold pair during the late folding (Stringer and Treagus, 1981).

The second fold pair is situated 28 m farther south, and affects a pelite-dominated sequence. This fold is upright and very tight with a twofold axial thickening. It is nearly symmetrical with an axial separation of 1 m and a NE plunge of 5°. The main-stage cleavage is strong and rotated by some 15° clockwise relative to the anticlinal axis.

A third main-phase anticline at **Locality 6** [543 514] is tight and upright, and has a particularly thick and bright pink, felsitic dyke intruded into the core. This dyke is again unsheared, but also lacks marginal concentrations of aligned feldspar phenocrysts and may be entirely post-tectonic. There is little if any evidence of faulting along the axial surface of the anticline but it is displaced by a small ESE dextral strike-slip fault, one of only two observed within the area and now eroded to form a prominent gully parallel to the shoreline.

The boundary between the Mossyard steep belt and the Mossyard–Gatehouse buckle fold belt is well exposed on Ringdoo Point at **Locality 7** [545 513] and takes the form of an axially faulted anticline. Each limb is nearly vertical and the fault plane is marked by a narrow, quartz-filled crush zone. Poorly developed grading and occasional bottom structures (mainly drag marks) indicate southerly facing seaward of the fault and northerly facing to landward. Strong reddening and ochreous discoloration of the strata in the vicinity of the fault are ascribed to weathering during development of the major Permo-Triassic depositional basin whose present margin lies a short distance offshore.

A low west-facing cliff at **Locality 8** [552 516] displays a symmetrical and upright main fold pair with a comprehensive range of minor structures. The syncline is wide and open and the anticline to the south narrow and very tight. There is considerable thickening of the anticline hinge in association with both small-scale disharmonic folding and flat-lying faults with quartz veining. The axial separation is about 25 m, and there is a gentle easterly plunge. Main slaty and late crenulation cleavages are especially well developed and replicate the features observed on the Auchenlarie shore. The relationship of the late cleavage to the crenulations is especially convincing, as is displacement of the main by the late cleavage. There is also a strong development of a steep main fracture cleavage in the arenite beds. The late cleavage in the pelites has a SE dip of 30°, strongly refracted in the arenites to dip 45°. The strata in the syncline constitute a thinning- and fining-upwards greywacke sequence which rests on pelites forming the anticline. This anticline is aligned with the Ringdoo Point anticline (Figure 39) but is unlikely to be an extension of it since the fold styles contrast markedly. There is likely to be a strike-slip fault through the sandy bay to the west of this locality.

Another main fold pair is well exposed in the three Garvellan Rocks (**Locality 9**).

In the eastern rock [552 514] the anticline folds a fine-grained sequence, and the NW limb is slightly overturned. The main cleavage has a southerly dip of 40°–60° and is offset by small SE-facing monoformal folds with a 10 cm scale of wavelength. These folds are closely comparable in style to the late crenulations but are an order of magnitude larger and are associated with a weak crenulation cleavage. This has itself been coaxially refolded into a gentle anticline. A felsitic dyke which traverses the middle rock occupies a late fault trending ESE. Drag folds in the adjacent strata indicate a dextral strike-slip movement though there is no discernible displacement of the anticlinal axis. This is the second of the two dextral faults observed in the area.

Several folds within the Mossyard buckle fold belt crop out on intertidal skerries (**Locality 10**) between the Garvellan Rocks and the Cardoness shore [570 538]. The traces of these folds are assumed to terminate against faults trending between north and NNE, the prevailing trend of the late sinistral wrench set.

11 Skyreburn Bay: tectonic structures in the Kirkmaiden Formation

Return to the main road and continue east for 3 km, parking in a lay-by on the seaward side [576 545]. Pass through the wicket gate near the eastern end of the lay-by and descend to the shore.

A series of small folds is exposed on the wave-cut platform below the east end of the lay-by. These folds have vertical axial surfaces with a north–south strike and are strongly asymmetrical, with east-facing limbs several centimetres long and west-facing limbs a metre or more in length. They are thus open, sharply angled chevron folds with interlimb angles of around 150° and near-vertical plunges; they represent a late brittle kink-band phase with dextral sense of displacement.

Several medium-sized main-stage folds are exposed above high water mark at this locality. They are symmetrical, have vertical axial surfaces striking ENE, are open with rounded hinges and show no axial thickening. Dips range up to 70° and hinge plunges, which are variable, are mostly steeper than 45° ENE. Wavelengths vary between 10 and 50 m. These moderately to steeply plunging folds occupy a tract 2.5 km long trending WSW between Skyreburn Bay and Cardoness, the plunge lessening progressively south-westwards. Apart from the steep plunges, the style and associated cleavages of these folds correspond with the other main buckle folds, including the clockwise rotation of the main cleavage relative to the axial surfaces. Late crenulations have plunges parallel to those of the main fold axes. Steepening of the plunges thus postdates the crenulation cleavage, and may relate to fold rotation by a major fault, as yet unproved, following the Fleet valley.

One arenite interval, just above high water mark close to the western limit of exposure displays sigmoidal tension gashes filled with quartz. These indicate a sinistral sense of movement in accordance with the late transpressive episode but contradicting the dextral kink bands which probably represent the latest Caledonian effect.

J A Weir

Excursion 13

WHITHORN:
turbidite sequences and deformation in the Hawick Group

OS 1:50 000 Sheet 83 Newton Stewart &
Kirkcudbright
BGS 1:50 000 sheets 2 Whithorn,
4E Wigtown
Route map: Figure 40

Main points of interest D1 deformation
styles and post-D1 structures in Silurian turbidites, characteristics and stratigraphical
relationships of the Cairnharrow, Kirkmaiden, Carghidown and Ross formation,
syntectonic dykes.

Logistics All localities are easily reached
via the A75 from Newton Stewart or

Glenluce and small roads on the Whithorn
peninsula; Locality 4 requires vehicular
access across private land and permission
should be gained. The localities are described anticlockwise around the coastline
(Figure 40). Some exposure is usually available above the high water mark but most
localities are best visited at medium to low
tide; low water is essential at Locality 2. To
visit all six localities requires a long day; if
time is short, Locality 3 could be omitted.
**For general safety it is necessary to be
fully aware of the tide movements and be
wary when the rocks are wet as they are
likely to be very slippery. Some localities**

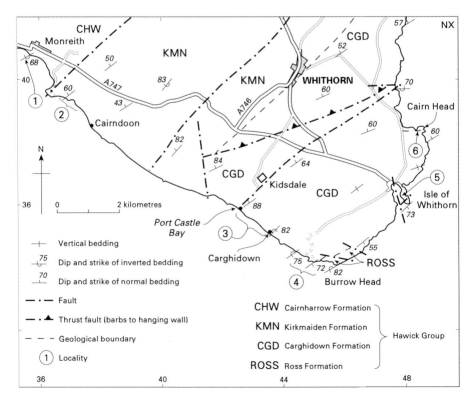

Figure 40 Locality map and outline geology for the Whithorn excursion.

include cliffs where special care is necessary, although no particularly difficult route for access is required. Whilst in the area visitors may wish to see something of the Whithorn archaeological excavations. The dig is investigating the 1500 year old church site founded by St Ninian and the ensuing Northumbrian monastery housing a shrine to the saint which became a centre of pilgrimage. A Viking trading centre was established on the same site and developed through a Scots take-over into a medieval town. Details of the up-to-date excavations and admission arrangements may be obtained from the Whithorn Trust, 45–47 George Street, Whithorn, DG8 8NS, Telephone 01988 500508.

Introduction This excursion aims to demonstrate the relatively complex deformation of the Hawick Group in the coastal exposures of the Whithorn promontory. Relationships can be demonstrated between the widespread, but here relatively variable, D1 deformation, the later folding and faulting, and the intrusion of suites of syntectonic dykes.

The Hawick Group crops out over the southern part of the Whithorn promontory (Figure 40). The Kirkmaiden Formation, named after the chapel at Kirkmaiden (between Localities 1 and 2), shows the general nature of the Hawick Group. It is characterised by medium-bedded $T_{a(bc)}$, $T_{b(c)}$ or T_c greywacke units with thin muddy partings, and includes packets (usually less than 3 m thick) of thinly interbedded T_c greywacke and silty mudstone, and thickly bedded massive sandstone in single beds or sequences of several beds. To the north, the Cairnharrow Formation typically includes a higher proportion of more thickly bedded $T_{b(c)}$ greywackes. To the south, two formations are defined on the presence of distinctive muddy interbeds in a sequence which is otherwise much like that of the Kirkmaiden Formation. The Carghidown Formation includes red mudstone beds, thin and infrequent in the north but increasing in importance southwards, accompanied by conspicuous detrital reddened mica in some of the sandstones. Soft-sediment deformation is also extensively developed in this formation, varying from disrupted bedding to mélange units. On the southern headland (Burrow Head, Locality 4) the red mudstone interbeds give way, up-sequence, to grey laminated siltstone beds in the Ross Formation. The siltstones contain graptolites of early Wenlock age (White *in* Barnes, 1989), providing one of only two direct biostratigraphical controls over the age of the Hawick Group in this area (White et al., 1990). The other is a sparse, late Llandovery graptolite fauna from the Kirkmaiden Formation near Monreith.

Tectonostratigraphy follows the regional pattern of the Southern Uplands. The younging direction of the strata is typically northwards yet the limited biostratigraphical evidence indicates that the formations become older in this direction. This paradox can only be resolved by inferring the presence of reverse faults parallel to the ENE strike of the rocks. These subvertical structures, spaced 2–5 km apart, define a series of parallel-sided tectonostratigraphical tracts. The faults are thought to have formed as thrusts in association with D1 folding and S1 cleavage formation but have since been rotated into a near-vertical attitude. The thrust front, detaching the turbidite sequence on the underlying Moffat Shale Group, effectively migrated southwards into progressively younger strata; the D1 event is thus diachronous, becoming younger southwards. This concept is discussed more extensively in the Introduction (see especially Figure 4).

D1, represented by gently plunging folds, was the only phase of deformation to have affected many of the rocks now preserved in the northern half of the Southern Uplands (Leadhills and Gala groups), later phases of deformation being apparent only rarely. To the south, in the Hawick Group, D1 was more complex and produced a wide range of fold plunge including steeply plunging sinistral folds. A second phase of deformation D2 is also relatively widespread, forming inclined, south-verging open folds and smaller recumbent folds associated with a locally well-developed subhorizontal cleavage (S2). Numerous lamprophyre and felsite dykes were emplaced into the Hawick Group at various times during the deformation history. The early, bed-parallel dykes are locally cut by the S1 cleavage, whereas other dykes have various relationships with D2 folds suggesting emplacement before or during D2 deformation. Examples of these relationships can be examined at Locality 2 of this excursion and at Locality 1 of Excursion 16.

Steeply plunging folds also occur elsewhere in the Southern Uplands, commonly adjacent to the tract-bounding faults. The Orlock Bridge Fault, for example, shows evidence of major sinistral strike-slip reactivation (Excursion 17). Many of these structures may have formed in response to a single sinistral shear event. At Locality 2 (below), folds of this nature can be shown to deform S2 and therefore to represent a third phase of deformation (D3). However, bearing in mind the diachronous nature of D1, these D3 structures may have formed at the same time as the steeply plunging D1 folds in the younger part of the Hawick Group (Figure 4).

Extensive coastal exposure through the Hawick Group on the Whithorn promontory allows study of its turbidite sedimentology and the effects of the deformation it has undergone. The tectonic structure is particularly well displayed. A study of the area by Rust (1965) was followed by British Geological Survey mapping (BGS, 1987; 1992c; Barnes et al., 1987; Barnes, 1989). The structure is dominated by D1, the effects of which are separated into two domains (Figure 40) by a D2 thrust fault (Barnes, 1989): in the northern zone folds plunge gently to moderately NE whereas in the southern zone fold plunges may be gentle, moderate or steep towards NE or SW. This excursion visits the localities where the main features of the stratigraphy and the inter-relationships between the deformation episodes can be seen.

1 Black Rocks, Monreith: steeply plunging D3 folding

From Newton Stewart follow the A714 to Port William (just over 30 km) then turn south on the A747 coast road for 5 km, parking on the seaward side of the road [NX 357 409] just before a sharp left bend into Monreith village. From here a flight of steps leads down to the beach where Black Rocks [359 408], forming a short section of exposure to the south, is accessible except at high water. Interpretation here is influenced by the style and chronology of D1 and D2 structures established at Locality 2, nearby.

Thin- to thick-bedded greywacke, often parallel-laminated even through thick beds, is interbedded with silty mudstone. These strata were formerly regarded as part of the Kirkmaiden Formation (BGS, 1987; Barnes, 1989) but are now assigned to the Cairnharrow Formation (BGS, 1992b; 1992c). They are deformed by steeply plunging folds, varying from minor folds with short limbs a few centimetres long, locally intensely developed in very thin-bedded units, to larger sinistral folds in more thickly bedded greywacke. The folds are associated with a steep, east-striking, near-axial-planar cleavage. The gently dipping S2 cleavage, which will be seen associated with recumbent D2 folds at Locality 2, is also developed in places here and the relationship between the various structures is critical to understanding the timing of the fold phases. The gently dipping S2 cleavage appears to be folded by the steeply plunging folds but, because these are at a high angle to one another, it is difficult to be certain. However, S2 is also crenulated by the steep cleavage, confirming that the steeply plunging structures are later. They can therefore be referred to the D3 phase of deformation.

Identical steeply plunging fold structures will be seen farther SE (Localities 3 to 6) associated with the late stages of D1. Given the diachronous nature of the D1 deformation, the same phase of sinistral shear may have been responsible for the formation of steeply plunging D1 folds in the youngest strata being deformed at any one time, contemporaneous with steeply plunging refolding (D3) structures in the older, previously deformed rocks of the thrust hinterland.

2 Back Bay, Monreith: Kirkmaiden Formation structure

Proceed through Monreith village on the A747 and about 1 km farther on turn right for Monreith golf course. The narrow road turns sharply to the left after 500 m, at which point a bronze otter, a memorial to the author Gavin Maxwell, is situated on a cup and ring marked rock to the right of the road. Drive through the golf course to the public car park at the shore [368 394] and walk along the beach towards the cliff at the east side of Back Bay. This is only accessible at mid to low tide.

The turbidites exposed in the cliff are typical of the Kirkmaiden Formation: thin- to medium-bedded greywacke with some thicker beds, and interbedded silty mudstone. Several D1 folds are well displayed. Two sets of later folds are also present, with steeply and gently dipping axial planes and opposed vergence. Their overall conjugate geometry forms open box folds (Figure 41; cf. Barnes, 1989, frontispiece) and they are therefore jointly referred to as D2. Recumbent D2 folds of small size are well displayed near high water (**A** on Figure 41) where they are associated with thrust faults which climb gently up through the cliff and have a small displacement up to the south. In the cliff to the south, larger recumbent D2 folds are apparent, the northern one of which passes down into a steeply inclined D2 fold (**B**) which refolds an isoclinal D1 syncline. An anticline and another syncline are more obvious a few metres to the south, bedding in the synclinal hinge (**C**) being deformed by recumbent D2 folds and associated cleavage. To the south (**D**), moderately inclined bedding in the north-younging limb of the fold includes a large, steeply inclined D2 fold with subhorizontal tension gashes apparently related to the S2 cleavage. Farther towards the headland (**E**) a south-verging

D1 fold pair is particularly well displayed, the shape of the fold hinges changing in response to the varying thickness of the bedding. An irregular lamprophyre dyke is also present near the headland (**F**).

At low tide it is possible to walk around the headland into the next bay, the deep embayment in the southern part of which is called Callie's Port. Alternatively, from just above the high water mark in Back Bay, follow the narrow path which winds up on to the headland then walk around the cliff top to the SE side of Callie's Port where the beach is easily reached. Several lamprophyre dykes are present in the north of the bay, particularly in the west-facing cliff where critical relationships with fold structures indicate post-D1 but pre-D2 intrusion. One large, irregular intrusion cross-cuts an anticlinal D1 fold hinge. Several bedding-parallel intrusions occur in the adjacent strata, a 1.5 m-thick dyke being folded by a small recumbent D2 fold and cut by fractures parallel to the S2 cleavage (Barnes, 1989, plate 1c). Immediately south of Callie's Port, a wide wave-cut platform presents easily accessible exposure in which both sets of D2 folds cause variations in the dip of bedding. About 100 m south of Callie's Port, a 1 m-thick lamprophyre dyke is exposed parallel to bedding but divided into a number of offset segments. At least one of the offsets is related to a recumbent D2 fold closure (Barnes, 1989, plate 1b), suggesting syn-D2 emplacement.

Proceed a further 50 m south, to the end of the wave-cut platform where deep gullies have been eroded along NW-trending fractures, and look at the cliff face immediately

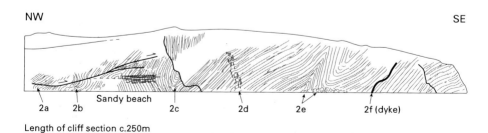

NW   SE

2a   2b   Sandy beach   2c   2d   2e   2f (dyke)

Length of cliff section c.250m

Figure 41 Sketch section of the Back Bay cliffs (Locality 2). Letters a to f identify points of particular interest discussed in the text.

to the east. Thin-bedded turbidites folded around an upright D2 fold include a bedding-parallel lamprophyre dyke, a few centimetres thick, which also passes around the fold. It is difficult in such circumstances to determine whether the dyke was intruded before or after folding. However, here the anticlinal hinge is fractured and the dyke is offset, suggesting that the dyke predates the folding. At low tide it is possible to proceed along the section to the SE where, over the next 120 m, D1 folds are deformed by recumbent D2 folds and related thrust faults.

To return to the car park, regain the cliff top and follow it almost to the golf course. After crossing a wire fence a path slants down over the steep grassy slope into the northern corner of Back Bay.

3 Port Castle Bay to Carghidown: Carghidown Formation structure

From Monreith take the A747 south for about 9 km towards Isle of Whithorn; at a cross-roads, turn right following a sign for St Ninian's Cave and after a further 2 km stop in the car park just before the farm of Kidsdale [NX 432 367]. A public footpath follows the track through the farmyard then turns right just after the house on the right, following the wooded valley for 1 km to the shore at Port Castle Bay [425 358]. St Ninian's Cave is along the shore to the north but the most informative geological section is to the south, towards Carghidown [435 351].

In passing, examine the small exposure of thin-bedded greywackes at the back of the beach a few metres south of the end of the path. This exposure includes gently plunging, south-verging D2 folds with a crenulation cleavage developed in the fold hinges only. Exposures towards the south of the beach show thin slickensided quartz coatings on bedding planes. These indicate subhorizontal shearing along the bedding, shown to be sinistral where the sense of movement can be demonstrated, and probably relate to deformation associated with a strike-parallel fault along the straight valley followed by the path to the beach.

The section south of the beach is similar in its sedimentology to the Kirkmaiden sequence but two features distinguish it as the Carghidown Formation: 1. thin red mudstone beds occur sparsely here but increase in frequency and thickness to the south; 2. short sections in which the bedding is disrupted are commonly interspersed with coherently bedded units. Faults form most of the boundaries to the disrupted zones which are themselves veined, probably because these units were initiated as zones of soft-sediment disruption but served to localise subsequent deformation. South of the beach, the strata are cut by several lamprophyre dykes which postdate well-developed, west-plunging folds but display variable relationships with faults.

Two fault sets, NW- and NNE-trending with conjugate geometry, are present throughout the Whithorn area, the straight coast at Locality 3 being developed along a zone of the NW-trending set. These cut the bedding and most of the bed-parallel dykes with clear evidence of dextral lateral displacement, although polyphase oblique slip is shown by several generations of slickensides. Later dykes have been emplaced into these faults. One example, exposed about 50 m from the start of the main coastal section, shows evidence of intrusion during fault movement. Bedding, including a 25 cm bed-parallel dyke, is displaced by a minor fault trending 125°. A 40 cm-thick lamprophyre dyke has been emplaced into the fault and carries a fabric in its margins consistent with dextral movement on the fault. Both dykes are folded by steeply plunging, dextral kink bands. A short distance to the south, D1 folds are well displayed in a north-verging fold pair which plunges moderately SW. A thick dyke forms a cliff immediately to the south and clearly postdates the folds.

The cliff prevents further access but a walk south along the cliff top for 100 m allows the shore to be regained in the south side of a small bay. However, before descending to the shore, walk 50 m further along the cliff top to where a steeply plunging sinistral D1 fold pair is particularly well exposed. The anticlinal hinge, plunging at about 87° at the top of the cliff, curves sharply to plunge 66° west lower down. Return along the cliff top, descend to the shore and examine the steeply plunging folds on the wave-cut platform. Cleavage is best developed in the muddy beds between sandstones and is axial planar to the folds. To the south, the same cleavage is related to several minor folds, affecting thin-bedded greywacke and silty mudstone alike; this emphasises that, despite their widely variable attitude, all the folds are the products of one phase of deformation. The cliff to the south exposes several minor thrust faults which displace the D1 folds and were probably formed during the D2 event; similar relationships were seen at Locality 2.

Return to the cliff top and walk back via Port Castle Bay to Kidsdale. Alternatively, if appropriate transport arrangements can be made, the cliff top can be followed for a further 2 km SE to Locality 4, near Burrow Head. In passing, the shore can be accessed to examine the characteristic features of the Carghidown Formation, including red mudstone beds, slumped units, folds of variable attitude and cross-cutting faults and dykes.

4 Burrow Head: Carghidown/Ross formation junction

From Kidsdale, return to the A747 and proceed 4 km SE to Isle of Whithorn. Turn right shortly after entering the village, following the sign for Burrow Head caravan park. Stop at the reception office to gain permission for access, then drive to the south part of the site and park near the cliff top [451 342]. Most of the exposure here is above high water mark, although the critical section across the junction between the two formations is difficult to reach when the tide is high; access to the foreshore is otherwise not difficult. Burrow Head [453 341] is important because it is the only place in Wigtownshire where the junction between the fossiliferous Ross Formation and the unfossiliferous Carghidown Formation can be examined. The same junction in Kirkcudbrightshire (Excursion 5) occurs in a more complete sequence where the Ross Formation is transitional between the Hawick and Riccarton groups (Kemp and White, 1985). The Ross Formation was formerly regarded as part of the Riccarton Group (Clarkson et al., 1975) because it includes the characteristic finely laminated

dark grey siltstone. However, it is more similar in its overall sedimentology to the Hawick Group and is now regarded as the highest formation thereof (White et al., 1992). Structurally it also has more in common with the Hawick Group, being strongly deformed and, at Burrow Head, forming part of the zone characterised by widely variable D1 fold plunge as seen at Locality 3. At Burrow Head the distinctive siltstone occurs sparingly, in beds from 1 cm to 1 m thick, interbedded with turbidites which are in other respects similar to those of the Kirkmaiden Formation. The disrupted bedding and red mudstone beds characteristic of the Carghidown Formation are confined to stratigraphical levels below the laminated siltstone bed which marks the base of the Ross Formation. However, the sporadic occurrence of reddened mica in sandstone above the lowest siltstone indicates that the boundary is to some extent gradational. The junction is situated in a broad zone of south-younging strata, implying that the Carghidown Formation is older than the Ross Formation. Unfortunately, the section at Burrow Head is cut by many faults, mainly of the conjugate, dextral and sinistral sets trending NW and NNE but also by some strike-parallel faults. These may be associated with minor folds and serve to make the continuity of the succession rather uncertain.

From where the vehicles are parked, walk round the coast to a stream at the east margin of the caravan park. The stream is incised into the raised beach and enters the sea along a small north-trending sinistral fault. Descend to the shore west of the stream close to two lamprophyre dykes, one north-trending and the other parallel to bedding. Bedding dips steeply SW and can be shown from sedimentary structures to be the right way up. The southward-younging nature of the succession is consistent with a minor, north-verging fold pair plunging 10° SW, immediately west of the stream. Note that the plunge changes to about 30° NE across the fault.

Two red mudstone beds, about 20 cm thick, occur on the foreshore either side of the stream; the intervening greywacke beds contain reddened mica which is conspicuous (particularly with the aid of a hand-lens) on freshly broken surfaces. These features indicate that the strata are part of the Carghi-down Formation, which makes up the coastal section for 4 km to the NW (see Locality 3).Return to the cliff top and walk on to the small headland about 50 m to the SE. Here the turbidite sequence is essentially similar to that seen previously, but instead of red mudstone beds it includes grey laminated siltstone, indicating that these strata are part of the Ross Formation. The first siltstone, about 30 cm thick, crosses obliquely through the centre of the headland; two more beds, each about 45 cm thick, occur close together about 20 m to the SE. Locally, the interven-ing sandstones contain red mica. The south-ward younging of the sequence is again shown by grading in the sandstone beds, congruent with a north-verging D1 fold pair which plunges 32° NE on the east side of the headland.

The transition between the two forma-tions is exposed in the west side of the headland. However, the transition zone is confused by a fold pair with a hinge separa-tion of about 25 m and some faulting. The occurrence of red mica in strata which are clearly part of the Ross Formation suggests that the disruption is minor.

The shore can be accessed from the cliff top at various places to west and east of this locality, allowing a wider examination of the Carghidown and Ross formations. Grey silt-stone can be found in various places and may yield graptolites if carefully split along the lamination. Graptolites of the early Wenlock *Cyrtograptus centrifugus* and *Monograptus ric-cartonensis* biozones have been collected (Barnes, 1989; White et al., 1992). Apart from the frequent disruption of bedding in the Carghidown Formation, the structure of the two formations is essentially the same, with beds dipping steeply south and frequent folds varying from moderate SW- to moder-ate NE-plunging. Steeply plunging sinistral D1 fold pairs are also common, related to the S1 cleavage which transects the gentle to moderately plunging folds but is axial planar to the steeply plunging folds.

5 Isle of Whithorn: Carghidown Formation structure

From the Burrow Head caravan park return to Isle of Whithorn; turn right into Main Street and drive around the harbour, park-ing on the wharf or in the small car park at the south end of the harbour [478 362].

The Isle of Whithorn (really a peninsula) and the area to the north are largely formed of Carghidown Formation turbidites like those at Localities 3 and 4, with common red mudstone beds. The south end of the Isle includes a tectonically complex sliver of Ross Formation. Several folds and strike-parallel faults cause changes in the young-ing direction of the strata. Lamprophyre dykes up to 3 m thick are commonly bed-parallel or fault-parallel, but include a few of ESE trend which are not related to any obvious structural weakness.

Well-bedded turbidites, dipping steeply SE but overturned to young NW, are exposed in the shore below the car park. About 70 m to the south these pass into a 20 m wide zone disrupted by slumping. Massive sandstone blocks and disorientated bedded slabs lie in a mudstone matrix with patches of red mudstone. Units of very thin-bedded greywacke and silty mudstone con-tain small slump folds with widely variable axial orientations. The mélange is cut by lamprophyre dykes which lie parallel to bed-ding in the adjacent strata, indicating that this attitude is tectonically controlled, not simply constrained by bedding as the easiest path for intrusion. The mélange passes southwards back into steeply SE-dipping tur-bidites, initially southward younging indicat-ing the presence of a fold or fault either with-in or at the southern edge of the mélange. After 50 m there is a return to north-young-ing across a bedding-parallel fault.

Hereabouts a narrow concrete path leads NE across the foreshore; follow it to where it crosses the high water mark. Immediately south of the path, a small anticlinal fold pair in very thin-bedded greywackes shows extreme variation in the plunge of the prominent anticlinal hinge, from 81°NE to 45°SW over a distance of 1–2 m along the axial plane. Cleavage, approximately axial planar, is continuous throughout the fold.

A short distance to the south a narrow bay called Chapel Port West has been deeply eroded along a strike-parallel fault. Cross to the opposite side of the Isle where a comparable bay (Chapel Port East) south of the ruins of St Ninian's Church marks the trace of the same fault. South of the fault the turbidite dominated sequence contains thick red mudstone beds. Irregular ESE-trending mica-lamprophyre dykes cut obliquely across bedding and show sinistral displacements ranging from a few centimetres to 3 m on faults lying nearly parallel to bedding. A red mudstone 6 m thick contains several such faults; a lamprophyre dyke is repeatedly offset sinistrally by 30 to 50 cm. Horizontal slickensides can be seen on some of the fault surfaces and are also commonly seen in thin veins along bedding, indicating that this late (post-lamprophyre) sinistral shear was mainly taken up by movement on discrete faults and by slip along bedding.

About 50 m SE of the bay on the east side of the Isle, a major anticlinal fold, plunging about 30°NE, is well exposed across the foreshore. The same fold is also exposed on the west coast, although here it is associated with minor folds and plunges more gently. Follow the western shore south; after about 40 m, a very thick sandstone bed with large flute casts on its base is well exposed above high water in an open, east-trending fold pair. A further 40 m south, several strike-parallel faults are apparent in an intensely deformed zone, 50 m wide, marked by discontinuous and contorted sandstone beds and blocks, with some gently plunging coherent folds, in a sheared matrix. Discontinuous beds of laminated, grey siltstone occur in the deformed zone and yield a sparse lower Wenlock graptolite fauna. These features are characteristic of the Ross Formation as seen at Burrow Head, although here at Isle of Whithorn the precise stratigraphical relationships are unclear.

Return to the car park by walking north around the shore or by following one of several paths across the Isle.

6 Cairnhead Mote: polyphase D1 folding

From Isle of Whithorn, take the B7063 north towards Wigtown. After 1.5 km, shortly before the road reaches the coast, the farm of Cairnhead is visible set back east of the road. Park at the road and, with permission from the farm, follow the track

through the farmyard for about 700 m until a small east-facing bay is reached. Cairnhead Mote [486 383], and the exposures of interest, are situated on a small headland (Cairn Head) not far to the south.

Bedding within the Carghidown Formation is here disrupted in a manner consistent with soft sediment deformation. However, two folds with axes plunging steeply west are clearly seen crossing the foreshore ENE of the mote; they form a sinistral fold pair and have minor folds locally in the short limb. Close inspection of bedding will reveal earlier tight folds which, despite poor preservation, can be seen to be refolded. A tectonic fabric is apparent in the early fold hinges, suggesting that they are not simply slump folds. This fabric is not discernable elsewhere, possibly due to the intense cleavage associated with the steeply plunging folds, or perhaps because it formed only in association with the early fold hinges. This evidence for two phases of folding was first described by Rust (1965). Elsewhere, throughout much of the Hawick Group outcrop, 'early' folds are characterised by widely variable hinge plunge and a mildly transecting cleavage; some isolated, steeply plunging sinistral folds appear to be related to the same cleavage. It is only at Cairn Head, where the two fold styles are superimposed, that one can be seen to postdate the other, but even here it seems likely that both are part of the D1 event. The variable relationships are probably due to a change in the stress regime during deformation, from one dominantly orthogonal to one involving a major component of sinistral shear.

Return directly to the road along the track, or follow the coast north around Cairn Head and then round the south side of Portyerrock Bay, meeting the road just north of Cairnhead Farm. If the latter route is taken the foreshore exposures of the Carghidown Formation can be examined. Changes in the direction of younging of the near-vertical bedding, shown by sole markings and grading in the sandstone beds, indicate the presence of major folds, although many of the fold hinges have been replaced by bed-parallel faults. Many minor fold pairs are present, the hinge plunges varying from moderate east to moderate west. This variation is sometimes seen in the same fold, producing markedly arcuate hinges. Several lamprophyre dykes are also present, usually bed-parallel and less than 2 m thick but including an 8 m-thick dyke through Cairn Head.

R P Barnes

Excursion 14

BARRHILL and NEWTON STEWART:
stratigraphy, provenance and structure of Ordovician turbidites

OS 1:50 000 sheets 76 Girvan,
77 Dalmellington to New Galloway
83 Newton Stewart & Kirkcudbright
BGS 1:50 000 sheets 8W Carrick,
4W Kirkcowan, 4E Wigtown
Route maps: Figures 42 and 44

Main points of interest Typical sections illustrating Kirkcolm/Galdenoch and Portpatrick/Glenwhargen formation relationships; Shinnel Formation; Moffat Shale Group; D3 folding.

Logistics A general north to south route starts from the village of Barrhill, about

20 km SE of Girvan on the A714, and ends near Newton Stewart. Most localities are accessed by narrow single-track roads with roadside parking adequate for 3–4 cars or a minibus. Localities 4 and 9 are adjacent to the main A714, with lay-bys adequate for larger coaches. Some rough walking is involved in Localities 1, 2, 3 and 8.

Introduction Several of the localities include sections within the Leadhills Group where critical stratigraphical relationships can be demonstrated. Such sections are particularly rare and valuable in the Southern Uplands, where exposure is generally poor

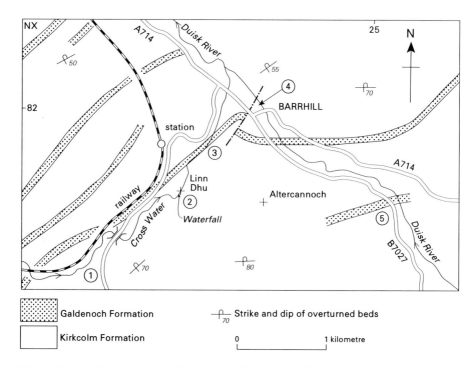

Figure 42 Locality map and outline geology for the Barrhill area (Localities 1–5).

and field relationships between rock units often inconclusive. The overall stratigraphical relationships are shown in Figure 2 and may also be compared with the stratigraphical transect of the Rhins of Galloway shown in Figure 46.

BARRHILL (Figure 42)

1 Cross Water: Kirkcolm Formation; folding in greywackes

From the crossroads at the village hall in Barrhill, take the moor road to New Luce as far as a small bridge (with concrete parapets) over the Cross Water, about 1 km SW of Barrhill Station. Cars may be parked at the roadside near the bridge [NX 221 806]. In the Cross Water, about 200 m upstream of this bridge, several good small-scale D3 fold pairs with sinistral vergence can be seen in medium-bedded quartz-rich greywackes of the Kirkcolm Formation.

The general strike locally is about 070° and the intermediate limbs of the folds strike about 130°. Axial planes trend east–west and the fold axes generally plunge steeply towards the west. Folds of this type are very common in the Northern Belt, particularly in the thinly bedded Kirkcolm Formation (also seen at Locality 2 of Excursion 6), and provide evidence for sinistral strike-slip movement.

The low rock ridge, which runs parallel to the river and crosses the field between the concrete bridge and the railway line, is the south-western strike continuation of the Galdenoch Formation, interbedded with the Kirkcolm Formation and described in detail at Locality 3.

2 Linn Dhu, Cross Water: greywacke and laminated siltstone with graptolites

From the concrete bridge, drive back 1 km towards Barrhill, to where the road turns to run north, about 300 m south of Barrhill Station. Park at the roadside and walk SE about 200 m and down a steep bank into the Cross Water [229 812].

The river exposes a strike section in a thick succession of grey and black striped and laminated siltstones. The black laminae have yielded graptolites of the *Nemagraptus*

gracilis Biozone at several localities, including an exposure just downstream from a high cliff of boulder clay on the west bank. Such siltstone units are commonly interbedded with the Kirkcolm Formation greywackes and, about 50 m downstream from this cliff, in an attractive waterfall known as the Linn Dhu, thickly bedded quartz-rich greywackes of the Kirkcolm Formation are well displayed in water-polished exposures.

3 Cross Water, Barrhill: contact between Galdenoch and Kirkcolm formations; greywackes and laminated siltstones

From the Linn Dhu, return to the road, drive back towards Barrhill for about 1 km and park at the old cattle market about 400 m beyond the cemetery. From the market, walk back up the road away from Barrhill for about 150 m to a sharp bend in the road near a covered water-supply reservoir. Use the gate in the wall on the south side of the road and cross the field into the river gorge at Locality 3 [230 815].

The Cross Water hereabouts displays an excellent section where interbedding of the Kirkcolm and Galdenoch formations can be reliably demonstrated. From the Linn Dhu (Locality 2), the river continues north for 200 m, cutting through greywacke and thick laminated siltstone, until it is deflected to the NE by a resistant bed of massive greywacke forming the base of the Galdenoch Formation. The river follows this bed for almost 300 m along strike to the NE before it finally breaches the obstacle and continues north across strike. The resulting cross-strike section forms Locality 3, about 300 m upstream from the old cattle market. It is the proposed type section for the Galdenoch Formation, a unit characterised by greywackes rich in andesitic detritus, including pyroxene- and hornblende-andesite lithoclasts as well as remarkably fresh grains of detrital pyroxene and hornblende. Some specimens contain up to 25 per cent pyroxene and are virtually resedimented crystal tuffs. The andesitic material is thought to have come from a volcanic island arc which was active during deposition of the greywackes. Andesitic detritus is conspicuously absent from the greywackes of the Kirkcolm Formation.

A measured section through the Galdenoch Formation here (Figure 43) proves it to be about 25 m thick and dominated by thickly bedded, medium- to coarse-grained greywacke with very little interbedded siltstone. The Galdenoch Formation greywacke is succeeded conformably by grey and black laminated siltstone of the Kirkcolm Formation, the contact being exposed in the field north of the river. Beds strike 050° and dip 60° to the south but young towards the north and are therefore overturned.

The presence of several parallel outcrops of pyroxenous greywacke in the Barrhill area (Figure 42) suggests that the Galdenoch Formation occurs as a series of packets which interfinger with the Kirkcolm Formation. Such a situation could arise as a result of repeated overlapping of distinct fan systems derived from opposite sides of the depositional basin. This interpretation is supported by contrasting palaeocurrent directions in the two formations. The numerous large flute casts which occur on the undersides of greywacke beds at the base of the Galdenoch Formation (Figure 43b) all indicate a sediment source to the south or SE, whereas current directions deduced for the Kirkcolm Formation immediately downstream (Figure 43a) indicate sediment transport from the opposite (northerly) direction (Stone et al., 1987; Evans et al., 1991).

4 War Memorial, Barrhill: Galdenoch Formation greywackes

Drive back into Barrhill, turn right at the crossroads and park by the War Memorial at the south end of Main Street [236 820]. The memorial is built on a knoll of massive Galdenoch Formation greywacke, part of the same packet of beds which forms the type section (Locality 3). The Kirkcolm Formation laminated siltstone underlying the Galdenoch Formation greywacke may be seen again in a small quarry nearby.

5 Altercannoch Quarry: Galdenoch Formation greywackes

Leave Barrhill on the B7027 and drive SE for about 2 km to a small quarry on the south side of the road [252 810]. Park in the quarry to examine a good section in thickly bedded NW-younging greywackes of the Galdenoch Formation. An interesting feature is the large lenticular block of black shale which occurs as a rip-up clast in a bed towards the top of the section. This clast has yielded a large collection of graptolites of the *N. gracilis* Biozone.

NEWTON STEWART (Figure 44)

6 Clachaneasy Quarry: Portpatrick Formation greywackes

Return to Barrhill and continue south on the A714 towards Newton Stewart. At Clachaneasy, about 14 km south of Barrhill and 1.5 km south of Bargrennan, turn left off the A714 on to the minor road which crosses the River Cree. About 200 m beyond the bridge, park at the roadside [358 753] to examine, on the right (south) side of the road, a large abandoned quarry in greywacke of the Portpatrick Formation (Figure 44). This is a good place to see the massive thickly bedded units which are typical of this formation.

The greywackes of the Portpatrick Formation are characteristically poor in quartz but rich in andesitic detritus and fresh grains of pyroxene and hornblende. Occasionally, as here, they also contain rare fragments of blue amphibole, both as individual detrital grains and as crystals within schist lithoclasts. Although originally loosely described as glaucophane, the amphibole has now been identified as the closely related mineral crossite. Glaucophane/crossite schists are metamorphic rocks of the blueschist facies and are usually associated with deep burial and low thermal gradient (high-pressure, low-temperature conditions), as found in metagreywacke terranes above subduction zones. Their presence in the Portpatrick Formation indicates that a terrane of this sort was exposed to erosion during the late Ordovician.

7 Minnoch Bridge: Glenwhargen Formation greywackes

From Clachaneasy Quarry, continue east along the minor road for a further 200 m

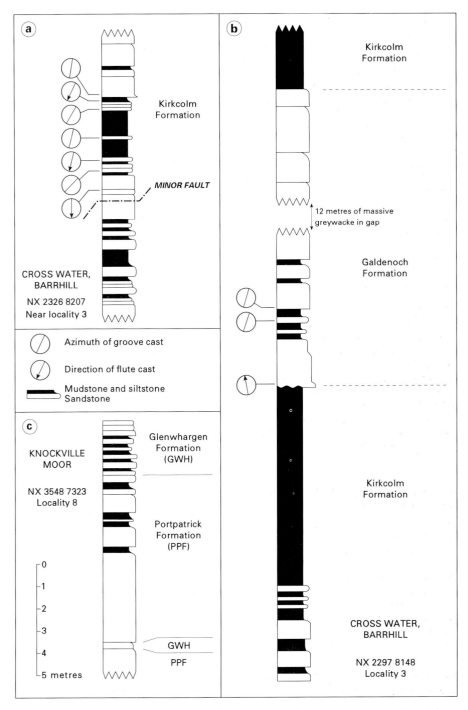

Figure 43 Measured sections in the Lower Palaeozoic strata between Barrhill and Newton Stewart.

and turn right at a T-junction. After about 1 km this road crosses the Minnoch Water at a large stone arch bridge over a rocky gorge. Park in the large car park just beyond the bridge on the left and walk down to the river below the bridge.

The bridge is built on greywacke of the Portpatrick Formation but the greywacke exposed about 20 m downstream belongs to the Glenwhargen Formation. This formation is highly quartzose and, in sharp contrast to the Portpatrick Formation, almost totally devoid of andesitic material. Bedding is generally vertical, strikes about 045° and youngs south. A north-verging fold pair can be seen on the east bank of the river, plunging about 20° towards 030°. At this locality the contact relationship between the two formations is unclear but at the next locality they are demonstrably interbedded.

8   Knockville Moor: contact between Portpatrick and Glenwhargen greywackes

Return to the A714 and continue south towards Newton Stewart for about 3 km from Clachaneasy. If the party is small (1–2 cars), turn right through the gate on to the rough track to Knockville Farm and park, with permission, at the farm [362 724]. Alternatively, park in one of the large laybys on the A714 and walk up to the farm (c.500 m) to request access permission. From the farm, walk NNW about 600 m across two fields to the gate near a T-junction between two drystane dykes. From the gate in the dyke, walk NW out on to the moorland for a further 500 m to a large *roche moutonnée* which lies 330 m NE of the prominent cairn [3525 7295]. An undoubted conformable stratigraphical contact between older Portpatrick and younger Glenwhargen formations is exposed on the north side of the *roche moutonnée*.

Greywackes of the two formations are visibly different in the field. Those of the Glenwhargen Formation are pale grey, often weather white, and are commonly rich in quartz pebbles. They are usually well bedded and often show obvious lamination even in coarse-grained units. By contrast, Portpatrick Formation greywackes are dull bluish grey, weather with a brown

rusty crust and tend to form rounded exposures of massive sandstone in which bedding is often obscure.

A measured section at the Knockville Moor locality (Figure 43c) shows that the basal units of the Glenwhargen Formation (at the top of the section) are relatively thinly bedded and fine-grained, in strong contrast to the underlying top units of the Portpatrick Formation sequence. Beds are vertical and young north. An interesting feature is the presence of a single thin quartzose greywacke bed interbedded near the top of the Portpatrick Formation. More typical thicker-bedded and coarser-grained greywackes of the Glenwhargen Formation can be seen in numerous isolated exposures on the moorland to the north.

The Portpatrick/Glenwhargen interbedding is analogous to that at the Kirkcolm/Galdenoch boundary (Locality 3) except that in this case the andesite-rich greywacke is predominant. The outcrop of the Glenwhargen Formation, which sometimes bifurcates into two distinct subunits, is mappable for over 35 km to the NE, as far as the Cairnsmore of Carsphairn granite. Further NE, and also towards the SW, the unit becomes much thinner and is represented by only a few sporadic quartzose beds in the Scaur Water (Floyd, 1982) and on the Rhins of Galloway (Excursion 15, Locality 4). As with the Kirkcolm/Galdenoch interbedding seen at Locality 3 of the present excursion, the Portpatrick/Glenwhargen relationship is interpreted as the result of repeated interfingering by submarine fans derived from strongly contrasting source areas, probably on opposite sides of the depositional basin.

9   A714 at Glenhapple: Moffat Shale Group black cherty mudstone

From Knockville, continue south on the A714 for a further 1.2 km to a roadside cliff section near Glenhapple [375 715] which exposes black cherty mudstone and

Figure 44   Locality map and outline geology for the area north-west from Newton Stewart (Localities 6–10).

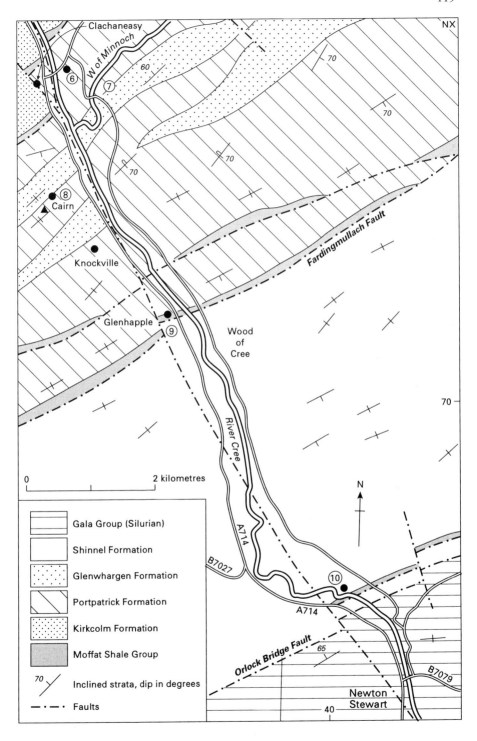

Gala Group (Silurian)

Shinnel Formation

Glenwhargen Formation

Portpatrick Formation

Kirkcolm Formation

Moffat Shale Group

70 — Inclined strata, dip in degrees

— · — · — Faults

thick greywacke. The mudstone is probably part of the Moffat Shale Group underlying the Portpatrick Formation and has been brought up along a splay of the Farding-mullach Fault. The greywacke immediately to the south of the mudstone belongs to the Shinnel Formation and its contact with the cherty mudstone is sheared and veined and probably tectonic. A 4 m-wide porphyritic microdiorite (porphyrite) dyke trending 015° cuts the greywackes and cherty mudstones here.

10 River Cree: Moffat Shale Group black shales; Shinnel Formation siltstones and greywackes

Continue south on the A714 to Newton Stewart, turn left across the Bridge of Cree into Minnigaff and turn left again almost immediately on to the Wood of Cree road. Continue north out of Minnigaff and take the left turn over the Penkiln Burn bridge and past the church. About 2 km north of Minnigaff and 400 m north of Boreland Lodge, a fisherman's path on the left leads down about 300 m to the River Cree [401 669].

At this locality, a large bend of the River Cree exposes deformed black shales on the north bank and on some small islands in the river. These black shales belong to the Moffat Shale Group, which underlies the Shinnel Formation at this locality and has been brought up along a splay of the Orlock Bridge Fault. Graptolites obtained from the shales indicate the presence of the *D. clingani* or *P. linearis* biozones. This is one of the few localities where black shales are exposed along the line of the Orlock Bridge Fault, which forms the boundary between the Northern and Central Belts in the Southern Uplands.

A short distance upstream, and round the bend in the river, there is a 150 m section in laminated siltstones which are typical of the Shinnel Formation and form its basal beds hereabouts. Beds strike about 055° with a general steep dip towards the north. NW across a small fault the succession becomes coarser grained and there is a good section in medium- to thickly bedded Shinnel Formation greywackes on the east bank of the river. Groove casts and graded bedding indicate that the succession youngs north. Rip-up clasts of dark shale can be seen in several of the greywacke units.

Petrographically, the Shinnel Formation is quite similar to the Kirkcolm Formation, with little or no andesitic detritus, but with a generally higher, though more variable, quartz content.

J D Floyd

Excursion 15

Rhins of Galloway:
a coastal traverse across the Northern and Central belts of the Southern Uplands

OS 1:50 000 sheets 76 Girvan and 82 Stranraer, Glen Luce & surrounding area BGS 1:50 000 Sheet 1 and 3 with parts of 7 and 4W The Rhins of Galloway Route map: Figure 45

Main points of interest Ordovician and Silurian structure; turbidite sedimentology (conglomerate, greywacke and shale) and stratigraphy; Caledonian folding and thrusting.

Logistics The itinerary suggested for this relatively remote area can be used as the basis for a 2- or 3-day excursion centred on Portpatrick. Some of the localities in Excursions 17 and 18 can also be visited from here. All the localities are readily accessible to small vehicles, but anything larger than a minibus will not be able to negotiate the narrow roads. All the localities are coastal, so more rock will be seen at low tide. Localities 2, 9 and 10 are the most tide dependent and should be visited out of sequence if necessary. Most of the localities require scrambling over steep rock outcrops which may be wet and slippery; the longest walk required is about 4 km.

Introduction The coast sections of the 45 km-long Rhins of Galloway peninsula provide an unsurpassed traverse through the Lower Palaeozoic outcrop of south-west Scotland. The sections chosen (Figure 45) build up a complete cross-strike traverse through the imbricate thrust sheet of late Ordovician and early Silurian turbidite strata. Biostratigraphical ages quoted are based largely on recent determinations by A W A Rushton and S P Tunnicliff summarised in Stone (1995). The summary of tectonostratigraphy given in Figure 46 encapsulates the stratigraphical paradox of the Southern Uplands: within each fault-bounded tract the exposed strata become younger towards the NW, though the tracts themselves become sequentially younger towards the SE. The strike faults separating

the tracts are therefore thrust faults which originally propagated mostly towards the SE, carrying older beds over younger. Each thrust slice steepened upwards before its sole thrust stuck and was replaced at a lower level by a new thrust. In some interpretations one of the faults is given special importance as a possible terrane boundary along which a large displacement has occurred. This structure, the Orlock Bridge Fault, is examined in Excursion 17. In the Rhins of Galloway traverse described here Localities 1–5 are within the Ordovician Northern Belt of the Southern Uplands and Localities 6–10 are in the Silurian Central Belt to the south.

The introductory section of this guide which deals with the Lower Palaeozoic regional geology is particularly relevant to this excursion. Also of great value is the BGS 1:50 000 Rhins of Galloway map, but note the alternative interpretation at Locality 9. Much of the evidence to be seen is pertinent to the debate over the origin of the Southern Uplands: forearc accretionary prism or backarc to foreland basin thrust belt. The regional palaeocurrent pattern (at least in the Ordovician) and the interdigitating siliceous and volcaniclastic turbidites at locality 4 provide evidence of a volcanic source to the south of a backarc Southern Uplands (Stone et al., 1987); the opposing younging and vergence of D1 thrusting and folding on either side of the Port Logan Fault (Localities 7, 8 and 9) provide evidence of obduction accretion comparable with that in the Washington–Oregon forearc (McCurry and Anderson, 1989). Descriptions for Localities 1, 2 and 5 have been prepared by P Stone, for Localities 3, 7, 9 and 10 by J McCurry, and for Localities 6 and 8 jointly.

1   Finnarts Bay: Kirkcolm Formation

Finnarts Bay is on the east side of Loch Ryan. If approaching from the east on the

122

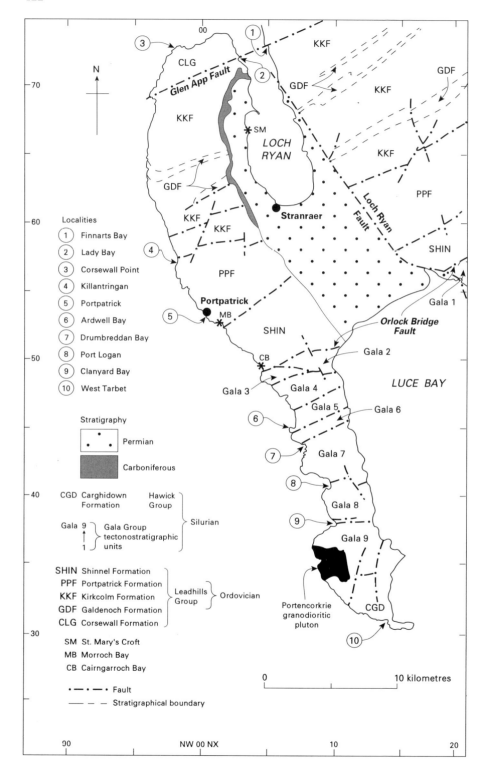

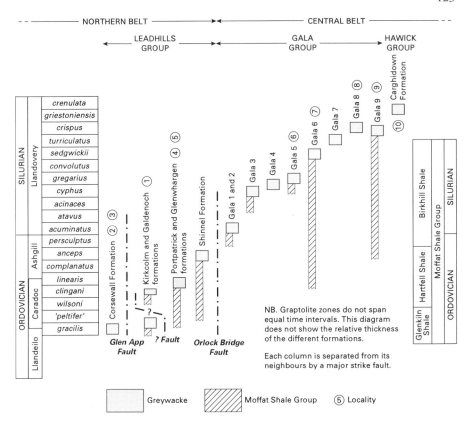

Figure 46 Summary of Lower Palaeozoic stratigraphy on the Rhins of Galloway.

A75 turn north on the A751 and follow the A77 through Cairnryan. About 4 km north of Cairnryan a large, disused quarry is seen on the right; shortly after take the left turn signposted for the Fish Farm and at the bottom of the hill turn abruptly left to park on the extensive raised beach [NX 051 725]. If approaching from the north, follow the A77 down the valley of Glen App and, when the road reaches the coast and swings south, turn right towards the Fish Farm. The itinerary (Figure 47) has two sections, a coastal traverse and a nearby road section along the A77. For the latter part there is parking for one or two cars at the entrance to the rough track leading into

Figure 45 Locality map and outline geology for the Rhins of Galloway.

the old quarry [053 720] or in the lay-by on the opposite (seaward) side of the road. If a larger number of vehicles is involved it is safer to leave them parked on the raised beach and walk back to the quarry entrance and road section.

Coastal traverse At the south-west end of the raised beach an extensive rocky area is exposed below the high tide mark. This outcrop consists of very thinly bedded, fine-grained greywacke and siltstone. At low tide and subject to the movement of beach shingle, a low northward extension of the main outcrop shows an intrusive porphyritic dyke (**a** in Figure 47). The dyke is up to 2 m across and contains abundant feldspar phenocrysts set in a fine-grained micro-dioritic groundmass. It has sharp margins against the host siltstone and contains no

124

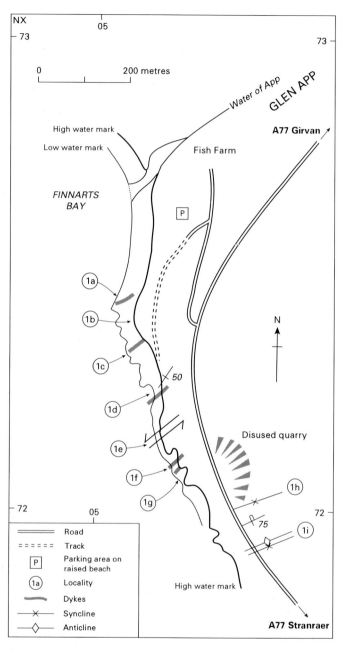

Figure 47 Locality map and outline geology for the Finnarts Bay area (Locality 1).

NX 73 / 05 / 73

0 — 200 metres

High water mark
Low water mark

Water of App   **GLEN APP**

A77 Girvan

Fish Farm

FINNARTS BAY

P

(1a)
(1b)
(1c)
✕ *50*
(1d)
(1e)
(1f)
(1g)

N

Disused quarry

(1h)
✕ *75*
(1i)

72 / 05 / 72

	Road
======	Track
P	Parking area on raised beach
(1a)	Locality
	Dykes
✕	Syncline
◇	Anticline

High water mark

A77 Stranraer

trace of tectonic foliation. It was clearly intruded after deformation. The surrounding sedimentary strata, best seen on the larger exposures to the south of the dyke (**b** in Figure 47), form a thinly bedded interval within the Kirkcolm Formation and contain a sparse *gracilis* Biozone graptolite fauna (Figure 46). Seemingly chaotic deformation has affected the siltstone and greywacke, with folding on a variety of scales and styles. Brittle dislocation of the thin beds in both an extensional and a compressional sense is also apparent. The folding may well be polygenetic, with tectonic deformation superimposed on syndepositional slump-related folding. Within the chaotically folded zones diagenetic carbonate concretions are fairly common, forming disc-shaped bodies up to 1 m across. These weather brown and may project from the eroded surface of the host strata. Significantly, when such concretions are surrounded by chaotically deformed layers they may preserve internal undisturbed lamination. The concretions are therefore thought to have formed before deformation occurred which suggests that much folding was post-diagenetic.

About 20 m south into the next small bay another felsic dyke is intruded into the laminated siltstone (c). However, in this case the dyke is pervasively foliated with a fabric parallel to, and apparently continuous with, that seen in the surrounding sedimentary strata. If possible, dig out the sand to expose the contact of dyke and siltstone; locally it is quite irregular but, whereas the dyke cuts across the overall bedding trend at an angle of about 10°, the cleavage fabric is continuous across the contact. Clearly the dyke was intruded prior to the imposition of the cleavage. The contrast with the dyke examined earlier, which is of very similar composition, suggests that dyke intrusion spanned the cleavage-forming deformation.

Slightly farther south within the same bay thick greywacke beds up to 1.5 m across appear in the sequence. These are medium-grained quartzofeldspathic representatives of the Kirkcolm Formation. Another thick greywacke bed forms part of the cliff at the south end of the bay, exposed beneath the World War II gun emplacement (Loch Ryan was a convoy assembly point and flying boat base, hence the fortifications). Bedding dip in the cliff section (d) is about 50° SE but sedimentary structures such as ripple crests and shale flames show that the beds are inverted. A well-developed slaty cleavage dips more steeply than the bedding and therefore cannot be a simple axial-planar cleavage. Various explanations are possible. Either the bedding and cleavage have been jointly rotated or the cleavage has been imposed on bedding already tilted out of the horizontal; both situations require at least two

deformation episodes. Alternatively a non-axial-planar cleavage, developed coevally with the folding, could locally give this relationship. Examples of the latter phenomenon are widespread in the southern part of the Rhins of Galloway.

Seaward from the inverted greywacke beds the chaotically deformed siltstone lithology reappears. It is intruded by a porphyritic dyke (feldspar phenocrysts in a microdiorite groundmass) up to 2 m across which runs oblique to bedding and has irregular margins. Examination of the dyke margins shows that the cleavage in the siltstone continues for up to a centimetre into the chilled margins. This dyke was clearly intruded before the end of cleavage-forming deformation.

Continue south along the beach and scramble up the low cliff on to the slightly higher rock platform; this is easiest at the inland end of the cliff. A narrow track leads south but after about 20 m leave it and scramble across the rock outcrops to seaward. The thinly bedded siltstones are here deformed in a slightly more orderly fashion and, if the beds are traced out, a sequence of steeply plunging 'S' folds can be established (e). A spaced cleavage can be seen subparallel to the axial plane of the folds. Note the similarity between the attitude of this cleavage and that in the inverted greywacke beds seen previously. The associated steeply plunging 'S' folds may be the result of the late sinistral shear (D3) imposed on this part of the Southern Uplands.

Regain the track and continue south for a short distance and descend into the next small inlet. The most prominent feature here (f) is a 2 m-thick felsic dyke containing abundant feldspar phenocrysts. At first sight the dyke appears compound, with a discrete central zone, but examination of thin sections has proved it to be a homogeneous porphyritic microdiorite. There is no cleavage in the dyke and so, like the first example seen, it is probably post-tectonic.

The less agile should retrace their route to the parking area, but the more sure-footed can scramble over the next two rocky spurs; the distance is only about 50 m but is quite arduous at anything but very low tide. The reward is a magnificent array of flute casts on the base of a greywacke bed, slightly overturned to dip steeply SE (**g**). The rock face must therefore be viewed looking north. The linear nested flutes indicate a current flow from top right to bottom left. If you imagine the bedding plane restored to the horizontal, an original eroding current flowing from the SE is suggested.

Return to the raised beach at Finnarts Bay. If several vehicles are being used the party should walk back to the A77 and **proceed with care** (the road carries **much heavy traffic** to and from the Irish ferry terminals) to the entrance track for the large disused quarry [053 720]. One or two vehicles can be parked in the rough track entrance or on the hard shoulder area on the opposite (seaward) side of the road. The quarry itself is structurally complex and has loose, dangerous faces. It should not be entered. Fortunately the more accessible cliffs forming the roadside section running south from the quarry (Figure 47) are both secure and instructive.

Roadside traverse This section is only slightly lower in the sequence than the flute casts viewed earlier at sea level. The entrance to the quarry coincides with an overturned F1 synclinal hinge zone with short limb partly eliminated by faulting (**h**). Closest to the quarry entrance the greywacke beds are the right way up and dip moderately south whereas, to the south in the roadside section, beds dip steeply south but are slightly overturned and young north. The direction of younging can be readily established from the array of sedimentary structures. The greywacke beds range from about 10 cm to over 1 m in thickness. Many beds are clearly graded and contain weak cross-lamination in places. Bed bases commonly carry small flute casts and more bulbous load casts.

The roadside section continues south becoming progressively lower and more obscured by bushes. Initially the attitude of the greywacke beds remains uniform with steep dip to SE and northwards younging. However, about 100 m SE from the quarry the greywackes are folded about an F1 anticline–syncline pair with both hinge zones broken and faulted (**i**). The anticline lies to the north of the syncline in a structural

pattern characteristic of much folding throughout the Southern Uplands (Types 1 and 2, Figure 3). No cleavage is developed in association with these folds and cleavage is in fact absent from the whole roadside section.

The greywackes exposed on the shore and roadside are all in the Kirkcolm Formation (Figure 46). They are quartzofelds-pathic greywackes with a few accessory grains of spilite, schist, garnet and zircon; the quartz content averages about 45 per cent. Full compositional details are provided by Kelling (1962), Floyd and Trench (1989), Evans et al. (1991) and Stone (1995).

2 Lady Bay: Glen App Fault and Corsewall Formation

Leave Finnarts Bay and drive south on the A77 to Stranraer; pass through the town following signs for Leswalt and Kirkcolm and leave on the A718 heading NW. After passing the Stranraer golf course turn right at the Craigencross roundabout, still following the A718 for Kirkcolm. About 3.5 km beyond the roundabout it is worth stopping briefly beside the sea at St Mary's Croft [034 659]. Here, on the foreshore, are exposed the Permian breccias which fill the 1500 m-deep Stranraer basin (Stone, 1988 and references therein). The east side of the basin is formed by a major fault which defines the east coast of Loch Ryan. This contrasts with the west side of the basin, where the Permian (and some Westphalian) strata lie unconformably above the Lower Palaeozoic greywackes; the structure is a classic half-graben (Figure 45). The breccias consist of greywacke pebbles up to about 6 cm across, contained in a matrix of coarse red sand. Thin interbeds of red sandstone and siltstone are also present. The most extensive outcrop is near the low water mark.

Continue north on the A718 through Kirkcolm. About 2 km beyond the village, fork right following signs for Corsewall Point and about 1 km beyond the fork turn right following signs for Lady Bay. The road is metalled as far as Low Portencalzie Farm but thereafter deteriorates into a rough track. Nevertheless continue on down towards the sea where there is a paved parking area with adjacent picnic tables.

It is essential to visit this locality around low tide. The Glen App Fault zone is exposed, subject to the vagaries of shifting sand and shingle, at the north end of the bay [027 718] below high water mark. All the rocks in the vicinity are pervasively reddened, a reminder of the nearby Permian sequence of red sandstone and breccia. A complex array of shear zones and quartz veins cuts through the reddened greywackes defining a fault zone about 5 m across and trending approximately NE towards Finnarts Bay and Glen App on the far side of Loch Ryan. The character and geometry of the structures within the fault zone suggest that ductile deformation occurred with a sinistral sense of shear, followed by small-scale brittle effects with a dextral shear sense.

Thickly bedded greywackes abut the fault zone on its north side and it is well worth scrambling over the cliffs a little way northwards to examine their sedimentary features. A well-trodden track provides a route. The greywackes are all part of the Corsewall Formation and are compositionally immature, with abundant clasts of igneous lithologies including spilite, gabbro and serpentinite probably derived from an ophiolitic source. The quartz content is only about 14 per cent on average. Compositional details are given by Kelling (1962), Evans et al. (1991) and Stone (1995). The lithic composition gives the greywackes a dark appearance which contrasts with the pale grey Kirkcolm Formation greywackes seen at Locality 1.

Immediately north of Lady Bay the Corsewall Formation greywackes are thickly bedded (up to 1.5 m) graded turbidites. Beds are steeply inclined and the grading, together with the weak cross-lamination in the top part of some beds and the bottom structures on their bases, establishes a consistent direction of younging towards the north. Slightly farther north (up sequence) the thick greywacke beds are separated by thinly bedded intervals of greywacke and siltstone showing classical turbidite structures such as grading, cross-lamination and rippled bed tops. Some of the thick, coarser interbeds have pockets of pebbly greywacke along their bases.

3 Corsewall Point: Corsewall Conglomerate

Return to the parking area in Lady Bay and retrace the route to the Kirkcolm–Corsewall Point road. Turn right and continue towards the lighthouse. Just over 1 km NW from the Lady Bay road junction be sure to take the right fork; thereafter the route is fairly obvious, though occasionally gated. At Corsewall Point park on the right side of the road by the wildlife information board [NW 982 727]. From there walk NW on to the fault-bounded promontory (3a on Figure 48). On this and the two promontories to the east (3b and 3c) the sedimentary features of the conglomeratic member of the Corsewall Formation (late Llandeilo–early Caradoc) can be examined. This site has been mapped and logged in detail by Holroyd (1978) who interprets its rocks as an inner fan channel sequence deposited at the base of a deep-sea slope. The steeply SE-dipping beds are slightly overturned and young north. The sequence consists of extrabasinal conglomerates interbedded with coarse, massive sandstone units. Individual units are up to 4 m thick. Tertiary igneous activity is evidenced by thin cross-cutting dolerite dykes and, offshore to the north, by the microgranitic plug of Ailsa Craig.

The conglomerates are variably clast and matrix supported and consist of well-rounded pebbles and boulders up to 1.5 m in diameter set in a sandy matrix (3a and 3b). Granites and acid volcanic clasts predominate, but spilites, gabbros, greywackes and cherts are also found. Although mostly disorganised, the conglomerates display increased organisation eastwards across the three promontories. Organisation is shown by the alignment of the long axes of clasts parallel to bedding and, in places, by a crude lamination in the matrix. Both normal and reverse grading are present, but rare. Bedding is lenticular and channelised, in places clearly eroding the underlying unit (3c). The massive sandstone units are coarse grained and frequently contain outsize extrabasinal clasts. Rare sole markings indicate palaeoflow from the NW. Further east the boulder conglomerates are less common so that massive and graded sand-

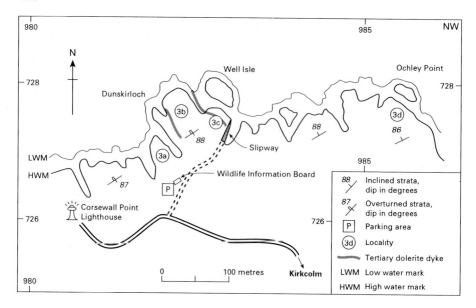

Figure 48 Locality map and outline geology for the Corsewall Point area (Locality 3).

stone units predominate. At Ochley Point [986 728], about 300 m east of the parking area, fine-grained sandstone, laminated siltstone and mudstone form interbedded units up to 1.5 m thick in an overall fining- and thinning-up sequence (**3d**). This facies assemblage represents an interchannel environment on a submarine fan.

Work by Elders (1987) on the provenance of the granite clasts has highlighted the tectonic importance of the site. He identified a suite of five granitic clast types within the conglomerate. The most distinctive of these is a weakly foliated, muscovite-bearing biotite granite dated at 1265 Ma. Two of the other granites yielded ages of 600 Ma and 475 Ma. Combining these dates with petrographic and geochemical evidence, Elders identified north-west Newfoundland as the only area with a plutonic and tectonic history to match that of the clasts. The Corsewall conglomerate was obviously deposited close to source and a sinistral strike-slip movement of 1500 km during closure of the Iapetus Ocean would therefore be needed to account for its present position. This controversial conclusion has not been universally accepted; Kelley and Bluck (1989) refute it based on radio-

metric work of their own from the Southern Uplands (see discussion, Elders, 1990); whilst Owen and Clarkson (1992) argue that faunal evidence supports at most a few hundred kilometres of strike-slip movement along the Southern Upland Fault (but see also McKerrow and Elders, 1989). In view of its importance this locality has been designated a Site of Special Scientific Interest (McCurry, 1994).

4 Killantringan: Portpatrick Formation

From Corsewall Point return via minor roads to the A718 north of Kirkcolm. Drive south through the village to the Craigencross roundabout and proceed straight on along the Glenstockadale road; at the end turn left on to the A764 towards Portpatrick. After about 3 km turn right on to a single-track road signposted for Killantringan Lighthouse. This road forms part of the Southern Upland Way footpath and is marked accordingly. When the road reaches the coast cars should be parked on the right-hand side overlooking Killantringan Bay [NW 982 567]. At low tide a broad sweep of sandy beach allows easy access to the cliffs; when the tide is high the sea reaches the foot of the cliffs and isolates a number of small coves. These may then be accessed via the cliff top path.

Walk north on to the sea cliffs, either at beach level or by way of the cliff path, where thinly bedded greywackes and siltstones of the Portpatrick Formation are extensively exposed (**4a** in Figure 49). Sporadic thicker greywacke beds are also present and isoclinal fold structures can be picked out in places by careful examination. However, the probability of folding is most readily deduced from the sedimentary younging indicators, mostly grading, which show local reversals. Despite these, the dominant younging direction is to the north. Structural complexity is illustrated at one place (**4b**) where a synclinal hinge is exposed in a section which the sedimentary younging indicators show is broadly anticlinal. A strong slaty cleavage dips moderately to the SE, compatible with the bedding attitude in an axial-planar relationship. A fragmentary graptolite fauna recovered from this vicinity indicates a *linearis* Biozone age (Figure 46).

Return past the parking area and move on to the rocky outcrops around high water mark to the west. A different facies of the Portpatrick Formation is exposed with thicker greywacke beds ranging up to 1 m. Cleavage is still strong but is generally confined to the finer-grained, upper part of the greywacke beds and is markedly curved, refracting through the bed as the grain size varies. Some beds preserve bottom structures on their bases (the south side of the bed so view looking north) including some large flute casts indicating current flow from the SW (**4c**). The greywackes are dark and immature, and on fresh surfaces it may be possible to discern with a hand lens the abundant detrital mafic minerals, dominantly pyroxene and amphibole. This composition, rich in andesitic debris, is characteristic of the Portpatrick Formation.

Leave the south end of Killantringan Bay and walk south and inland to join the Southern Upland Way. The route skirts the inlet of Portamaggie where the wreck of the Craigantlet may still be visible; the ship ran aground in February, 1982. Continue for about 200 m south from Portamaggie and then drop down on the right-hand side

towards the coastal rocks and cliff line. Thickly bedded Portpatrick Formation greywackes are well exposed; bedding is uniformly upright and youngs north. Many of the greywacke beds are coarse and gravelly at the base and show marked truncation of the cross-laminated tops of underlying beds. Bed bases also preserve abundant bottom structures, including flute casts which uniformly indicate current flow from the SW (**4d**). A few tens of metres farther south the cliff section recommences, coincident with a decrease in average bed thickness. Most of the greywackes have the characteristic dark colour of the Portpatrick Formation but thin interbeds (up to 25 cm) of pale grey quartz arenite can be seen (**4e**). These are correlated with the Glenwhargen Formation which develops as a thick sequence of quartzose greywackes farther east (see Excursion 14). The interbeds illustrate the interfingering of two different turbidite fan systems derived from very different source areas. Portpatrick Formation greywackes contain on average about 15 per cent quartz grains whereas the Glenwhargen Formation arenite contains about 65 per cent quartz. Full compositional details are given by Stone (1995) and a sedimentological analysis is included in Kelling et al. (1987). Return to the parking area via the Southern Upland Way.

5 Portpatrick: Portpatrick Formation, folding and fault zone

Drive back along the lighthouse road to the A764 and turn right for Portpatrick. After about 4km turn right again into the village. Part of the described route requires a lowish tide and it may be necessary to arrange the sequence of localities to accommodate this. If time allows, a walk south along the cliff path to Dunskey Castle [004 534] is a worthwhile diversion from the geology. The path is reached via steep steps just beyond the SE margin of the main car park on the south side of the harbour. The castle is about 500 m from the top of the steps. It occupies an impressive position on the cliff edge and is built mainly of local greywacke, with dressed corner stones and lintels of Permian red sandstone most probably brought in from Dumfries. It was built around 1510 by Adair of Kilhilt on the site

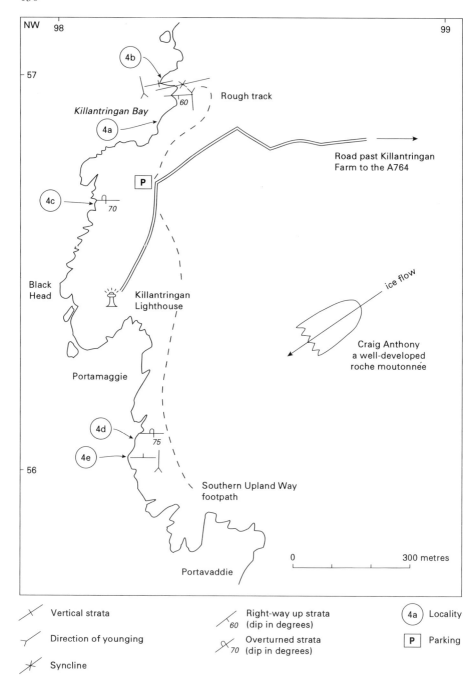

Figure 49 Locality map and outline geology for the Killantringan area (Locality 4).

of an earlier stronghold but was in a ruinous condition by 1684 and has remained so.

Folded Portpatrick Formation greywackes are well exposed in and around Portpatrick Harbour and exposure is more or less complete southwards to Morroch Bay. At Morroch Bay the basal beds of the Portpatrick Formation conformably overlie the Moffat Shale Group and are interbedded with shales containing *clingani* Biozone graptolites (Figure 46). Full details are given in Excursion 18.

A spectacular exposure of the greywackes is provided by an old quarry, 250 m SE from the southern harbour car park. The quarry is paved and landscaped. The main face, viewed looking east, exposes a magnificent F1 monoclinal fold. Remember, as you view the fold, that north is to your left. On the left the beds are vertical at ground level but higher in the cliff face assume a more gentle northward dip. The axial plane of the monocline dips moderately south (towards your right) and so the upper, gently dipping limb of the fold descends to ground level in that direction. A fine selection of turbidite features includes gravelly bed bases, shale rip-up clasts and cross-laminated bed tops. These make it easy to confirm the younging directions. In the north of the quarry the bedding at ground level is vertical and youngs north; in the south of the quarry it is the right way up and dips gently northwards.

Continue NW across the intertidal rocks towards Portpatrick Harbour. Bedding dip is variable and by applying younging criteria it can be seen that the beds are right way up and are folded about several open F1 synclines and anticlines. The hinges are mostly replaced by faults or shear zones but one good example of an open syncline is preserved slightly farther north in the back wall of the outer harbour and, at lowish tide, is accessible from the beach. The hinge plunges about 15° NE. A strong slaty cleavage is developed throughout this section, striking NE, and is either vertical or dips steeply SE.

Ascend the steps at the back of the harbour near the synclinal hinge. Turn left at the top and walk to the NW corner of the inner harbour [997 542]. Thence continue west past the paddling pool and the Southern Upland Way start/finish indicator. A rocky gully continues west and the remains of a red sandstone archway at its seaward end marks the outfall of an old (perhaps Victorian) sewer. As you approach the archway **take care on the slippery rocks** and note the abundant quartz veins. The modern sewer follows the same line as its ruined predecessor and this outcrop is occasionally polluted. The gully utilised by the sewer pipes follows a major fault zone, the internal structure of which is exposed at low tide beneath the red sandstone archway. A black shaly siltstone is pervasively sheared and cut by several generations of quartz veins which are themselves sheared and folded. At least some of the deformation appears to have been ductile and the fold style suggests an overall sense of sinistral shear. An important feature of this fault is its separation of two contrasting structural domains. To the south lies the open folding just traversed; to the north the bedding is upright and youngs almost consistently northwards into the Killantringan section (Locality 4). This uniform section extends for almost 3 km, interrupted only sporadically by tight F1 fold pairs.

From Portpatrick Harbour return to the car park, and take the A77 Stranraer road to Ardwell Bay. Time may be available *en route* for diversions to Morroch Bay or Cairngarroch Bay. The former exposes a conformable contact between the Portpatrick Formation and the Moffat Shale Group (Excursion 18, Locality 3). The second locality allows examination of the Orlock Bridge Fault zone (Excursion 17, Locality 1).

6   Ardwell Bay: Gala Group, contrasting fold styles

From Portpatrick travel via the A77 and B7042 to join the A716 at Sandhead. Just south of Sandhead turn right at the signpost for the early Christian site at Kirkmadrine and continue on to the Clachanmore crossroads [084 467]. (If Morroch Bay or Cairngarroch Bay have been visited continue south along minor roads for 10 km or 5 km respectively to Clachanmore crossroads). At the crossroads continue SW for 2 km along the road and then the rough track (which may be gated) to Ardwell Bay. Parking is available in a paved area with a picnic site [071 449]. This journey crosses the major sinistral Orlock Bridge Fault, which separates Ordovician greywackes to the north from Silurian greywackes to the south. Ardwell Bay is on the south (Silurian) side of the fault (Figure 45) and exposes quartz-rich greywackes, the Stinking Bight beds (Gala Group 5) of *gregarius* Biozone age (Figure 46).

At the north end of the sandy bay [071 453], where a fence meets the coast, a series of eight upright F1 folds are exposed over a 25 m section. These tight to open folds are developed in interbedded mudstones and sandstones with beds of less than 50 cm thickness. The folds display characteristic F_1 geometry with curvilinear hinges plunging gently to moderately SW and axial surfaces inclined steeply SE. A vertical fault in one synclinal hinge has a minor downthrow to NW. Cleavage fans are centred on the axial surface of the folds and show strong refraction between sandstones and mudstones in all the hinges. This indicates that the cleavage is contemporaneous with folding, not superimposed later. In the second anticlinal hinge from the south a 'finite neutral point' is particularly well formed in the mudstones. This represents a point of zero stress during fold deformation of the adjacent sandstones, now marked by the bifurcation of the cleavage in the mudstone. Clockwise rotation of the S_1 cleavage by 10–20° out of the axial surface in plan view is particularly well displayed. Bedding/cleavage intersection lineations are less steep than fold plunge (or have a reversed plunge) on SE-younging limbs and plunge more steeply than the hinge on NW-younging limbs. This has produced downward facing bedding/cleavage relationships on some NW-younging limbs. Clockwise transecting S1 cleavage is common throughout the Silurian rocks of the Rhins and is believed to result from sinistral transpression acting during D1 deformation.

Return south along the beach past the parking area and continue to the south side of Ardwell Bay. The strata here are overturned so that the gently dipping bedding planes are the inverted bases of greywacke turbidite beds. These carry an impressive array of bottom structures and it is worth spending some time examining them under low tide conditions. Thereafter continue south and take the footpath up the slope past the ruined fortification of Doon Castle on Ardwell Point (labelled *Broch* on some OS maps). This path leads round the top of the cliff skirting the Hooies inlet [069 446]. The agile can scramble down to beach level where dark graptolitic shales with pale bentonite layers are apparently interbedded among the Gala Group greywackes. Graptolites may be collected from several of the intertidal outcrops and prove the *gregarius* Biozone (Gala 5; Figure 46). If the graptolite localities are visited it is possible, **with care**, to climb out of the bay on the south side. Otherwise follow the cliff path around the back of the bay and then descend to the promontory on its south side. The bedding on the south side of the Hooies is steeply inclined and youngs to the south but on the headland it is folded about vertical hinges in a sinistral sense. The slaty cleavage developed subparallel to the bedding is also folded about the same hinges whilst maintaining its angular relationship to the bedding planes. Two generations of deformation are thus evident here: the main cleavage forming event was probably related to the fold and thrust episode (D1) with subsequent sinistral shear (D3) responsible for the steeply plunging hinges. If the steeply plunging hinge zone is followed seaward as far as possible the final exposure shows bedding, cleavage and fold hinge all cut across by a thin (and definitely post-tectonic) lamprophyre dyke. This instructive outcrop therefore also provides evidence for the local relationship of deformation and intrusion.

From the Hooies return via the cliff path to Ardwell Bay.

7 Drumbreddan Bay: Gala and Moffat Shale groups

Drive back to Clachanmore crossroads, turn right and proceed SE for 1.5 km to a prominent left-hand bend. Turn right at the bend and continue first south and then SW for 2 km to Drumbreddan Farm where permission to park and to visit Drumbreddan Bay should be obtained. Walk west through the farm for 150 m to the track which leads past the cattle sheds [083

439]. Follow this track SW for 600 m to the coast.

This locality is part of the Drumbreddan Bay Imbricate Zone and provides remarkable structural and sedimentological exposure across three imbricate thrust slices of Moffat Shale, each overlain by Gala Group greywackes of the Grennan Point Formation (Gala 6, Figure 46). The Moffat Shales acted as a decollement during thrusting and so form the lowest beds exposed. A rich graptolite fauna may be recovered from the shales (Excursion 18, Locality 4). Bedding youngs north but is overturned with a steep dip SE. Like most Gala Group lithologies the Grennan Point Formation has a siliceous petrography.

The southernmost imbricate thrust slice is exposed in a 100 m-wide promontory between two bays at the end of the track (**7a** in Figure 50). As the Moffat Shales exposed at the SE edge of the promontory are only visible at low spring tide, proceed NW across the bay to examine the more accessible exposure within the Grennan Bay Site of Special Scientific Interest (Treagus, 1992). Along the NW edge of the bay [077 437] (**7b**) Birkhill Shales (Moffat Shale Group) of the *gregarius* and *convolutus* biozones young into the overlying Grennan Point Formation to the NW. The black fissile Birkhill Shales contain numerous pale bentonite layers (originally volcanic ash), one of which has been dextrally imbricated in response to a minor post-D2 steeply plunging dextral fold. The progradational sedimentary sequence from black shales into coarse well-graded turbidite beds with load, scour and tool (sole) markings, takes place over 8 m. Transitional parallel-laminated, shales and siltstones with rare cross-lamination yield graptolites of *convolutus* Biozone age. Flute casts indicate flow derivation from the NE, a trend supported by the general NE–SW alignment of groove casts.

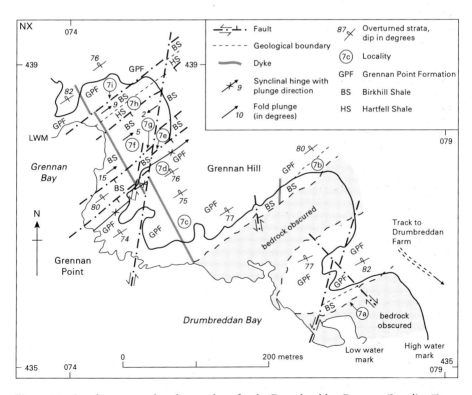

Figure 50 Locality map and outline geology for the Drumbreddan Bay area (Locality 7).

The nature of turbidite sedimentation can be examined in more detail at the edge of Grennan Point [076 437] (7c). The coarse- to fine-grained turbidites are well graded and in places display complete Bouma T_{a-e} sequences. Convolute and cross-lamination are present in T_c divisions, and load structures are common on bedding soles. Amalgamation of beds is observed in places. Thickening-upward cycles range from 5 m to 20 m, and 80 m above the base of the formation a 20 m-thick sequence of shales and thin base-absent (T_{cde}, T_{ce}) turbidites is present. The facies associations at Grennan Point indicate progradation from a basin plain and outer fan into a mid-fan lobe environment. The latter predominates throughout the succession apart from a temporary regression to outer fan deposits marked by the shaly section 80 m above the base.

At the north end of Grennan Point [075 438] an inclined F1 synclinal hinge with a steeply inclined axial surface (7d) is deformed by the fault forming the base of the next imbricate thrust slice (7e). Beyond this fault a 100 m-thick outcrop of Moffat Shale is again overlain by the Grennan Point Formation. The structures associated with major D1 thrusting can be seen in detail. The fault at the base of the slice appears to dip steeply SE and contains brecciated greywacke lenses within a sheared black shale (7e). The S1 cleavage is in places disturbed, so is earlier than at least some of the movement. No conclusive movement indicators are apparent, although the synclinal hinge SE of the fault, and subvertical slickensides within the fault zone, suggest a south-easterly downthrow compatible with the regional stratigraphy. The fault is itself displaced by a series of small post-D2 sinistral wrenches trending NNE.

Within the Moffat Shales beyond the fault a series of neutrally verging F1 folds with wavelengths less than 1 m plunge gently NE (7f). A few steeply plunging folds are also present. At this locality S1 cleavage is axial planar to the folds (cf. Locality 6– Ardwell Bay). About 20 m NW of the fault an antiformal hinge within the Moffat Shales has had its SE limb removed by a subvertical fault (thrust?) developed preferentially along a 12 cm bentonite horizon

(7g). The incompetent nature of bentonite relative to black shale is demonstrated by extreme thickening of the bentonites in the fold hinge. In the most north-westerly 25 m of this Moffat Shale outcrop a 12 m-thick structural inlier of black Lower Hartfell Shales and pale grey Barren Mudstones of the Upper Hartfell Shales (both of Ordovician age) are exposed NW of a steep SE-dipping fault (7h). Graptolites collected from the Lower Hartfell Shales indicate a *wilsoni* or *clingani* Biozone age. These beds young north into the Silurian Birkhill Shales thus exposing the Ordovician–Silurian boundary. Graptolites ranging from the *persculptus* to the *atavus* Biozone have been identified in the Birkhill Shales here. A synform in the Birkhill Shales south of the fault is compatible with the regional stratigraphy in suggesting a downthrow to the SE. However, local biostratigraphical evidence indicates some, possibly late, movement with downthrow to the NW (cf. Excursion 18, Locality 4).

The boundary between the Moffat Shale sequence and overlying Grennan Point Formation to the NW is a poorly exposed fault (7i). The fault has a steep south-easterly dip and separates black Moffat Shales from grey siltstones. Brecciated lensoid greywackes set in a sheared silty matrix are present for 8 m north of the boundary, beyond which are seen NW-younging brecciated greywackes of the Grennan Point Formation.

8 Port Logan: Gala Group

From Drumbreddan Farm drive along minor roads to join the A716 at Ardwell. Follow this road south for 2.5 km and then take a right turn for Port Logan. This road leads past the renowned Logan Botanical Gardens, which are well worth a visit. At Port Logan drive along the seafront and park by the pier at the SW corner of the bay [095 404]. Beneath the bay, but not exposed, is the Port Logan Fault, a major D1 tectonic boundary separating north-younging, SE-verging folds and thrusts to the north, from south-younging, NW-verging fold and thrust structures to the south.

The outcrop extending SW from the car park is formed by well bedded greywackes of the Port Logan Formation (Gala 8, Figures 45 and 46). These rocks retain a diagenetic mineralogy (Merriman et al., 1991), making the grade of metamorphism here one of the lowest recorded in the Rhins of Galloway area (see Introductory chapter for further discussion). Turbidite features are well developed, both in terms of Bouma divisions and of bottom and top bed-surface structures. A short walk SW along the coast into the next small bay will in addition traverse the following features:

1   A cross-cutting, Tertiary dolerite dyke 2 m thick forms a vertical wall trending NW within a small inlet. Note the unusual honeycomb weathering of the dyke surface.

2   A zone of open folding with one well-preserved open synclinal hinge and evidence of bedding imbrication in the limbs.

3   Sequences of dark, interlaminated siltstone and shale up to 5 m thick interbedded with the greywacke.

4   A spectacular array of ripple marks on large, steeply dipping slabs at the south side of the small bay [091 401].

Retrace the coastal route to Port Logan.

9   Clanyard Bay: Gala and Moffat Shale groups

To reach the next locality, Clanyard Bay, continue SE along the B7065 for 3.5 km to an offset crossroads. Turn right and drive for 800 m to just beyond the point where the road bends sharply south. Branching off to the right is the track to Low Clanyard Farm [107 376]. Park carefully at the road adjacent to the track, or drive to the farm where permission should be obtained to visit Clanyard Bay. This locality provides evidence for the reversed sense of D1 thrusting and allows a comparison with the Drumbreddan Bay Imbricate Zone (Locality 7). The Moffat Shale outcrops at Clanyard Bay are locally rich in graptolites and the locality is also described in Excursion 18, Locality 5.

One important difference in interpretation is adopted here to that shown on the BGS 1:50 000 Rhins of Galloway geological map and described by Stone (1995). The Cairnharrow Formation shown therein as a part of the Hawick Group is considered

by McCurry (1989) to be the most southerly Gala Group unit (Gala 9, Figure 46). McCurry places the northern boundary of this unit to the north of Clanyard Bay and thus overlaps with a part of the Gala 8 unit shown on the BGS map. The critical area is examined in this excursion at locality 9 and visitors may judge for themselves.

From Low Clanyard Farm follow the track first NW and then west for 800 m past the derelict mill to Clanyard Bay. Walk to the north end of the bay [101 381] where there is an exposure of Moffat Shale 60 m thick (Figure 51). This forms part of the 1.5 km-wide Clanyard Bay Imbricate Zone within the south-younging sequences south of Port Logan. The Moffat Shale exposure is divided in two by an east–west-trending felsitic dyke 6 m thick. The northern margin of the dyke is formed by a steep SE-dipping fault. South of the dyke the Moffat Shales are folded by a large synformal F_1 hinge plunging gently west (**9a** in Figure 51). This hinge folds a faulted contact between intensely sheared Birkhill Shale in the core of the fold and Barren Mudstone (Upper Hartfell Shale) away from the core. The fault is interpreted as an early thrust formed within the Moffat Shale decollement prior to folding. The northern limb of the synform is displaced by a late-D1 fault dipping steeply NW. At the core of the synform the Birkhill Shales range from *atavus* to a possible *gregarius* Biozone age. The surrounding Barren Mudstones are variably red, grey, blue or brown in colour and contain numerous irregularly shaped siderite nodules of diagenetic origin. The red mudstones have been reduced to produce a buff or green reaction rim around each nodule. Both F1 and post-F1 (probable F2) isoclinal folds are present in the Barren Mudstones.

North of the dyke Birkhill Shales are exposed for 30 m and have an anomalous WNW bedding strike. Graptolites indicate an age range spanning the *atavus* to the *sedgwickii* biozones in an overall north-younging sequence. At the northern boundary of the Birkhill Shales two prominent felsitic dykes, each 1 m thick, are spaced about 2 m apart. The shales are intensely sheared and contain brecciated greywacke lenses. This sheared zone con-

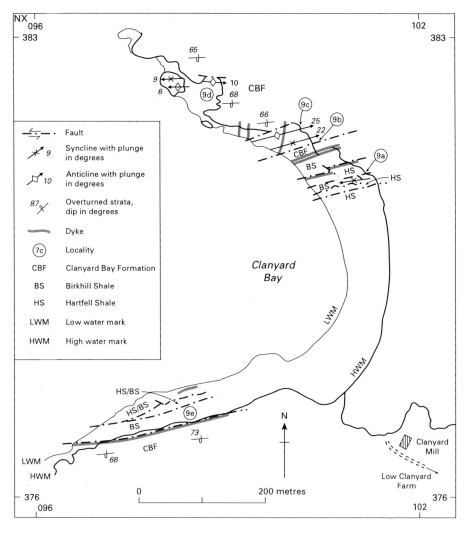

Figure 51 Locality map and outline geology for the Clanyard Bay area (Locality 9).

tinues for about 7 m north of the dykes to a distinct gouge plane with an associated S1 fabric intruded by a thin (10 cm) felsitic dyke (**9b**). The attitudes of the fabric and breccia zones marginal to the fault indicate a downthrow to the NW. An adjacent large synclinal F1 hinge plunging gently NE has had its SE limb sheared and removed by the fault consistent with NW downthrow. There is therefore evidence for two phases of thrusting associated with the Moffat Shale decollement: the first was probably pre-F1 folding and the second was syn- or post-F1 folding. The NW downthrow is the opposite to that suggested earlier within the Drumbreddan Bay Imbricate Zone (Locality 7) and is atypical of the Southern Uplands generally. It is consistent though with the SE-younging and NW-vergence of D1 structures south of the Port Logan Bay Fault (McCurry and Anderson, 1989).

From the north end of Clanyard Bay [100 382] continue WNW across the south-younging turbidites of the Clanyard Bay

Formation (Gala 9, Figs. 45, 46). Grapto-lites collected from rare black shale interbeds indicate a *turriculatus* or *crispus* Biozone age. After 30 m an upright F1 anticlinal hinge with a moderate westerly plunge is reached (**9c**). Some of the irregular joints developed in the hinge contain rare radiating sheaves of haematite. About 5 m north of the anticlinal hinge the beds are once again intensely brec-ciated in association with a number of mod-erate to steeply plunging post-F1 folds of wavelength 1–2 m.

Continue WNW for 70 m across a fence and over a prominent grassy ridge to a small bay (**9d**). On an island in the bay a superbly exposed NW-verging chevron fold pair is developed in overturned south-younging strata. The regular geom-etry of the fold pair represents in micro-cosm the structure demonstrated through-out the south-younging sequences south of the Port Logan Fault. The extreme angularity of the hinges and the straight-ness of the limbs characterise major fold structures, which dramatically increase in wavelength to over 1.5 km away from the boundaries of individual thrust sheets. The overturned bedding on the long limbs of folds is inclined steeply NW whereas the right-way-up flat limbs are inclined gently NW. These flat limbs are often intensely folded.

In the cliff at the north end of the bay another NW-verging F1 fold pair affecting thinly bedded turbidites can be examined in detail. A thrust is developed in the syn-clinal hinge and progressively excises the short limb westwards. The same style of chevron folding continues north for 400 m to the sole thrust of the sequence just north of Dunbuck [094 382]. Within this zone the south-younging strata are intensely brecciated and disrupted by numerous faults. There are few precise movement indicators on the faults, but fold geometry, younging directions and stratigraphy all suggest downthrow to NW. Note once again the major regional difference in structure between these sections and the north-younging sequences seen further north.

Return to the south end of Clanyard Bay, to about 150 m beyond the mouth of the burn at Clanyard Mill. Here the Moffat Shales are divided in two by an ENE fault which forms a small gully through the exposure (**9e**). North of the fault gully a complex sequence of Upper Hartfell Barren Mudstones and Birkhill Shales (visible only at low tide) appears to young north despite disruption by a series of strike-parallel faults. To the south of the fault gully Birkhill Shales are isoclinally folded with hinges plunging gently to moderately NE or SW. Some folds display clockwise cleav-age transection of up to 8°. Graptolites indicate *cyphus* and *convolutus* Biozone ages (Excursion 18, Locality 5). At the south margin of the Moffat Shale outcrop a prominent east–west felsite dyke dips steeply north. Beyond the dyke intensely brecciated south-younging greywackes are present.

10   West Tarbet: Hawick Group

From Low Clanyard continue south and then east on the minor road to join the B7041 at Kirkmaiden. Drive south on the B7041 for 3 km and take the left-hand fork for the Mull of Galloway. On reaching the narrow isthmus at West Tarbet (Figure 52) turn right and park at the side of the road next to the track [142 309]. This locality must be visited within three hours either side of low tide.

The platform between the bays at East and West Tarbet (**10a** in Figure 52) is cov-ered by a layer of rounded pebbles and may be a late-glacial kame terrace. A small area of raised beach is visible in the bay below. The isthmus has formed by erosion along the major ENE trending Tarbet Fault. From the platform walk down to the northern foreshore of the bay at West Tarbet [140 309]. The position of the fault is indicated by a felsitic mass intruded along it and exposed in the centre of the bay (**10b**). The pale green Hawick Group lithologies exposed both north and south of the fault are turbidites, but much finer grained than those of the Gala Group seen at the previous three localities, and with a calcareous matrix. They are part of the Carghidown Formation and north of the fault form the Leucarron Member of McCurry (1989). This is a sequence of fine-grained T_{ace}, T_{ade}, T_{ce}, and T_{de} tur-

138

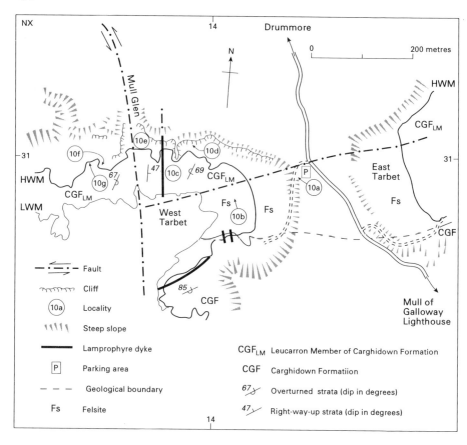

Figure 52 Locality map and outline geology for the West Tarbet area (Locality 10).

bidites with thick mudstone interbeds intercalated with packets of coarser channelised T_{ade}, T_{ace} turbidites.

For 120 m along the northern shore of the bay the strata are contorted into a series of unusual tight-to-open, post F1 folds (**10c**). With increased distance from the Tarbet Fault the folds develop a strong sinistral vergence and plunge moderately to steeply SE. They approach a parallel style, with little or no hinge thickening, and have a chevron geometry. Towards the fault they become increasingly brecciated, develop strong coaxial refolding and plunge moderately NE. Although they fold the S1 cleavage, only a few hinges have developed a weak coaxial crenulation cleavage. Examples of this planar crenulation can be seen in folds within the cliffs 30 m east of

the prominent shallow cave (**10d**); since the cleavage is axial planar to the folds its orientation varies with the hinge orientation. Commonly both hinge and cleavage are coaxially refolded by later uncleaved folds of the same deformation, showing that this weak cleavage is an early-formed feature. These distinctive folds are probably linked with isomorphic folds seen elsewhere in the southern Rhins which are spatially associated with major late D1 thrusts. The folds at West Tarbet are restricted to a 120 m-wide zone between the Tarbet Fault and a major north–south-trending sinistral wrench fault. The latter structure has been eroded to form the prominent Mull Glen [139 310] within which the folds are spectacularly exposed (**10e**).

Proceed over the promontory on the west side of the glen, crossing overturned, south-younging beds on the steep limb of a major NW-verging F1 fold pair. On the far side of the promontory, a bedding sole is covered in large well-formed flute casts (**10f**). Like most sole current structures in the Leucarron Member these indicate palaeoflow from the SE. This contrasts with the NW- and NE-derived currents that typify the Hawick Group elsewhere in the Southern Uplands. Ripples on a bedding surface on the opposite side of a small bay (**10g**) indicate palaeoflow at a high angle to that of the flute casts. This strong divergence in flow direction between sole markings and ripples is not uncommon.

From West Tarbet visitors may wish to continue to the Mull of Galloway lighthouse. This windswept spot is the most southerly point in Scotland and affords splendid views across to Ireland, the Isle of Man and English Lake District. There are numerous exposures of thinly bedded Carghidown Formation greywackes but the sea cliffs around the headland are high and extremely precipitous and should not be approached too closely.

J A McCurry and P Stone

Excursion 16

CREETOWN and CAIRNSMORE OF FLEET: igneous intrusion and tectonic deformation

OS 1:50 000 sheets 83 Newton Stewart & Kirkcudbright, 77 Dalmellington to New Galloway
BGS 1:50 000 sheets 4E Wigtown, 8E Loch Doon
Route maps: Figures 53 and 54

Main points of interest Structural relationships of igneous intrusions, from pre- to post-tectonic, at a range of scales; evidence for the early development of thermal (contact) metamorphism relative to igneous intrusion.

Logistics The itinerary utilises the A75, between Gatehouse of Fleet and Newton Stewart, and the A712 Queen's Way, from its intersection with the A75 just east of Newton Stewart to Clatteringshaws Loch en route to New Galloway. Locality 1 is coastal and the critical exposure is obscured at high tide. Localities 2 and 5 are on open fell-side and involve some rough walking, particularly in the latter case where a round trip of about 10 km is involved. Localities 3 and 4 are quarries where protective helmets must be worn; Kirkmabreck Quarry (Locality 4) is worked intermittently and particular care should be taken near the unstable faces. The quarry is owned by Tarmac Ltd and it is essential that permission for access is obtained in advance. Localities 6–8 are in the Kirroughtree Forest, and Locality 9 is in the Glentrool Forest, both owned by the Forestry Commission.

Introduction The Ordovician and Silurian turbidite sequences of the Southern Uplands are contained in a series of ENE-striking, vertical, fault-bounded slices and show three phases of deformation (see Introduction chapter and Figures 1–4). The major, tract-bounding faults, now spaced 2–5 km apart, originally formed as north-dipping thrust faults in association with D1 folding and cleavage (S1) formation but were then rotated into their present near-vertical position. Thrusting detached the turbidite

sequence within the basal Moffat Shales, the thrust front effectively migrating southwards into progressively younger strata. Hence this D1 event, the only phase of deformation to have affected many of these rocks, was diachronous, becoming younger southwards (Figure 4). Locally it was succeeded by minor refolding (D2), forming inclined, south-verging open folds and small recumbent folds, the latter associated with a sporadically well-developed subhorizontal cleavage (S2). A third phase of deformation (D3), marked by steeply plunging sinistral folds, occurs in places, often in association with the tract-bounding faults. This deforms the S2 cleavage at one locality (Excursion 13, Locality 1). One of the strike-parallel faults, the Orlock Bridge Fault, shows evidence of major sinistral, strike-slip reactivation (the Moniaive Shear Zone, Excursion 17) which may have been associated with the D3 event.

The earliest intrusions in the Southern Uplands thrust stack were swarms of lamprophyre and felsite sheets (Barnes et al., 1986; Rock et al., 1986a and b) which, although dominantly emplaced parallel to bedding, are commonly referred to as dykes since they are broadly upright. They are concentrated in a strike-parallel zone in the south-central part of the Southern Uplands, the part in which all three phases of folding also occur. Relationships between dykes and tectonic features show some of the dykes were emplaced during the deformation (Localities 1 and 2 and Excursion 13). Later dykes were emplaced along conjugate NW- and N-trending minor faults. These were largely succeeded by dioritic and granodiorite intrusions of intermediate size (Localities 3 and 4) and the three large, zoned diorite to granitic plutonic bodies of Loch Doon, Cairnsmore of Fleet and Criffell. The latter are known from isotopic dating (Halliday et al., 1980) to be of late Silurian or early Devonian age and are probably largely post-tectonic. However, aspects of the aureole to the Fleet intrusion (Locality 5c) suggest that

Figure 53 Locality
map for the
Creetown,
Cairnsmore of Fleet,
Clatteringshaws and
Glentrool excursion.

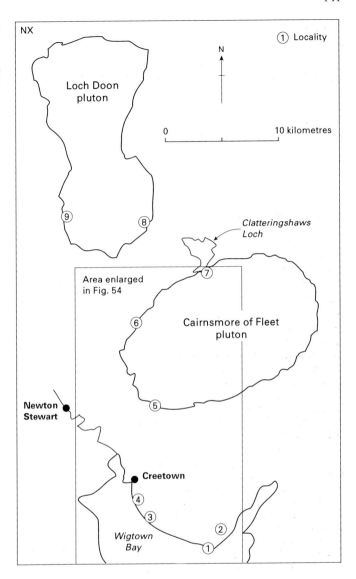

it formed before or during a late phase of
deformation, perhaps associated with
movement on the Moniaive Shear Zone
(Excursion 17), although the granite itself
shows little evidence for deformation (e.g.
Localities 5a and 5b).

Metamorphism associated with the
dioritic and granitic intrusions has usually
produced a relatively simple biotite hornfels aureole, which is seen in the field as a
colour change to purple in the host turbidites due to the development of microscopic biotite. Such aureoles are usually
explained by the conduction of heat away
from an igneous body as it cools after
emplacement (Kerrick, 1991). However,
the Cairnsmore of Fleet and Kirkmabreck
intrusions (Figure 54, Localities 4 and 5)
have much more complex aureoles, indicating that several events intervened between
formation of the hornfels and the emplacement of the associated igneous body.

1 Shore at Low Auchenlarie: pre-, syn- and post-D1 lamprophyre dykes

Medium to low tide is needed to see the best exposures, although there is no danger of becoming stranded by the rising tide. An alternative account of the section is given in Excursion 12, Locality 3. Access is through the caravan park adjacent to the A75, 10 km south of Creetown; permission for access should be sought from the reception office at the entrance to the park. The shore is reached using a path at the west side of the public house in the SE corner of the site, where there is ample parking space. On reaching the shore [NX 540 517] follow the high water mark to the SE, passing medium-bedded fine-grained turbidites with well-developed sedimentary structures. These are characteristic of the Hawick Group, Kirkmaiden Formation. Bedding dips moderately NW but is variable due to open, steeply inclined, south-verging D2 folds. An almost bed-parallel S1 cleavage is generally overprinted by a subhorizontal cleavage (S2). The latter is related to a conjugate set of recumbent D2 folds not developed here but seen at Excursion 13, Locality 2.

After about 125 m, a small upright fold pair, plunging gently seawards, can be seen just below high water mark. At first sight a 33 cm 'sandstone bed' is continuous around the fold, although close inspection will confirm that it is actually a bedding-parallel lamprophyre dyke. Although the dyke is altered, it is distinct from the enclosing sandstone, particularly in the inclusion of green chlorite pseudomorphs after mica. In the anticlinal hinge the dyke is fractured, with some mudstone injected upwards; cleavage in the lamprophyre indicates that the dyke was folded with the enclosing sediments and not passively intruded around a pre-existing fold. Looking down on the fold hinge it can be seen that the trace of the cleavage on the upper, bedding-parallel surface of the dyke is not quite parallel to the fold axis, a feature characteristic of D1 folds in this area. This is the only clear example known in the Southern Uplands of a dyke which is deformed by such a fold.

A further 70 m to the south a field boundary reaches the shore. About 30 m south of here a felsite dyke 4 m thick has been intruded along a NW-trending sinistral wrench fault with a displacement of about 3 m. This is an example of the huge number of later dykes which were emplaced into such faults.

Follow the high water mark around the small headland a short distance (30 m) to the south and move seawards across the foreshore a little way (tide permitting) to look back at the low cliff where an overturned D1 anticline is well exposed. Several small recumbent D2 folds are developed in the steep, overturned, southern limb associated with a cleavage dipping gently south. A lamprophyre dyke up to 1 m thick, with conspicuous thin zones of amygdales 20–30 cm from either margin, cuts stepwise up through this structure and, in this case, clearly postdates the formation of the D1 fold.

The section can be followed a further 600 m south to Ringdoo Point, across intensely folded strata with dykes frequently emplaced into the fold hinges. Return by the same route.

2 High Auchenlarie to Ben John: syn-D1 felsite dykes

Ben John is best approached from the farm of High Auchenlarie [538 532]. From the Low Auchenlarie caravan park, turn right on to the A75 and then left after just over 1 km. Follow the minor road for about 1 km and turn right along the track to High Auchenlarie Farm. There is little space to park vehicles on the roadside so permission to park in the farmyard should be sought from the farm. Permission for access should also be gained, although the exposures of interest are situated on land belonging to the adjacent farm of Laggan. On a clear day, the superb view from Ben John [544 548] over Kirkcudbrightshire and Wigtownshire in itself makes the walk worthwhile.

A track immediately west of the farm buildings leads north through two fields

Figure 54 Locality map and outline geology for Creetown and Cairnsmore of Fleet.

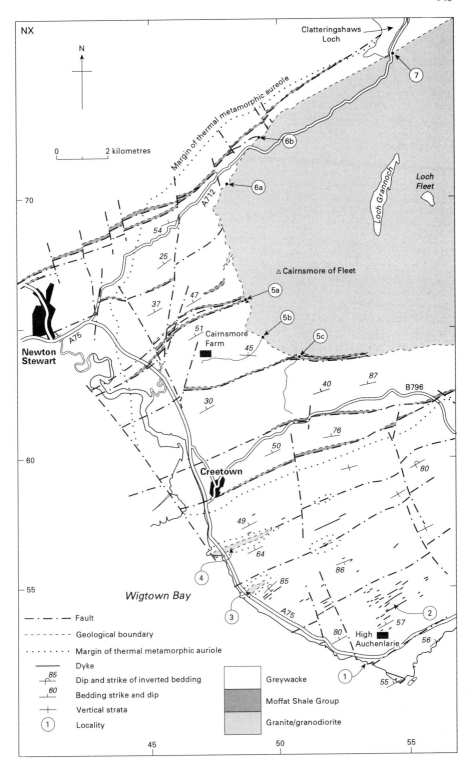

NX

N

Clatteringshaws Loch

⑦

Margin of thermal metamorphic aureole

⑥b

⑥a

0   2 kilometres

Loch Grannoch

Loch Fleet

— 70

54

25

A712

△ Cairnsmore of Fleet

47

37

⑤a

51

⑤b

⑤c

A75

45

Cairnsmore Farm

40

87

B796

Newton Stewart

30

50

76

80

— 60

Creetown

49

80

64

86

⑦

85

⑦④

High Auchenlarie

— 55

⑦③

A75

80

57

②

56

Wigtown Bay

— · — · — Fault

– – – – – Geological boundary

· · · · · · Margin of thermal metamorphic auriole

———— Dyke

85 Dip and strike of inverted bedding

60 Bedding strike and dip

+ Vertical strata

① Locality

55

①

55

	Greywacke
	Moffat Shale Group
	Granite/granodiorite

45   50   55

before ending at a gate. Pass through the gate and turn immediately east along the wall to the intersection with another wall which can be crossed using a large boulder. The exposure just over the wall is analogous structurally to that at Locality 1. Well-bedded turbidites dipping NW have been folded by open, steeply inclined D2 folds and a later subhorizontal cleavage has been superimposed in association with minor recumbent folds. A pale-coloured felsite dyke, about 2 m thick, is conspicuous parallel to bedding and passes around the open folds; has it been folded or passively intruded into previously folded strata? Close inspection of the dyke will reveal a cleavage fabric within it at about 90° to its margins. This angle is more or less constant at various positions around the folds, indicating that the dyke was folded after the cleavage was formed. The cleavage in the dyke is the early (S1) fabric, which is nearly parallel to bedding in mudstone but refracts to a high angle in sandstone beds and the dykes. This dyke was therefore intruded before the S1 cleavage was formed but its relationship to D1 folding cannot be established at this locality.

Those who do not wish to go farther can retrace their steps to the farm, but the recommended route continues obliquely up the hill in a NNE direction. After about 350 m the slope begins to flatten out on to a shoulder of the hill from which an area of extensive exposure will be visible; this should be reached a further 400 m in the same direction. There are no clear landmarks here to identify individual exposures but, by moving around, numerous variably cleaved felsite dykes can be seen. The dykes, usually bed-parallel, range from vertical to steeply NW-dipping whereas the cleavage typically dips moderately southwards. If the junction of a dyke with the enclosing sandstone or mudstone is located, the cleavage in the dyke can be seen to be continuous with that in the host rock. Where a dyke is adjacent to sandstone then the dip of the cleavage in both lithologies is similar. If the junction is against mudstone, the cleavage will refract into a steeper dip in the latter. The same effect will be seen where this cleavage passes between interbedded sandstone and

mudstone, such refraction at lithological boundaries being a common feature. However, in these exposures, the early cleavage in the mudstone is typically overprinted by the subhorizontal S2 cleavage which is not developed in the sandstone beds or dykes. The cleavages can be distinguished locally in mudstone where the less intense S2 cleavage can be seen to crenulate the S1 fabric; the latter continues, though refracted, into adjacent sandstone. Careful attention should also be paid to the attitude of bedding and its younging direction. Younging is mainly indicated by grading (emphasised here by the rotation and increased development of cleavage in finer-grained sandstone) which will point to the presence of a number of large-scale upright folds. There is no indication that the dykes are folded by these structures and examples can be found where dykes have been emplaced along fold axial planes. However, the cleavage in the dykes is clearly that which relates to the folds, and it seems most likely that the dykes were emplaced soon after the folding but before the imposition of a cleavage.

3 Bagbie Quarry, Carsluith: post-tectonic, zoned diorite intrusion

From High Auchenlarie, return to the A75 and drive NW until Carsluith Castle is passed on the left. A new by-pass continues the A75 from this point, but take the old road which requires a right turn to Carsluith. After crossing the burn at the margin of the village the road swings to the left; 120 m on from the bend, park opposite the row of cottages on the right and follow the short track immediately south of the cottages. This leads into Bagbie Quarry [489 549].

The intrusion that was quarried is wedge shaped, being at its widest here (200 m) and pinching out rapidly to the NE along the trace of the strike-parallel fault into which it is interpreted to have been emplaced. It is characteristic of the smaller dioritic intrusions in the Southern Uplands in that they are zoned from a more basic margin into a granitic core. Here there are simply two phases, a porphyritic dark grey diorite and a white granodiorite. The latter forms the back face of the quarry and the former can be seen in the faces either side, where the nature of the junction between the two lithologies is well displayed. The contact is sharp and steeply dipping, although irregular in detail. In the SE face the coarser, white granodiorite includes two slabs of the diorite, about 2 and 4 m thick, indicating that the latter was emplaced first. The granodiorite in the back of the quarry is well jointed with slickensides on some of the fracture surfaces. A basalt dyke (probably of Tertiary age), 30–40 cm thick, takes an irregular course through the north face of the quarry, cutting both diorite and granodiorite phases of the main intrusion.

From the track in the entrance to the quarry it is possible to walk SE through the wood to the Carsluith Burn which flows along the junction between the diorite and the host turbidites of the Cairnharrow Formation. Although the contact is relatively smooth and subparallel to the vertical bedding in the host sandstone, small steps allow thin dykes of the diorite to penetrate along bedding planes. The sandstone has been altered by contact metamorphism, with biotite extensively developed in the matrix. This is too fine grained to be observed directly but it gives the sandstone in particular a distinctive purple coloration on a freshly broken surface. Cleavage is obliterated by the recrystallisation and it is apparent that this intrusion is, here at least, post-tectonic.

As the lower part of the burn passes through the garden of a private house it is necessary to return through the wood to the quarry and thence to the road.

4 Kirkmabreck Quarry, Creetown: post-tectonic granodiorite with metasomatic alteration of aureole

The complex contact relationships of a 500 m-thick granodiorite sheet, emplaced into a strike-parallel fault, are well exposed in Kirkmabreck Quarry [480 565] adjacent to the A75, 2.5 km south of Creetown. At this locality the development of the biotite hornfels aureole and emplacement of the granodiorite are seen to have been separated by an interval during which several other veining and intrusive events

occurred. This quarry, one of several in the granodiorite, was originally developed for building stone but more recently has been intermittently worked for aggregate. **Permission for access must be sought from the quarry owners** in advance of any visit (Tarmac Roadstone (Scotland) Ltd, 134 Nithsdale Drive, Glasgow) and **particular care should be taken near the steep quarry faces where protective helmets are essential.**

Park at the quarry entrance or in the yard on the opposite side of the road and walk up the track around the north side of the quarry. A little way up the track a view over the whole quarry shows the essential features. The south wall, dipping at about 60° north, is cut along the footwall contact of the granodiorite. The hanging wall contact is visible in the north side of the quarry, above which a suite of subparallel dykes can be seen within the dark grey metasandstone host-rock of the Gala Group. The detail of the hornfels, the granodiorite margin and the dykes can be seen in three benches accessed from further up the track.

The hornfels exposed on the benches shows greenish bands of skarn alteration, typically a few mm thick, due to replacement of the biotite in the matrix of the metasandstone by epidote and actinolite. Close to the granodiorite contact, and particularly well displayed in some of the large loose blocks, this alteration encloses veinlets and some larger, irregular pods filled by quartz and bronze-coloured grossular garnet. In this situation the alteration is sometimes zoned symmetrically away from the vein, with an inner pale green zone dominated by diopsidic pyroxene and the epidote-actinolite forming a darker green outer zone. This skarn alteration must have been caused by the passage of calcium-bearing hydrothermal fluids because there is typically little calcium in the unaltered sandstone. The skarn veins are cut, and therefore postdated, by quartz-carbonate veins, sometimes irregular but often in the form of tension gash arrays. The quartz-carbonate veins are best developed in the exposure adjacent to the upper bench. Here they are locally very intensely developed in narrow lenses or screens of hornfels between the anastomosing dykes. The veins never penetrate the dykes which must have been emplaced after the veining, a relationship confirmed by the rare occurrence in the dykes of hornfels xenoliths with quartz-carbonate veining. The dykes, composed of a porphyry of similar geochemical composition to the main granodiorite sheet, have sharp, smooth contacts and are generally less than 1 m thick. They are best exposed on the lower bench where narrow chilled margins and a strong, wall-parallel flow-banding is apparent in some examples. An unusually thick (c.2 m) dyke is present at the margin of the granodiorite. Although broadly parallel to the dykes, the granodiorite margin is irregular in detail with narrow offshoots extending into the porphyry dyke. A narrow (c.5 cm) granodiorite dyke can also be seen at the margin of the next porphyry dyke. There is no sign of chilling of the granodiorite and the contact with the porphyry may be quite diffuse across a 2 cm-thick biotite-rich zone. The main granodiorite sheet seems to postdate the porphyry dykes, a relationship supported by the tendency for the contact to obliquely cut across the undulating dykes up through the quarry sections.

Old quarries higher up the hill, along the strike of the granodiorite sheet, are reached on foot by continuing to the top of the track past Kirkmabreck Quarry and then proceeding up the hill to where large piles of granodiorite blocks are visible. Alternatively, vehicles can be taken (with permission) up the narrow access road off the A75 just south from Kirkmabreck Quarry and parked inside the gate to the upper quarry area. The two largest quarries here are both flooded but the hanging wall contact of the granodiorite with the hornfels, again including porphyry dykes, is visible in the north side of both. The dykes and the granodiorite contact here have a similar orientation to those in the lower quarry. Angular blocks of porphyry can be seen as xenoliths in the granodiorite below the hangingwall contact, confirming the age relationship between the two. Aplite dykes occur locally within the granodiorite, marking the final intrusive phase.

5 The south-western contact of the Cairnsmore of Fleet granite pluton

The Cairnsmore of Fleet granite, one of three major plutons which outcrop in South-west Scotland, has been dated at about 395 Ma by the Rb-Sr method (Halliday et al., 1980), a date confirmed by a new zircon U-Pb age (J Evans written comm., 1994). The outcrop of the granite is elliptical. The northern and southern margins are largely parallel to bedding in the host rocks, apparently being controlled by the location of mudstone units of the Moffat Shale Group and/or associated strike-parallel faults. The western side of the granite is almost perpendicular to the regional strike. Three localities at the SW side of Cairnsmore of Fleet serve to demonstrate contradictory relationships between the development of the strong tectonic fabric in the host rocks (probably related to the Moniaive Shear Zone and discussed further in Excursion 17), the contact metamorphism, and the emplacement of the granite.

At McClave's Pantry (Locality 5a) and Graddoch Burn (Locality 5b) the granite contact and thin granite veins in the adjacent hornfels cut across the tectonic fabric and are not themselves deformed, although one granite dyke is locally cleaved. Cordierite is widely developed in the aureole and locally, as at Culcronchie Burn (Locality 5c), it is seen to predate at least part of the development of the tectonic fabric. However, the fabric and the cordierite are overprinted by the biotite hornfelsing. Evidence for local metasomatism of the Cairnsmore of Fleet hornfels, comparable with that exposed at Kirkmabreck (Locality 4), is also seen and again this postdates formation of the biotite hornfels but is cut by the granite. Together, these aspects suggest a similar situation to that at Kirkmabreck (locality 4), with evidence for the intervention of two events (cleavage development and skarn alteration) between the initial phases of contact metamorphism and the emplacement of the intrusion.

5a McClave's Pantry

The craggy exposures at McClave's Pantry [490 660] provide the best place to study the south-western granite contact. Access involves a significant walk; use the forestry track which climbs the hill behind Bardrochwood House, leaving the road along the east side of Bargaly Glen at [461 650]. The track climbs to the Cairnsmore Burn [478 654] from which strike directly up the hill between the burn and the forestry fence. From the point where the fence turns towards the north, McClave's Pantry lies about 350 m uphill to the NE.

In the approach up the side of the Cairnsmore Burn there are numerous exposures of Gala Group greywacke which display both a well-developed foliation and a linear fabric. In places both of these are cut by quartz veins, and at one locality [4856 6569] ramifying quartz veins have produced a breccia zone with disorientated blocks of lineated greywacke.

The granite contact is well exposed amongst a jumble of large granite boulders. Veinlets and apophyses of the granite occur over a zone of about 2–3 m in the hornfels adjacent to the main granite mass. They markedly cross-cut the bedding and the bedding-parallel foliation, here with a strongly developed linear component; neither the veins nor the main granite are deformed.

5b GRADDOCH BURN

The next two localities are best reached from Cairnsmore Farm [471 640] where a parking and picnic area has been provided just north of the farm path for walkers to Cairnsmore of Fleet. A visit to both localities involves a total walk of about 10 km, partly on tracks but generally over exposed countryside, and a total climb of about 500 m.

From the parking area, follow the track south past the farm, turning east at the cottage after 400 m. After a further 300 m the track crosses the Graddoch Burn, where exposures of medium-bedded Gala Group greywacke dipping moderately northwards are visible beneath the bridge, then passes along the edge of a field. A conspicuous exposure in the field shows massive greywacke with a purple colouration on freshly broken surfaces due to the development of biotite in the matrix. The rock contains a foliation, distinguished by mm-scale, flattened biotite clots possibly representing pseudomorphs after cordierite, dipping moderately northwards. Oblate, foliation-parallel lenses of greenish alteration

mark replacement of the biotite by skarn minerals similar to those seen at Locality 4. Continue along the track which, once out of the field and on to open moorland, becomes more distinct and closely follows the burn. Exposures of metagreywacke in the burn hereabouts also include closely spaced, discontinuous zones of skarn alteration, typically 5–10 cm thick. Bedding may also be distinguished in these exposures, lying parallel to the ubiquitous north-dipping foliation.

The burn forks 700 m east of the field and the track continues along the southern branch towards Locality 5c. To examine the contact between the hornfels and granite at Locality 5b, leave the track and follow the northern branch of the burn for just over 1 km until the wall bounding the forestry plantation to the north crosses the burn. Medium- to thick-bedded greywacke interbedded with black mudstone is intermittently exposed for 25 m either side of this point. An irregular granite dyke is exposed 35 m west of here in the south side of the stream. The dyke cuts narrow skarn zones in the hornfels and contains angular xenoliths of the foliated metagreywacke, but is itself locally foliated parallel to the steeply dipping fabric apparent in the metagreywacke immediately to the west. The margin of the main granite is exposed about 120 m east of where the wall crosses the burn [496 646]. The granite, extensively exposed upstream, is free of xenoliths and no chilling is noticeable at the contact. Small irregular veinlets of granite and quartz aplite extend from the granite over a zone about 5 m wide, markedly cross-cutting the bedding and skarn zones in the metagreywacke. The foliation in the host rock near the contact is masked by the hornfelsing and the granite and aplite are undeformed.

5c CULCRONCHIE BURN

To return to the vehicles, retrace the route taken from Cairnsmore. To proceed to Culcronchie Burn, walk for 1.5 km SE across the moorland strewn with granite boulders. After about 1 km you should meet the track from Cairnsmore. From this point a cliff can be seen on the southern flank of Cairnsmore of Fleet to the NE. This feature is formed by a narrow screen of metagreywacke within the granite, parallel to the southern contact but 500 m in from it. From the track, descend into the valley to where the wall, apparent on the far side, crosses the burn [510 638]. In addition to the foliated metagreywacke, a dark cherty lithology is exposed hereabouts and is interpreted as a contact metamorphosed mudstone of the Moffat Shale Group. The local existence of extensive quartz veining, in a network of brittle fractures, has encouraged a mine trial which cuts through the bend in the burn. Lenticular cordierite pseudomorphs, up to 5 mm long, occur widely in the hornfels here but are particularly well developed, up to 2 cm long, in metagreywacke exposed in a small knoll a few metres west of the stream. The intense fabric in the hornfels wraps around the pseudomorphs, which are flattened and also define a gently plunging lineation, indicating that they predate at least part of the deformation which formed the foliation. Return to Cairnsmore Farm by walking westwards up the hill to regain the track that leads back to the car park.

6 The northern contact of the Cairnsmore of Fleet granite pluton

The northern contact between the granite and the metamorphosed sedimentary host rocks is generally poorly exposed. It is near-parallel to the regional strike of bedding and cleavage fabric in the enclosing strata, and occurs just south of the linear outcrop of Moffat Shale along the Orlock Bridge Fault (Figure 54). Two localities showing the parallel junction between the granite and hornfels are easily reached from the A712 (Queen's Way) between Newton Stewart and Clatteringshaws Loch.

6a Bar

Exposures of the granite contact in the forest at Bar [483 705] are best accessed from the Glen of the Bar picnic site on the A712 [483 711], 1.3 km SW of the campsite at Talnotry. A narrow footpath leads south through the forest from the car park and should be followed for 400 m until it joins a forest road (it is worth marking the road to enable the foot path to be found on return). Turn east along the forest road for about 250 m to the top of an up-hill section then walk NNE into the forest for about 70 m, towards a large exposure which will gradually become visible through the trees. Here the granite forms a low cliff, the junction with the hornfels occurring near the top; the hornfels is also exposed in a higher cliff.

The junction is sharp, generally parallel to the strong banding and foliation in the hornfels but stepping across it locally, and without xenoliths in the granite. Immediately above the granite contact in the west part of the exposure, bedding is apparent in the hornfels dipping about 10° more steeply than the foliation — a typical relationship between bedding and S1 cleavage. Thin quartz veins, developed parallel and oblique to the fabric, are a characteristic feature of the hornfels in the northern part of the aureole. The banded hornfels can be examined further in the higher cliff. Retrace the route to the car park at Glen of the Bar.

6b Craigdews Hill

This craggy hill, in the wild goat park at Talnotry, provides a spectacular exposure of the granite/hornfels contact at the northern edge of the Cairnsmore of Fleet pluton. From the Glen of the Bar picnic site drive 3 km east and park in the lay-by [502 721] provided for viewing the wild goats which live on Craigdews Hill [497 723]. The crags in the hillside are mostly composed of pinkish grey granite but the contact with the darker grey hornfels above, slanting gently to the west, is visible in crags near the top of the hill. The junction actually dips NW, near-parallel to the pervasive bedding-parallel cleavage in the host strata. As at Bar (Locality 6a), the junction is sharp and no xenoliths are present in the granite.

Note that other localities in this vicinity are described in Excursion 17.

7 Clatteringshaws Dam Quarry: outer facies of the Cairnsmore of Fleet granite pluton

The Cairnsmore of Fleet pluton comprises an inner medium-grained granite facies and an outer coarse-grained facies. The outer phase can be examined at the quarry [547 754] near Clatteringshaws Dam. The quarry lies just off and slightly above the A712 immediately SE of the dam. It can be accessed by a rough track which leaves the road about 100 m south of the north end of the dam. Parking is simplest at the entrance to the Raiders Road (forestry track) about 200 m farther south on the main road [547 752].

The quarry is in coarse-grained grey granite characterised by large (3–4 cm) tabular feldspar crystals. These are commonly aligned and, along with preferred orientation of the micas, impart a marked N- to NNW-dipping foliation to the granite. In thin-section the foliation may be marked by zones of granulation, implying a tectonic rather than a magmatic origin. The disposition of the foliation across the mass as a whole, however, suggests that it may relate to the forceful intrusion and ballooning of the mass rather than later post-intrusive deformation.

At various points in the quarry the granite is cut by aplite and pegmatite veins ranging up to 15–20 cm across. Many of these appear to cut and postdate the foliation, supporting the above views. However, two-thirds of the way along the long wall of the quarry (from left to right facing the quarry wall) the foliation in the granite can been seen to be continuous with a conspicuous cleavage apparent in a flat-lying aplite dyke. This fabric, dipping moderately north, is parallel to the foliation in the hornfels a short distance to the north. Foliated aplite dykes are also apparent in the road cutting to the north of the quarry, although **any investigation of these roadside exposures should be made with extreme caution** due to the lack of visibility for vehicles entering the cutting. These features suggest a tectonic element to the development of the foliation in the granite.

8 River Dee, Clatteringshaws: Loch Doon pluton, granodiorite/greywacke contact

The marginal facies and contact relationship of the Loch Doon pluton can be examined a little farther NW. Return SW along the A712 for about 500 m and then turn north (right) on to a minor road which leaves the A712 about 400 m west of the bridge over the River Dee below Clatteringshaws Dam. Continue on this minor road along the west side of Clatteringshaws Loch for about 8 km and park at the car park near Craigencallie [504 780]. Continue on foot through the gate and along the forestry road for about 1.5 km and, at a T-junction, turn right on to the road leading north across a bridge over the River Dee. The contact of the granodiorite with the local greywackes is exposed on the north side of a second T-junction, just beyond the bridge [496 795].

The contact may be examined over a 60 m section exposed in small crags at the side of the forestry road. At the east end of the section, dark purple hornfelsed greywackes of the Shinnel Formation are largely devoid of veining. About 5 m to the west of a small stream, small (1–2 mm) acid veinlets appear, broadly parallel to the NE-trending strike. Westwards these increase in abundance, the foliation in the greywackes becomes less regular and the rock develops a brecciated appearance. Calcareous concretions are broken and cross-cut by the veinlets. About 10–15 m east of the contact, granitic veins become relatively abundant and are markedly cross-cutting in relation to the greywacke bedding. The veins are generally 1–2 cm in thickness although locally they coalesce to form patches up to 50 by 70 cm. Immediately adjacent to the contact the greywacke is recrystallised with the loss of primary bedding features, giving the rock a massive appearance. The marginal facies of the pluton is here a quartz diorite. It is massive and unfoliated and here, at least, free of xenoliths. Note that the granitic veins in the greywacke are more acid than the main granodiorite mass, and that this does not itself vein the country rock. This implies that the material in the veins was generated as a contact effect.

In the quarry behind these roadside exposures, further excellent sections through the purple hornfelsed greywackes may be examined. On the east side, massive sandstone beds alternate with thin (50 cm) siltstone beds, with little acid or quartz veining present. To the west side of the quarry, dark siltstones become more abundant and contain lines of calcareous concretions. These siltstones contain many more quartz veinlets and lenses than do those to the east, a contrast which may have more to do with the overall host lithology than with proximity to the igneous contact.

9   Buchan, Glen Trool: Loch Doon pluton, granodiorite/greywacke contact

From Craigencallie, return to the A712, continue west to Newton Stewart and take the A714 towards Girvan. At Bargrennan, about 12 km north of Newton Stewart, turn east on to the minor road leading to Glen Trool. Drive to the end of the Glen Trool road and park at the car park [416 803]. Proceed east on foot along the track past Buchan House and, just beyond the house, strike up the hillside on the well-marked path to Loch Valley. After 500 m the path goes through a gate in a stone wall and some 70 m beyond this, the granodiorite contact is exposed on a series of crags rising steeply to the north [426 808]. The contact runs up the crags with an approximate north–south trend, parallel to the local bedding strike of the greywacke country rocks.

The granodiorite contains abundant xenoliths of greywacke, with the long axes generally orientated parallel to the contact. Most xenoliths are only 10–20 cm long, although large elongate relics up to 1 m

long can be seen in places; some xenoliths are cut by late acid veining. Locally the granodiorite exhibits a weak foliation which is also orientated parallel to the contact. At the contact, the country rock (here greywacke turbidites of the Portpatrick Formation) shows the local development of feldspar porphyroblasts along some bedding planes, giving the rock a coarse gneissose appearance. Calcareous concretions are relatively unaffected by the feldspathisation, and the calcareous pods lying within the feldspathised greywackes give the metagreywacke a superficial resemblance to the igneous rock with its sedimentary xenoliths. New feldspar is only observed within a zone between 50 and 90 cm wide adjacent to the contact. Beyond this the greywackes contain some minor acid veinlets but these, in turn, disappear within a few metres of the contact. It is notable that no veins of granodiorite extend from the main mass. These relationships were formerly cited as evidence for a 'front' of granitistation, although the intrusive nature of the granodiorite is no longer in dispute. Despite the similarity in appearance between the feldspathised greywacke and the foliated and xenolith-rich igneous rock, close examination shows that the contact between them is sharply defined.

R P Barnes and D J Fettes

Excursion 17

THE ORLOCK BRIDGE FAULT and THE MONIAIVE SHEAR ZONE: sinistral displacement and high strain at the Ordovician–Silurian boundary structure

OS 1:50 000 sheets 82 Stranraer & Glen Luce, 77 Dalmellington to New Galloway, 78 Nithsdale & Annandale, 72 Upper Clyde Valley
BGS 1:50 000 sheets 1 & 3 Rhins of Galloway, 4W Kirkcowan, 8E Loch Doon, 9W New Galloway, 15E Leadhills, 24W Biggar
Route map: Figure 55

Main points of interest This excursion examines the range of structures developed along the trace of the Orlock Bridge Fault and within the adjacent Moniaive Shear Zone across southern Scotland. In Northern Ireland and south-west Scotland the Orlock Bridge Fault forms the boundary between Ordovician and Silurian turbidite sequences although this relationship may not hold further east. The fault zone, originally described in Ireland, shows evidence for major post-D1 sinistral displacement and has been proposed as a terrane boundary of regional significance. This interpretation has not been universally accepted although recent work in the Southern Uplands has defined a zone of ductile deformation (the Moniaive Shear Zone) associated with part of the fault.

Logistics This is a two-day excursion, with localities spread along the length of the Southern Uplands (Figure 55). New Galloway is a convenient break with Localities 1 to 4 (or 5) on the first day and localities 5 (or 6) to 9 on the second. Alternatively some of the localities described here could be linked with other excursions. Localities 1–3 are easily accessed using the A75 from Stranraer to Newton Stewart, the A712 via New Galloway and the A702 to Moniaive. Thence the A702 leads past locality 7 through the Dalveen Pass to Elvanfoot and, after 10 km southwards on the A74, the B719 links to the A701 from which Localities 8 and 9 are easily reached. Locality 1 is coastal, but most of the exposure there is

accessible at all but very high tides. At some of the localities parking and access are on private land and appropriate permission should be sought.

Introduction The strike-fault at the boundary between the Ordovician and Silurian turbidite sequences in the Southern Uplands was termed the Kingledores Fault by Leggett et al. (1979), from a major feature in the central Southern Uplands. Anderson and Oliver (1986) subsequently described the equivalent structure in the Longford–Down inlier of Northern Ireland, where a 200 m wide fault zone is exposed on the coast at Orlock Bridge. To the SW, a 1 km wide shear zone is associated with the fault at Slieve Glah. They correlated the 'Orlock Bridge Fault' with the Kingledores Fault in the Southern Uplands, describing exposures of a narrow zone of deformation at Cairngarroch Bay on the Scottish coast (Locality 1) and near Garvald east of Edinburgh. A high strain zone up to 5 km in width (the Moniaive Shear Zone, Lintern et al., 1992; Barnes et al., 1995; Phillips et al., 1995), comparable with the Slieve Glah shear zone, has since been recognised in the Southern Uplands. The Orlock Bridge Fault in Scotland can be divided into five distinct sectors from west to east as follows:

i) Glenluce sector: Cairngarroch Bay to the River Cree near Newton Stewart. The fault zone is relatively narrow (up to 50 m), and is marked by predominantly brittle structures except in the immediate vicinity of the fault where more ductile fabrics may occur in a very narrow zone.

ii) Talnotry sector: Newton Stewart to New Galloway. Several anastomosing faults are marked by narrow outcrops of Moffat Shale Group in this complex sector. These faults occur near the northern edge of a wide zone of ductile deformation partly contemporaneous

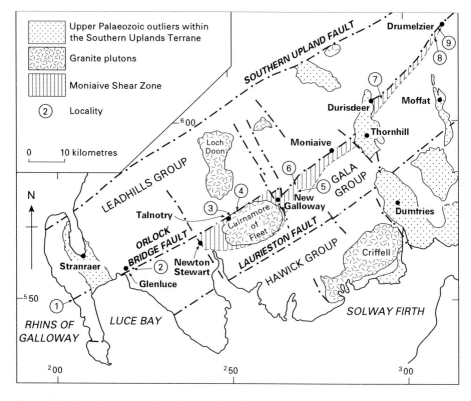

Figure 55   Locality map and outline geology for the Moniaive Shear Zone excursion.

with the early stages of contact metamorphism. This subsequently overprinted all the fabrics as the Cairnsmore of Fleet pluton was emplaced.

iii) Moniaive sector: New Galloway to Thornhill. The fault forms the sharp, northern margin to a zone of locally intense ductile deformation up to 5 km wide. Both planar and linear fabrics are well developed.

iv) Durisdeer sector: Thornhill to Peebles. The shear zone narrows eastwards from about 2 km width east of Thornhill. Brittle and ductile components are present and as the shear zone narrows it bifurcates with discrete strands affecting Ordovician and Silurian strata on either side of the Orlock Bridge Fault.

v) Garvald sector: Peebles to Dunbar (not shown in Figure 55). A narrow fault zone at the boundary between the Ordovician and Silurian strata is known at one locality only, where mainly brittle shearing and sinistral refolding of S1 cleavage structures were described by Anderson and Oliver (1986).

In the Glenluce sector the Orlock Bridge Fault can be examined at Cairngarroch Bay and Wood of Dervaird (Localities 1 and 2). At the eastern margin of the Glenluce sector a cross-cutting NNW-trending fault along the River Cree at Newton Stewart effectively marks the start of the Moniaive Shear Zone. A large down-west displacement across the NNW fault causes an abrupt eastward increase in the grade of regional metamorphism (BGS 1992c, inset map), accompanied by the appearance of an unusually intense bedding-parallel foliation in the massive sandstone of the Silurian Gala Group. The foliation is characteristic of the Moniaive Shear Zone, a major, regional high-strain zone up to 5 km wide, which extends for over 50 km to the NE, with the Talnotry and Moniaive sectors of the Orlock Bridge Fault forming its northern boundary. The occurrence of Moffat Shale in the Talnotry sector indicates that the Orlock Bridge Fault is essentially comparable to the other tract bounding faults in the Southern Uplands (see Introductory chapter) but is associated with an unusual degree of post-D1 reactivation.

In the aureole of the Cairnsmore of Fleet granite pluton (Localities 3 and 4), the Moniaive Shear Zone fabric is characterised by an intense bedding-parallel foliation with fine, parallel quartz segregations. Outwith the aureole the shear zone is best developed around Moniaive (e.g. Localities 5 and 6) where the planar foliation is intermittently developed but the shear zone includes a strong linear component. Farther east the shear zone narrows (e.g. Locality 7) and breaks into at least two strands (Localities 8 and 9) where the close association between the Orlock Bridge Fault and the Ordovician/ Silurian boundary is lost. In the most easterly Garvald sector the fault becomes a narrow zone of brittle deformation; it is poorly exposed and correlation of its various possible strands is uncertain.

In Northern Ireland, the belt of fault-deformation associated with the Orlock Bridge Fault ranges in width from 200 m to 1 km and typically comprises three structural zones (Anderson and Oliver, 1986). These contain increasingly intense deformation fabrics in sequence from 1 to 3.

Zone 1   The regional S1 cleavage is overprinted by a phyllonitic fabric and sandstone beds are cut by numerous sinistral extensional shear fractures at an acute angle to bedding.

Zone 2   Bedding and cleavage are transposed by a strongly developed foliation subparallel to the fault. Numerous quartz segregations, of variable thickness, occur parallel to the fabric and increase in intensity towards the boundary with Zone 3. An S-C fabric is develped usually.

Zone 3   Abundant, discontinuous, tightly folded quartz segregations are embedded in intensely foliated phyllonite.

These zones are best developed at Slieve Glah where the fault zone is up to 1 km wide; zone 1 forms broad areas of shearing at the margins of the fault zone and zones 2 and 3 occur in the central part. At Orlock Bridge the fault-associated deformation is about 200 m wide, although it is very asymmetrical and affects the formations on either side of the fault in different ways. Zone 1 is recognisable south of the fault but cannot be distinguished to the north where the regional D1 deformation is relatively intense. Zone 2 deformation occurs north of the fault in a number of bands, 1–10 m wide, which coalesce southward towards the fault-trace. Zone 3, about 16 m wide, is coincident with the fault trace and has a sharp boundary with zone 1 to the south; a lamprophyre dyke at this boundary postdates most of the fault-related deformation.

Fault-deformation is thus apparent on both sides of the Orlock Bridge Fault in Northern Ireland and a comparable situation occurs in the Glenluce sector in the Southern Uplands, with the most intense deformation (Zone 3) along the trace of the fault. However, in the Talnotry and Moniaive sectors the Moniaive Shear Zone, essentially a major development of Zone 2, is situated south of the fault and may be very wide, encompassing at least two tectonostratigraphical tracts and one other tract-bounding fault. Deformation continues north of the fault for a short distance at Talnotry (Locality 4) before dying out gradually northwards.

Regional constraints on the timing of movement on the Orlock Bridge Fault

Evidence for the timing of movement on the Orlock Bridge Fault is at present contradictory and may indicate a long history, with phases of movement from Wenlock to early Devonian times (Barnes et al., 1995; Lintern et al., 1992). The structures in the Glenluce sector have features in common with the D3 deformation elsewhere and thus the main phase of movement may have occurred in the Wenlock (c.425 Ma; Figure 1–4 and Lintern et al., 1992). It is unclear to what extent the origin of the Moniaive Shear Zone is related to that of the Orlock Bridge Fault but there are certainly geometrical affinities with the structures developed in the Slieve Glah Shear Zone, regarded by Anderson and Oliver (1986) as being formed before 400 Ma. The shear zone foliation apparently represents a progressive development of the S1 cleavage. Local refolding of the shear zone foliation by structures similar in style to D2 is also consistent with it being related to S1. However, the shear zone foliation locally deforms dioritic intrusions of probable late Silurian or early Devonian age, and cordierite and garnet porphyroblasts in the thermal aureole of the Cairnsmore of Fleet granite pluton (see Excursion 16, Locality 5) also predate at least part of the development of the foliation. An overlap between the development of foliation and thermal metamorphism is indicated, although subsequent biotite horn-felsing overprints the foliation. The granite itself is largely undeformed and cuts the foliation in the host rocks (see Excursion 16, Localities 5, 6 and 7). The cooling age of the granite is 392 ± 2 Ma by the Rb-Sr method (Halliday et al., 1980), a date recently confirmed by U-Pb on zircon (J A Evans written communication, 1994). This places a minimum age limit on the ductile deformation in the high-strain zone although it also suggests that significant deformation occurred in the late Silurian (Figure 4). At its northern margin the Orlock Bridge Fault was probably reactivated as a brittle structure during the late Palaeozoic.

Kinematic indicators

Interpretation of the movement direction of the fault zone depends on identification of minor structural features. The four main shear criteria encountered in this excursion are described below and summarised diagrammatically in Figure 56.

a. Asymmetry of steeply plunging folds
Steeply plunging fold pairs may be described as having sinistral or dextral vergence, the description being based on the sense of rotation of the short limb (sinistral = anticlockwise) but also applying to the overall sense of the lateral component of movement on the zone in which they were formed.

b. S-C mylonites
An S-C fabric represents the development of two foliation surfaces within a shear zone (Berthe et al., 1979). The C-surfaces develop parallel to the shear zone boundary while the S-surfaces are initiated at 45° to the boundary and rotate towards the C-surfaces as deformation progresses. The C-surfaces have the same sense of shear as the overall zone and this can be determined from the rotation of the S-surfaces (Lister and Snoke, 1984).

c. Asymmetric augen structures
These develop where resistant particles, such as feldspar and quartz grains or cordierite and garnet porphyroblasts, are contained within a more ductile matrix. The foliation may be asymmetrically distributed around the augen and recrystallised grains of the porphyroclast extend along the foliation plane forming 'tails'. The asymmetry of these tails defines the sense of shear (Passchier and Simpson, 1986).

d. Extensional crenulation cleavage
Extensional crenulation cleavages form oblique to the shear zone boundary and develop after the main shear zone fabric (Platt, 1984; Platt and Vissers, 1980). The sense of movement is such as to cause extension along the older foliation, the new fabric forming along the limbs of open folds of the foliation.

1 Cairngarroch Bay

OS 1:50 000 Sheet 82 Stranraer & Glen Luce
BGS 1:50 000 Sheet 1 & 3 The Rhins of
Galloway

The most westerly manifestation of the Orlock Bridge Fault within the Southern Uplands can be seen on the coast about

10 km SE from Portpatrick. The locality may be reached from the A75 by travelling westward past Glenluce and turning left on the A715 towards Sandhead. This road links with the A716 just north of Sandhead; continue south towards the village but at its outskirts turn right (west), initially on the B7042 but thereafter utilising a network of minor roads towards Cairngarroch. Continue straight on at the Cairngarroch crossroads to West Cairngarroch Farm. Access and parking arrangements should be agreed at the farm. Walk down the rough track leading south from the road about 300 m east of the farm near Cairngarroch Croft. After a short distance the track swings WSW to follow a narrow valley for 1 km down to the shore.

Much of Cairngarroch Bay is underlain by granodioritic intrusive rocks (Stone, 1995), intruded subsequent to movement on the Orlock Bridge Fault. The fault itself forms a narrow inlet at Calves Hole, about 100 m SW of the cottage on the south margin of Cairngarroch Bay. Scramble over the rocky cliffs until a narrow gully leads down to the WSW. The belt of fault-associated deformation is about 50 m across with structures typical of Zones 1 and 2; the following description is based on Anderson and Oliver (1986, p.217 and Figure 8).

The Orlock Bridge Fault is represented by a few square metres of intensely foliated and quartz-veined strata in Calves Hole which show an S-C fabric referable to Zone 2. Closely spaced upright S-surfaces trending 065°, together with quartz segregations, are clearly cut by steeply inclined C-surfaces with approximately 3 mm spacing and at some 10° to 30° anticlockwise of the S-surfaces. There are other, less regular, shear planes and some local refolding of the fault fabric. Late carbonate veins cut across both S- and C-surfaces. South of the Calves Hole gully, sandstone and mudstone (Gala Group) are sheared into lenses characteristic of Zone

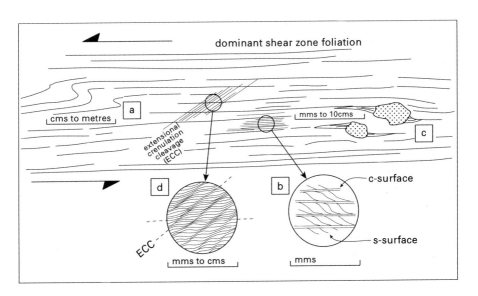

Figure 56 Schematic illustration of kinematic indicators within a sinistral shear zone. For more detailed illustrations see White et al. (1986).

a. asymmetry of steeply plunging folds.
b. S-C mylonite.
c. asymmetric augen structures.
d. extensional crenulation cleavage.

Scale range for each kinematic indicator shown.

1. Bedding becomes obvious about 10 m south of Calves Hole and the intensity of shearing and density of fractures both decrease rapidly southward, with the fault-associated deformation ceasing to be distinguishable from the regional S1 cleavage.

The north side of Calves Hole is a cliff 4 m high formed by a fault trending about 070°. This forms the northern margin of the Zone 2 outcrop and separates it from a complex of felsite sills and numerous lenticular screens of hornfelsed Shinnel Formation sandstone which are moderately NW-dipping. The lowest sill is clearly truncated by the fault. The felsite sills are foliated approximately parallel to their margins but this fabric is not obviously tectonic and is clearly not related to fault movement. In the hornfelsed sandstone at the base of the 4-m cliff, tight folds with a strong axial-planar cleavage are probably products of the main D1 regional deformation. Local refolding of that cleavage may be due to fault movement or may be a consequence of felsite intrusion. The relationship between intrusion and faulting is complex but it seems likely that the intrusion post-dated the main fabric-generating movement on the Orlock Bridge Fault but was followed by one or more phases of brittle movement.

2   Wood of Dervaird

OS 1:50 000 Sheet 82 Stranraer & Glen Luce
BGS 1: 50 000 Sheet 4W Kirkcowan

Return eastwards on the A75 and, near the east end of the Glenluce bypass, turn right into a gated farm track 2 km after the junction with the A747 to Port William. Drive 600 m south along the track, keeping right at the intersection with a forestry track, and park near the Wood of Dervaird Farm buildings [NX 226 578]. Permission for access should be sought at the farm if not already arranged in advance.

The ENE-trending Orlock Bridge Fault passes a few metres south of the farmhouse, separating a thick unit of laminated silty mudstone at the base of the Ordovician Shinnel Formation (to the north) from thickly bedded greywacke of the early Llandovery Gala Group (to the south). Deformation is largely concentrated in the

siltstone and is best seen in exposures which extend over a distance of about 200 m west from the farm before the Orlock Bridge Fault is displaced southwards by a cross-fault. Fault-related deformation in the Gala Group is restricted to the immediate vicinity of the fault where intensely foliated sandstone containing suggestions of an S-C fabric is exposed at the southern edge of the farmyard near the gate.

Proceed through the sheep pens west of the farm track and follow the wall to the right for about 50 m. Exposures in small knolls to the left and just beyond the sharp angle in the wall are composed of grey silty mudstone with a distinct cleavage and thin quartz veins parallel to the steeply dipping bedding-lamination. The lamination, cleavage and veins are distorted by numerous sinistral minor folds with axial plunge ranging from moderate to vertical. Walk SE to a small WSW-trending and N-facing bank with small exposures at the base. These show intensely foliated silty mudstone with abundant parallel quartz veins up to 2 cm thick. The veins are folded by small, steeply plunging, sinistral fold pairs. The overall characteristics are of Zone 3, suggesting that these exposures and the bank feature mark the trace of the fault.

3   Murray's Monument, Talnotry

OS 1:50 000 Sheet 77 Dalmellington to New Galloway
BGS 1:50 000 Sheet 8E Loch Doon

Return to the A75 and proceed east to the junction with the A712, 1.5 km beyond the roundabout south of Newton Stewart; turn left on to the A712 and continue for about 9 km towards New Galloway. Murray's Monument [NX 488 719] is a monolith situated on a knoll named Big Doon to the left of the road and is served by a car park [491 721] a little further on at the foot of the Grey Mare's Tail waterfall (Locality 4). From the car park, follow the path which leads SW to the top of Big Doon. The monument was erected in honour of the self-educated son of a local shepherd who became a professor in oriental languages at Edinburgh University.

A number of exposures in meta-greywacke near the top of Big Doon are characteristic of the Zone 2 style of deformation immediately south of the Orlock Bridge Fault in this northern part of the Cairnsmore of Fleet aureole. An intense foliation, dipping moderately NW, transposes all original structure and carries fine, parallel quartz veins. Conjugate kink bands are locally well developed.

4 Grey Mare's Tail Burn, Talnotry

OS 1:50 000 Sheet 77 Dalmellington to
New Galloway
BGS 1:50 000 Sheet 8E Loch Doon

A series of waterfalls in the Grey Mare's Tail Burn and forest trails through the adjoining woodlands (described in a leaflet available from the nearby campsite) are situated close to the A712 and are served by the same car park as Murray's Monument (Locality 3). The burn provides a discontinuous section across the relatively narrow aureole in the deformed Moffat Shale and interfaulted greywackes north of the Cairnsmore of Fleet granite and into the much less deformed Shinnel Formation outwith the aureole to the north. The Orlock Bridge Fault has at least two branches here. The intrusive granite contact, visible to the NE on Craigdews Hill (Excursion 16, Locality 6b), is not exposed here but probably passes beneath the burn just north of the A712. The three characteristic features of the western part of the aureole, the moderate dip, intense foliation and the contact alteration itself, die out gradually to the north.

From the car park, cross the burn by the road-bridge and walk along the east side of the burn. The exposures in the lower part of the burn are a fine-grained rock seen in thin-section to be a brecciated mylonite. This lithology can be traced for some distance either side of this locality and may represent the locus of ductile movement adjacent to the Orlock Bridge Fault. Its junction with the overlying metasandstone is a gently dipping fault exposed low in the steep bank on the opposite side of the stream. Near the waterfall scramble up the steep bank in front of the cliff, or walk back a few metres and

follow the main path which climbs more gently. The cliff is in metasandstone with an intense foliation marked by 1–2 mm quartz veins which are moderately NW-dipping. Near the top of the slope the fabric is folded by an open recumbent fold, similar in style to the D2 folds well developed to the south in the Hawick Group (Excursion 13). Continuing up the path, there are small exposures of metamorphosed black mudstone (which may mark a branch of the Orlock Bridge Fault) and then another large exposure in the foliated metasandstone. The path continues alongside the burn for a further 200 m to the intersection with a forestry track. North of the track, about 30 m east of the burn, a clearing is partly floored by intensely foliated metasandstone with uneven, fabric-parallel veining and alteration. In thin-section the latter is seen to be caused by replacement of the biotite in the hornfels by delicate, radiating arrays of sillimanite needles, indicating that no deformation has occurred after their formation in the aureole.

Return to the burn and continue upstream towards the steep bank visible to the north, which marks the main strand of the Orlock Bridge Fault. Exposure in the burn resumes near the foot of the bank, about 100 m north of the track. About 4 m of pyritous black mudstone/siltstone, with a foliation dipping 45° NW and a gently SW-plunging crenulation lineation, is followed by grey silty mudstone with medium to thick sandstone beds to the foot of a series of waterfalls. The lower waterfall cascades over a cliff in about 8 m of metamorphosed black mudstone. Two large greywacke lenses in the mudstone at the base of the cliff show no sign of the pervasive foliation seen hitherto. A zone of intensely brecciated mudstone 1–1.5 m thick, on both sides of the stream by the waterfall is probably a fault gouge formed by relatively late reactivation of this part of the fault. East of the burn the interbedded transition between the Moffat Shale and the greywacke of the overlying Shinnel Formation, dipping moderately north, is exposed above the path where it turns abruptly along the base of the slope.

Exposure in the deeply incised burn above is best accessed from the west bank, although this involves a scramble through the trees. Alternatively the path can be followed to the top of the waterfalls where massive, thickly bedded greywacke alternates with medium- to thin-bedded greywacke and interbedded silty mudstone. This assemblage is typical of the Shinnel Formation locally. Initially the pervasive foliation is still apparent in the metasandstone, dipping moderately NW and parallel to bedding, but northwards it weakens and within 100 m dies out. Evidence of the contact metamorphism, small dark cordierite spots and the purple colouration characteristic of the biotite hornfels, dies out about 250 m north of the waterfall.

The dip of bedding in the 300 m section north of the waterfall is variable between 60° and 80°NW. The burn then turns along strike for a short distance and the next exposure northwards, where its NW course is regained, shows bedding dipping steeply south and overturned. North of this point bedding displays its regional attitude, being near vertical or dipping steeply SE. This moderate NW dip of bedding and foliation is characteristic of the western part of the Cairnsmore of Fleet aureole but the reason for the departure from the regional attitude is unknown. The effect is approximately coincident with the western part of the thermal aureole so it may be related to the emplacement of the granite. This is consistent with the rotation of the dip of the foliation, confirming other evidence that the shear zone pre-dates the final emplacement of the granite.

5 Bread and Beer Cottage to Troquhain Hill

OS 1:50 000 Sheet 77 Dalmellington to New Galloway
BGS 1: 50 000 Sheet 9W New Galloway
Route map: Figure 57 with locality numbers referenced in the text

East of New Galloway the Moniaive Shear Zone causes locally intense deformation of the early Llandovery greywacke of the northern tract of the Gala Group (see below and Phillips, 1992; Barnes et al., 1995; Phillips et al., 1995). A variably developed penetrative planar fabric and subhorizontal stretching lineation are characteristic. On its north side the Shear Zone is bounded by the Orlock Bridge Fault, beyond which the pyroxene-bearing greywacke sequence of the Ordovician Glenlee Formation is at very low regional metamorphic grade and is only weakly deformed.

The section between Bread and Beer Cottage [NX 698 792] and Troquhain Hill [695 816] lies on the south (Silurian) side of the Orlock Bridge Fault and entirely within the Moniaive Shear Zone. Follow the A712 east from New Galloway, through Balmaclellan, towards Corsock. Bread and Beer Cottage is located approximately 6 km from New Galloway, near the junction of a single-track road. Turn left at this junction and park after the cattle grid (Locality 5a). Space is available for a small number of vehicles at the side of the road, but please avoid blocking access to the cottage. The section follows a northward route, across country, to the summit of Troquhain Hill (5f). Total walking distance is about 5 km. There is no footpath across the open and relatively featureless moorland so **this section should not be attempted in poor visibility**.

From the road (**5a**) walk northwards across scattered small exposures of Gala Group quartzose greywacke. Bedding and way-up evidence can be locally identified showing that the sequence dips and youngs NW. Clasts of quartz and feldspar plus various rock fragments are recognisable in the sandstone, despite a variably developed planar foliation and locally developed linear fabric. The foliation, typically steeply NW-dipping, is represented in places (**5b**) by a fine S-C fabric which yields a consistent sinistral sense of shear. The stretching lineation, plunging gently NE, is defined by highly attenuated lithic quartz and mudstone. Within the more pelitic bands the foliation takes the form of a weak to moderate slaty cleavage.

Proceed north, following the line of the exposures on to the slightly higher ground on the southern slopes of Troquhain Hill where the intensity of foliation and linear fabric in the metasandstone decreases. An altered apinitic lamprophyre dyke is poorly exposed (**5c**) but is seen to contain a variably developed foliation dipping steeply NW. The strike of this foliation is broadly parallel to the shear zone fabric developed

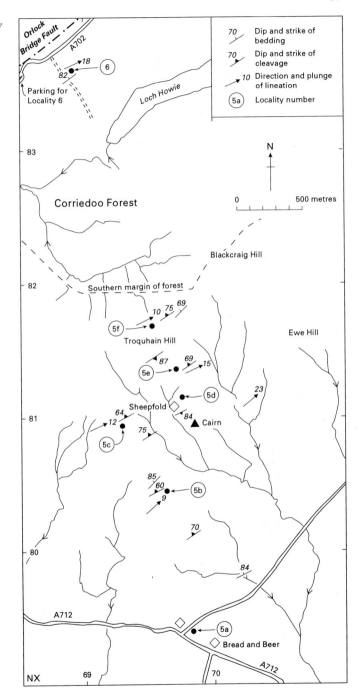

Figure 57 Locality map for the section from Bread and Beer (Locality 5) to Corriedoo (Locality 6).

within the country rocks, indicating that intrusion of the dyke occurred before or during, ductile deformation.

Traverse eastwards across two small streams to a group of exposures at the base of a cairn and proceed towards the summit of Troquhain Hill. In the vicinity of the cairn only a weak fabric is apparent but the intensity of ductile deformation progressively increases up the hill, resulting in the development of a locally intense lineation (5d) as well as a steep SE-dipping planar foliation which, in places, forms a sinistral S-C fabric (5d and 5e). Preserved detrital clasts are attenuated and the resulting augen may exhibit a pronounced sinistral asymmetry. At the top of Troquhain Hill (5f) the shear zone fabric is quite well developed, dipping NW. Minor variations in the intensity of the fabric occur, even within a single exposure, and may be related to the small-scale partitioning of deformation and/or a lithological control, with shearing being concentrated along the more pelitic partings. The same effect is seen regionally; variation in the intensity of ductile shearing can be related to the partitioning of deformation into a number of discrete belts of high strain within the Moniaive Shear Zone.

Return to the parking place by the most direct route down the hill.

6   Corriedoo Forest

OS 1:50 000 Sheet 77 Dalmellington to New Galloway
BGS 1:50 000 Sheet 9W New Galloway

Return towards New Galloway on the A712 but at Balmaclellan turn right to join the A702 and continue NE from St John's Town of Dalry towards Moniaive. Approximately 7 km from Dalry, past Corriedoo Farm, there is a forest track on the right hand side of the A702 immediately after a sharp right hand bend. Parking is provided by a large lay-by (a section of the old A702) [NX 689 836] immediately before the right hand bend (Figure 57). Locality 6 is situated approximately 100 m southwards along the forest track and about 20 m off to the left within Corriedoo Forest.

Coarse-grained Silurian (Gala Group) greywacke is exposed beside the track but the best exposures form a small rocky knoll about 20 m farther to the NE. There, large clasts of quartz, feldspar and lithic fragments are clearly recognisable. Mudstone clasts are locally flattened into the plane of a steeply NW-dipping foliation which wraps around the more rigid quartz and feldspar clasts with the development of asymmetric pressure shadows. Within the mudstone clasts the foliation takes the form of a variably developed slaty cleavage. Quartz and lithic clasts are also highly attenuated, the latter up to 10 cm in length, defining an exceptionally well-developed stretching lineation plunging gently NE and providing a spectacular illustration of a linear fabric. This locality is at the northern margin of the Moniaive Shear Zone and the Orlock Bridge Fault probably occupies the valley immediately to the north of the A702.

7   Durisdeer

OS 1:50 000 Sheet 78 Nithsdale & Annandale
BGS 1:50 000 Sheet 15E Leadhills
Route map: Figure 58 with locality numbers referenced in the text

This section provides an opportunity to examine the variation in intensity of fabric within the shear zone, the nature of the shear zone margins, and the relationship between the shear zone fabric and the regional folds. Kinematic indicators can also be seen within the highest strain segments of the zone. Follow the A702 to the NE, including its offset by a short section of the A76 from north of Thornhill to Carronbridge, following signs for Elvanfoot. Four kilometres NE from Carronbridge the small settlement of Durisdeer is signposted on the right; take this road and park in front of Durisdeer Kirk [NS 895 038]. Walk along the road which runs NE past the Kirk and then follow the Roman Road (now a farm track) on to the valley bottom and along to the Roman fortlet (7a).

Silurian greywacke of the Gala Group is exposed in a number of places on the flanks of the mound on which the fortlet was built. A well-developed penetrative cleavage, slaty in places, has a moderate dip NW and includes a stretching lineation plunging gently

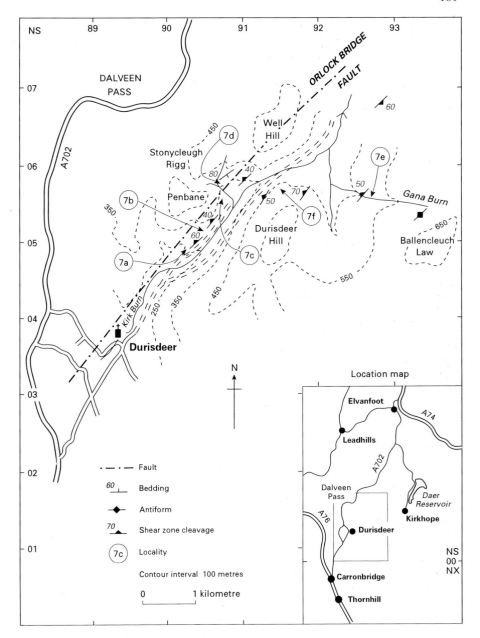

Figure 58   Locality map for the Durisdeer section (Locality 7).

NE. Within the phyllosilicate-rich layers the slaty fabric is deformed by an extensional crenulation cleavage. Open crenulation folds, with wavelengths of 1–3 cm, have zones of intensified cleavage associated with their limbs. The main cleavage rotates into these discrete zones, the sense of rotation indicating extensional displacement on the secondary cleavage and an overall sinistral sense of shear.

Following the Roman Road further up the valley an outcrop of mylonite can be seen above the road where it passes through the field boundary wall (7b). The fabric here is folded by open to close asymmetric folds with wavelengths of 2–30 cm. The axial surface of the folds dips moderately SW, the fold hinges having a moderate plunge NW. These folds are comparable in style and orientation to the widespread D3 structures and indicate further shear reactivation after the formation of the main fabric zone.

Proceed north on to the slightly higher ground above the Roman Road where two small exposures occur approximately 150 m SW of a sheepfold (7c). Here a penetrative cleavage and stretching lineation in silty mudstone are folded by open to close folds with wavelength of approximately 30 cm. The folds have a subhorizontal axial surface, marked by a weak axial planar crenulation cleavage, and plunge gently SW. These folds are comparable in style to the recumbent D2 structures seen elsewhere in the Southern Uplands and suggest a complex relationship between the sinistral strike-slipe folding (D3) and the regional D2 event. Both fold episodes were probably polyphase, diachronous and overlapping.

Follow the small stream (Glenhourie Burn) on to Stonycleuch Rig (7d). Coarse-grained massive sandstone beds form a small waterfall where the stream bifurcates. No cleavage is apparent within the sandstone here but it is intensely fractured and a narrow zone of quartz- cemented fault breccia is developed. The fracturing is probably a consequence of late, brittle deformation on the Orlock Bridge Fault, the trace of which probably runs along the break of slope at the NW side of the valley, marking the northern extent of the shear zone.

The variation in fabric development towards the southern margin of the shear zone can be examined by traversing east into the valley of the Gana Burn. A strong fabric is present within the greywacke exposed in the burn (7e) and a slaty foliation in the mudstone units is accompanied by fabric-parallel, mm-scale quartz veins. Both the cleavage and the veins are folded by close asymmetric folds, similar to those at Locality 7c, but here with a wavelength of about 2 cm and subhorizontal axial surfaces.

An initial expression of the domainal nature of fabric development can be seen on the NW flank of Durisdeer Hill (7f), these exposures being easily accessible from the track from Durisdeer where it passes through the col at the head of Kirk Burn. There, coarse-grained, thick-bedded to massive greywackes show a weakly developed planar fabric in zones 50 cm wide. Outside these narrow zones the greywackes are undeformed but the whole assemblage is interleaved between the zones of intense fabric development exposed to the north and south, by the Roman Road (Localities 7a, b and c) and in Gana Burn (7e) respectively. This contrast within the broad Moniaive Shear Zone may be a precursor to its bifurcation farther east (Localities 8 and 9).

8   Hearthstane

OS 1:50 000 Sheet 72 Upper Clyde Valley
BGS 1:50 000 Sheet 24W Biggar

This and the next locality (9) examine the north-easterly continuation of the Moniaive Shear Zone in an area where two separate belts of ductile deformation have been identified, one on each side of the Orlock Bridge Fault. At Hearthstane (Locality 8), deformation in the Silurian Gala Group appears to have a sinistral sense of displacement, continuing the character of the western part of the Moniaive Shear Zone; further north, at Drumelzier (Locality 9) a narrow zone of deformation in Ordovician rocks shows clear evidence of dextral movement. It is not yet clear whether these two belts, about 2.5 km apart, represent branches of a single zone or whether they were produced by two separate kinematic events.

From Durisdeer, return to the A702 and continue east to Elvanfoot, from where the southbound A74(M) should be followed for about 10 km before turning left on to the B719 signposted Greenhillstairs. Turn left at the junction with the A701 and continue for about 20 km towards Edinburgh. Hearthstane [NT 113 260] is situated on the right, 1.5 km north of Tweedsmuir; permission for parking and access should be sought at the farm house.

This section provides an opportunity to examine shear zone fabrics correlated with those within the Moniaive Shear Zone, last seen 50 km to the SW.

A well-developed fabric can be seen in the section exposed in Hearthstane Burn downstream from the small dam behind the farm buildings. A strong linear fabric, plunging gently NE, is present in the thick-bedded greywacke of the Gala Group which crops out immediately downstream of the dam. The fabric is largely caused by quartz grains with a preferential elongation. In thin section they show evidence of both ductile and brittle deformation with undulose extinction and sub-grain development around grain boundaries; mica beards form tails to the elongate quartz grains and show a sinistral sense of shear. Brittle desegregation of grains has also occurred, with fractures perpendicular to the stretching direction.

A planar fabric, dipping moderately NW, is developed within siltstone interbeds exposed in small cuttings beside the track running east along Hearthstane Burn. A gently NE-plunging stretching lineation is developed within the foliation. The southeastern margin of the zone cannot be located precisely, due to lack of exposure, but a linear fabric is present in loose scree blocks as far as the confluence of Glenheurie and Hearthstane burns approximately 1 km farther east.

9 Drumelzier Place

OS 1:50 000 Sheet 72 Upper Clyde Valley
BGS 1:50 000 Sheet 24W Biggar

From Hearthstane continue towards Edinburgh on the A701 and at Rachan Mill turn right on to the B712, which is signed for Drumelzier. The road takes a sharp left turn after it crosses the River Tweed; at the bend turn right, following the sign for Drumelzier Place, and follow this minor road to the turn off to Drumelzier Place

Farm [NT 125 336], where permission should be sought for parking and access.

Above the road to the SE, opposite the farm drive entrance, are a number of exposures of rhyolitic tuff forming interbeds in the Ordovician greywacke sequence. The tuff contains both scoria and crystals, the former up to 5 cm across, in a fine-grained chloritic matrix; the vesicles in the scoria are infilled with quartz, chlorite and calcite. The tuff horizons are closely associated with a limestone breccia, the Wrae Limestone, interpreted as a debris flow transported into deep water. The limestone has been worked in a small quarry a few hundred metres along strike to the SW. More extensive workings are present on Wrae Hill directly to the SW across the River Tweed (Floyd and Stone, 1992). Within the tuff both the clasts and crystals show chloritic deformation tails, though little desegregation of the crystals has occurred. A penetrative foliation is developed but there is no sign of the stretching lineation seen within the Moniaive Shear Zone further west. Shear sense indicators visible on near-horizontal surfaces include augen asymmetry, long-axis alignment of feldspar grains, and localised development of secondary cleavages. These dominantly indicate a dextral sense of movement but contradictory evidence is also apparent and a complex shear history seems likely.

Further up-slope, medium-bedded greywacke sandstones can be seen in a number of small exposures. The sandstone shows no indication of penetrative deformation and its position thus limits the southern extent of the shear zone. This strand of the shear zone lies entirely within the Ordovician sequence and it is clear that the close relationship seen farther SW between the Orlock Bridge Fault, the Moniaive Shear Zone and the Ordovician–Silurian boundary, is not maintained at this more easterly outcrop.

This completes the itinerary and the A701 may be followed south towards Moffat and the A74 or north towards Edinburgh. The only known outcrop of the Orlock Bridge Fault farther to the NE is the Garvald locality originally described by Anderson and Oliver (1986). This is near Haddington, about 70 km farther NE where the trace of the Orlock Bridge Fault is marked by a few metres of mainly brittle deformation. Anderson and Oliver (1986) describe anastomosing shear planes similar in some respects to their Zone 1 fabrics, and note that in the vicinity of the fault the S1 cleavage is refolded about steeply plunging sinistral hinges.

R P Barnes, M P Boland, E R Phillips and P Stone

Excursion 18

Graptolites:
Ordovician and Silurian biostratigraphy

By far the most commonly found fossils in the Lower Palaeozoic sequences of Southwest Scotland are graptolites. Unlike the Girvan area to the north, the region offers no localities where rich shelly fossil assemblages can be found; but for the graptolite collector there is as wide a selection of fossiliferous horizons as anywhere in the British Isles, ranging in age from the Arenig to the Wenlock.

The collecting of fossils, especially the zonal collecting of graptolites, is not a task to be rushed. Time and perseverance are needed to locate the fossil-bearing layers, especially those with the best-preserved specimens, and a fair number of fossiliferous slabs are needed if a fully representative fauna is to be obtained. Most of the localities described here require a day's study (or longer) to do justice to their biostratig-

raphy, and in each there is every possibility that new discoveries will be made. The graptolite zones recorded so far from each of the localities are shown in Table 3. Some of the mid-Ordovician to early Silurian species likely to be found are illustrated in Figures 59 and 60. Graptolites of Arenig (early Ordovician) age can be collected at Ballantrae, as described in Excursion 8, and additional fossiliferous localities with zones of the Wenlock Series (mid-Silurian) are visited in Excursions 5 and 11 to the Kirkcudbright area. The general stratigraphy of the Moffat Shale Group and the graptolite zones is summarised in Table 4.

If planning a fossil-collecting excursion, note that the availability of several of the localities depends on the state of the tide. Access to most localities is across farm land by way of farm tracks; local permission for

Table 3 Graptolite biozones recorded from:
1. Glenkiln Burn
2. Loup of Kilfeddar
3. Morroch Bay
4. Drumbreddan Bay and Grennan Bay
5. Clanyard Bay and Grennan Quarries (+)
6. Gillespie Burn.

biozone	1	2	3	4	5	6
crispus					(+)	
turriculatus s.l.	+				+	
sedgwickii					+	
convolutus				+	+	
leptotheca						
magnus				+		
triangulatus				+	?	
cyphus				?	+	+
acinaces					+	?
atavus				+	+	+
acuminatus				+		+
persculptus				+		
extraordinarius						
pacificus						+
anceps					?	
complexus						+
complanatus						
linearis						+
clingani	+		+	?		+
wilsoni	+		+			
'peltifer'	+	?	?			
gracilis	+	+	+			
	1	2	3	4	5	6

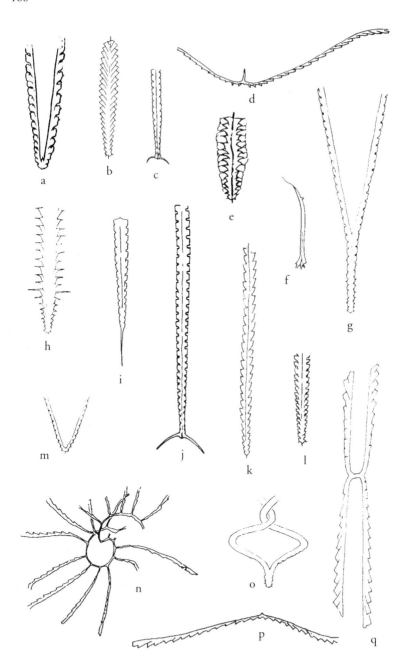

Figure 59 Examples of some of the Ordovician graptolites found in south-west Scotland, all about twice natural size.

a. *Dicellograptus anceps* (Nicholson) — *anceps* Biozone.

b. *Orthograptus abbreviatus* Elles & Wood — chiefly *anceps* Biozone.

c. *Climacograptus supernus* Elles & Wood — *anceps* Biozone.

d. *Leptograptus flaccidus* (Hall) — *clingani* and *linearis* biozones.

e. *Neurograptus margaritatus* (Lapworth) — *clingani* Biozone.

f. *Corynoides calicularis* Nicholson — *peltifer?* and *wilsoni* biozones to *clingani* Biozone.

g. *Dicranograptus ramosus* (Hall) — chiefly *clingani* Biozone.

h. *Orthograptus quadrimucronatus* (Hall) — *clingani* and *linearis* biozones.

i. *Climacograptus caudatus* Lapworth — lower *clingani* Biozone.

j. *Climacograptus bicornis* (Hall) — upper *gracilis* to *wilsoni* biozones.

k. '*Glyptograptus' euglyphus* (Lapworth) — chiefly *gracilis* to *peltifer* biozones.

l. *Amplexograptus leptotheca* (Bulman) — chiefly *peltifer* Biozone.

m. *Dicellograptus sextans exilis* Elles & Wood — *gracilis* and *peltifer* biozones.

n. *Nemagraptus gracilis* (Hall) — *gracilis* Biozone.

o. *Dicranograptus ziczac* Lapworth — chiefly *peltifer* Biozone.

p. *Didymograptus superstes* Lapworth — chiefly *gracilis* Biozone.

q. *Tetragraptus approximatus* Nicholson — *approximatus* Biozone, from the Arenig of the Ballantrae Complex.

entry and parking should always be sought. General advice on the collecting of graptolites is given in Chapter 11 of *Graptolites* edited by Palmer and Rickards (1991).

1   Glenkiln Burn [NY 007 895]

OS 1:50 000 Sheet 78 Nithsdale & Annandale
BGS 1:50 000 Sheet 10W Lochmaben
Route map: Figure 61 with locality numbers referenced in the text

The exposures of Moffat Shale in the Black

Linn section of Glenkiln Burn are historically important because they furnished Lapworth with one of his typical sections of their lowest unit, namely the Glenkiln Shales (Table 4). Typically the Glenkiln Shales yield fossils of the *Nemagraptus gracilis* and *Climacograptus 'peltifer'* biozones, and at this locality they are seen to underlie the Lower Hartfell Shales of the *Climacograptus wilsoni* biozone. The section at Black Linn is not recommended for excursion parties because many of the exposures are small and lie in the banks of a ravine above deep pools in the stream; there are larger and more accessible exposures of correlative strata at the Loup of Kilfeddar (Locality 2), Morroch Bay (Locality 3) and Hartfell Score (described by Rushton in McAdam et al., 1992). A brief guide to Black Linn is given here for the specialist who may be interested in this historic locality. The account is based on those of Lapworth (1878) and Peach and Horne (1899) and, for the lower end of the section, that of Williams (1994, Figure 3).

Take the A701 (Dumfries–Moffat) road to Kirkmichael Mains, and then the turning to Ae Village. After 1.5 km there is limited roadside parking near the bridge west of the chapel at Townhead [NY 004 884]. Access is via the farm track towards Kirkmichael Fell (obtain permission at Townhead). Follow the track for about 1 km, until it begins to ascend the flank of Kirkmichael Fell, whereupon leave the track and fork left, descending to Glenkiln Burn. Upstream lie inliers of Moffat Shale faulted among the outcrops of Gala Group greywackes, fine-grained interbeds of which contain late Llandovery graptolites of the *guerichi* Biozone (= lower part of the *turriculatus* Biozone). The type locality for the Glenkiln Shales, however, is downstream, past a right-hand bend, in the ravine known as Black Linn [007 895].

Downstream of the bend, on the left (south) bank, is a bluff of Glenkiln Shales, deformed but locally fossiliferous (**1a**). Hereabouts Lapworth's map shows an open shaft in the black shales where someone had 'foolishly excavated ... in search of coal' (Lapworth, 1878, p. 287). For about 50 m downstream the burn exposes unfossilifer-

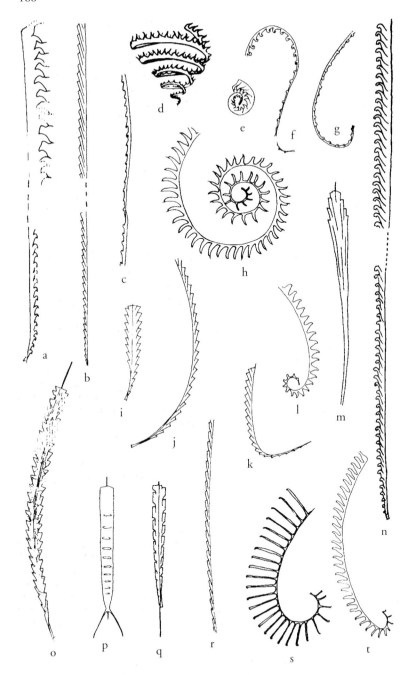

Figure 60 Examples of some of the Llandovery (lower Silurian) graptolites found in south-west Scotland, all about twice natural size.

a. *Monograptus sedgwickii* (Portlock) — *sedgwickii* Biozone.
b. *Pristiograptus regularis* (Törnquist) — chiefly *sedgwickii* Biozone.
c. *'Diversograptus' runcinatus* (Lapworth) — lower *turriculatus* Biozone.
d. *Monograptus turriculatus* (Barrande) — *turriculatus* Biozone to lower *crispus* Biozone.
e. *Monograptus discus* (Törnquist) — *crispus* to *crenulata* biozones.
f. *Monograptus crispus* Lapworth — *crispus* Biozone.
g. *Streptograptus exiguus* (Nicholson) — uppermost *turriculatus* Biozone to *griestoniensis* Biozone.
h. *Monograptus convolutus* (Hisinger) — *convolutus* Biozone.
i. *Dimorphograptus swanstoni* Lapworth — *acinaces* Biozone.
j. *Coronograptus gregarius* (Lapworth) — *cyphus* to *convolutus* biozones.
k. *Monograptus limatulus* Törnquist — chiefly *convolutus* Biozone.
l. *Monograptus triangulatus fimbriatus* (Nicholson) — *magnus* Biozone.
m. *Cephalograptus cometa* (Geinitz) — upper *convolutus* Biozone.
n. *Monograptus priodon* (Bronn) — *griestoniensis* Biozone? to lower Wenlock.
o. *Parakidograptus acuminatus* (Nicholson) — *acuminatus* Biozone.
p. *Climacograptus trifilis* Manck — *acuminatus* Biozone.
q. *Rhaphidograptus toernquisti* (Törnquist) — top *atavus* to basal *sedgwickii* biozones.
r. *Atavograptus atavus* (Jones) — chiefly *atavus* to *cyphus* biozones.
s. *Rastrites longispinus* Perner — *triangulatus* to *convolutus* biozones.
t. *Monograptus triangulatus triangulatus* (Harkness) — *triangulatus* Biozone.

Some Wenlock graptolites are illustrated in Figure 26

ous grey flaggy mudstones, but at the next left-hand bend, near the confluence of a tributary stream on the right bank, near-vertical fossiliferous black mudstones are seen striking approximately parallel to Black Linn (**1b**). Many strongly flattened

graptolites of the *Nemagraptus gracilis* Biozone can be collected, including *Climacograptus bicornis, Dicellograptus sextans* and *N. gracilis* itself. Downstream of the tributary the banks of the ravine become steep, and access is precarious. At about 40 m downstream the Glenkiln Shales pass up (=downstream) into grey mudstones of the Lower Hartfell Shales. These contain thin black beds that may locally yield well-preserved fossils of the *wilsoni* Biozone, including *C. wilsoni* and *Pseudoclimacograptus scharenbergi* (**1c**). Farther downstream is a faulted outcrop of Lower Hartfell Shale with fossils representing the *Dicranograptus clingani* Biozone (**1d**).

2 Loup of Kilfeddar [NX 152 674]

OS 1:50 000 Sheet 82 Stranraer, Glen Luce & surrounding area
BGS 1:50 000 sheets 1 and 3 The Rhins of Galloway
Route map: Figure 62 with locality numbers referenced in the text

The thick siliceous greywacke succession of the Kirkcolm Formation has been dated by the faunas collected from a number of graptolitic interbeds. One of the thickest and most fossiliferous of these interbeds occurs in the Main Water of Luce near a waterfall called the Loup of Kilfeddar, at the contact between the Kirkcolm Formation and the pyroxenous greywackes of the Galdenoch Formation.

From New Luce [NX 175 645], 8 km north of Glenluce, cross to the west side of the river and take the minor road that follows the west bank northwards. The Loup of Kilfeddar is reached after about 4 km; it is about 600 m east of Cairnerzean, where the Main Water of Luce makes a sharp bend to the left [152 674]. The main waterfall exposes part of the Kirkcolm Formation which, on the east bank below the waterfall, has yielded a few graptolites including *Pseudoclimacograptus scharenbergi*. Much more promising for the collector is the section upstream of the main waterfall on the west bank which exposes a succession of black graptolitic mudstone units for about 100 m. The beds are fossiliferous at several places and large faunas typical of the

Table 4 General succession of the Moffat Shale Group, correlated with the sequence of graptolite biozones (Figure 5).

Note that whereas Gala unit 7 overlies the highest Birkhill Shales, units 1–6 are laterally equivalent to the Birkhill Shales; the Leadhills Group is laterally equivalent to the Hartfell and Glenkiln shales.

Gala Group (unit 7)			turriculatus s.l. (base) to triangulatus	SILURIAN
Birkhill Shale	Upper			
	Lower		cyphus to acuminatus persculptus	
MOFFAT SHALE GROUP	Hartfell Shale	Upper ('Barren mudstones')	extraordinarius anceps complanatus	ORDOVICIAN
		Lower	linearis clingani wilsoni	
	Glenkiln Shale		'peltifer'	
			gracilis	
	chert and pillow basalt (base not seen)		(base not recognised)	

Nemagraptus gracilis Biozone can be collected.

At the broken footbridge, and just upstream of it, outcrops of black shale (**2a**) contain species of *Cryptograptus, Dicellograptus, Dicranograptus, Didymograptus, Diplograptus, Glossograptus, 'Glyptograptus', Lasiograptus, Nemagraptus* and *Orthograptus*. Some of the shales appear disturbed but in their midst are blocks of coherent shale with well-preserved graptolites.

Upstream the river broadens into a pool without exposure, but above this, where the river forms rapids, is a broad exposure of grey and black shale 15–20 m thick. Here the succession is interrupted by zones of disturbance (representing faulting and minor folding?) but graptolites including examples of *Thamnograptus* can be collected at places where the shale is less disturbed, for example near the downstream (**2b**) and upstream (**2c**) ends of the exposure.

Upstream of the rapids is a reef in the river where disturbed shales at the base of the overlying Galdenoch Formation again contain blocks of graptolitic black shale (**2d**) of the *gracilis* or *'peltifer'* Biozone.

3 Morroch Bay [NX 017 525]

OS 1:50 000 Sheet 82 Stranraer, Glen Luce & surrounding area
BGS 1:50 000 sheets 1 and 3 The Rhins of Galloway
Route map: Figure 63 with locality numbers referenced in the text

Morroch Bay displays the largest outcrop of the Moffat Shale in south-west Scotland. When the tide is out, mudstones and associated cherts of the Glenkiln and Lower Hartfell formations are exposed for nearly 400 m across strike and, at the north end of the bay, are interbedded with and overlain by the basal greywacke beds of the Portpatrick Formation. It is possible to collect graptolites representative of the *gracilis, 'peltifer?', wilsoni* and *clingani* biozones, and to use their distribution to infer the presence of structural imbrication. Peach and Horne (1899, pp.401–408) described the section in detail and their account and collections form a component of the present account. However, their structural interpretation for the northern end of the bay, of interfolded greywackes and shales is rejected here in favour of simple interbedding.

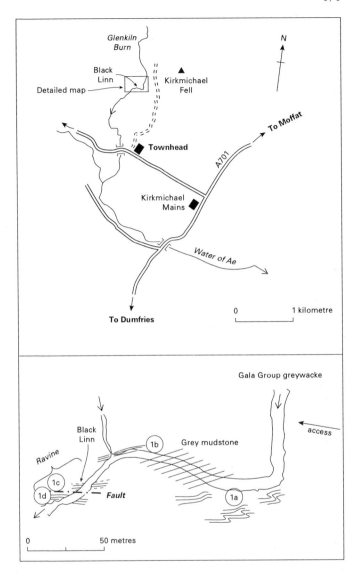

Figure 61 Locality map for Glenkiln Burn (Locality 1).

If using a car, take the minor road from Portpatrick towards Knockinaam and Port of Spittal. About 3 km SE of Portpatrick [at NX 023 527] there is a track down to the south end of the bay; park by the roadside and walk 1.5 km down the track to the bay. There is no room to park a bus. Morroch Bay can also be reached on foot from Portpatrick by the cliff-top path, a pleasant walk of about 3 km in each direc-tion, but involving **an arduous scramble down steep overgrown slopes** into the north end of the bay. The tide is not dangerous at this locality, but when it comes in, the bedrock geology is largely obscured.

The intertidal zone exposes a thick sequence of mudstone dipping steeply and striking roughly SW, out to sea. There are several intrusive igneous dykes, more or less concordant with the bedding, and these

172

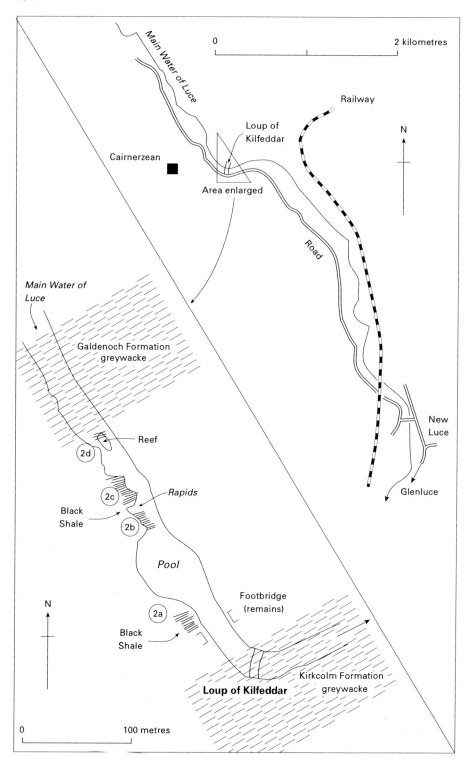

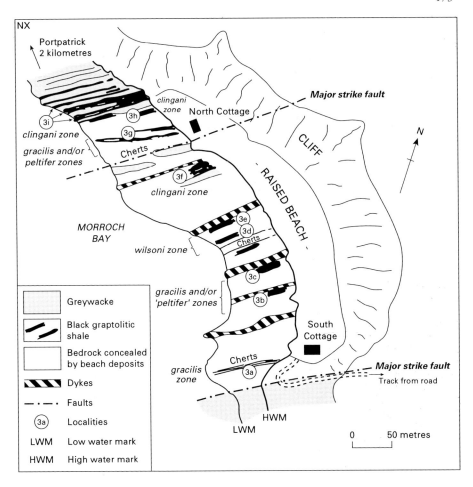

Figure 63 Locality map for Morroch Bay (Locality 3).

can serve as useful landmarks when studying the mudstone succession. The mudstones generally become younger from south to north but the distribution of fossil zones indicates at least one major structural repetition, whilst the anomalous thickness of some units, together with the presence of minor folding and faulting, shows that the structure is complicated in detail.

At the south end of the bay, black mudstones (**3a**), associated with cherts and red

Figure 62 Locality map for Loup of Kilfeddar (Locality 2).

and green mudstones have yielded a relatively diverse fauna of the *N. gracilis* Biozone, including a dozen species referable to *Climacograptus, Cryptograptus, Dicellograptus, Dicranograptus, Hallograptus, Nemagraptus* and *Orthograptus*. Conodonts have been recovered from red mudstones here.

The succession to the north consists largely of red and green mudstones with beds of chert, but about 100 m north of the cottage at the south end of the bay (**3b** and **3c**) you can collect faunas of the *gracilis* and possibly *'peltifer'* biozones from black Glenkiln Shales.

The *wilsoni* Biozone is found in black shale (**3d**) about 150 m NW of the cottage, between chert beds and a large dyke near the middle of the bay. *Climacograptus wilsoni* is associated with *Amplexograptus perexcavatus, Dicranograptus nicholsoni,* and *Glossograptus hincksii.* Close to the dyke is a bed (**3e**) with *Dicellograptus angulatus* and other graptolites.

Further north the mudstones are associated with some greywacke beds, and beside one of these (**3f**), about 50 m south of the northerly cottage, a fairly diverse *D. clingani* Biozone fauna can be found, with species of *Climacograptus, Corynoides, Leptograptus, Neurograptus* and several of *Orthograptus.*

The localities referred to so far are progressively younger northwards. However, a major strike fault to the north of here truncates the Hartfell Shale and reintroduces chert and Glenkiln Shale (**3g**) with fossils of the *gracilis* and *'peltifer'* biozones.

The northern end of the bay shows very clearly the interbedding of black mudstone with the basal greywackes of the Portpatrick Formation. Many of the mudstone beds (**3h** and **3i**) are fossiliferous, and faunas of the *clingani* Biozone, including *Climacograptus spiniferus, Dicellograptus morrisi, Dicranograptus ramosus, Neurograptus margaritatus* and various *Orthograptus* spp., are easy to collect. This locality shows that the base of the Portpatrick Formation lies within the *clingani* Biozone, whilst the top of the formation exposed some 5 km to the NW in Killantringan Bay (see Excursion 15) appears to lie within the overlying *linearis* Biozone (Figure 46).

4   Grennan Point and Drumbreddan Bay [NX 075 437]

OS 1:50 000 Sheet 82 Stranraer, Glen Luce & surrounding area
BGS 1:50 000 Sheets 1 and 3 The Rhins of Galloway
Route map: Figure 64 with locality numbers referenced in the text

Intertidal exposures around Grennan Point (about 13 km SE of Portpatrick) afford an opportunity to examine the Upper Hartfell Shale and several zones of the Birkhill Shale, and to see how they relate to the overlying greywackes of Grennan Point (Gala Group 6: Figure 46).

Approach on the A716 from Stranraer; 4 km south of Sandhead turn right, pass Ardwell House, and after 1.5 km turn left down the minor road to Drumbreddan [NX 084 440]. From the farm a walk of about 800 m takes you to Drumbreddan Bay.

There are two principal exposures of Moffat Shale, separated by the greywacke beds that make up Grennan Point. The northerly exposure is much the larger and displays a wider range of strata; the southerly exposure shows the relationship with the greywacke particularly well. Structural aspects of this locality are described in Excursion 15.

NORTH OF GRENNAN POINT (GRENNAN BAY)

The Moffat Shale Group is well exposed at low tide but largely covered when the tide is in. The structure is broadly an anticline–syncline fold pair, though complicated in detail (Figure 64). Somewhat north of the middle of the bay, the unfossiliferous grey 'barren' mudstones (**4a**) that typify the Upper Hartfell Shale are found [0748 4383]. They include thin black beds, and although these contain fragments of graptolites, it has yet to be shown whether they are referable to the *complanatus, anceps* or *extraordinarius* biozones.

Working north from the grey mudstones, the first black beds encountered are basal Birkhill Shales (**4b**). Here you can collect fossils of the *persculptus* Biozone. Further to the north, 5 m from the faulted contact with the Gala Group greywackes (**4c**), the succeeding zone of *Parakidograptus acuminatus* is present. The *atavus* Biozone is proved close to the greywackes, though the effects of strong faulting makes the collection of satisfactory material more difficult.

Turning south from the pale barren mudstones, the centre of Grennan Bay is occupied by a considerable thickness of Lower Birkhill Shale — massive black mudstones described by Lapworth as the 'vesiculosus Flags'. They yield fossils of the *acuminatus* Biozone in the centre of the bay (**4d**) and several species of the *atavus* Biozone (includ-

175

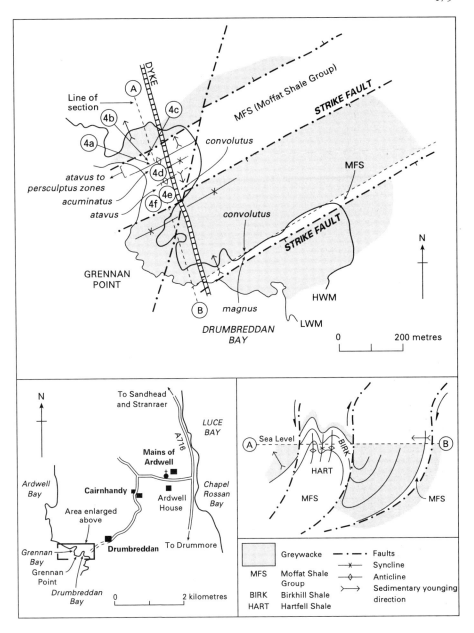

Figure 64 Locality map and geological cross-section for Drumbreddan Bay (Locality 4).

ing species of *Atavograptus, Coronograptus, Dimorphograptus* and *Normalograptus*) within 10 m of the greywackes of Grennan Point (**4e**). Closer still to the greywackes (**4f**), you can collect diverse faunas of the *convolutus* Zone, including species of *Coronograptus, Glyptograptus, Petalolithus, Rhaphidograptus* and several *Monograptus* species (*M. argutus, M. clingani, M. convolutus, M. limatulus*). Deformation associated with strong nearby faulting hampers collecting but excellent specimens were collected last century and the source of those remains to be rediscovered. The pale greenish or whitish beds of soft claystone interbedded in the Birkhill Shale are metabentonites (altered volcanic ash). These indicate frequent and large-scale eruptions, but the position of the volcanic source is unknown.

Drumbreddan Bay

On the south side of Grennan Point a relatively narrow exposure of the Birkhill Shale (**4g**) extends along the base of the greywacke cliffs. Despite the presence of a strike fault, some of the graptolites found here are well preserved. Examples representing the *cyphus* Biozone? and the *magnus* Biozone have been recorded.

The Birkhill Shale passes up into a few metres of thinly bedded grey shale and laminated siltstone (**4h**) followed conformably by massive greywackes. The thinly bedded unit contains thin black mudstone seams and with patience you can collect rare but well-preserved graptolites of the *convolutus* Biozone which serve to date the onset of greywacke deposition.

5   Clanyard Bay and Grennan Quarries [NX 101 380]

OS 1:50 000 Sheet 82 Stranraer, Glen Luce & surrounding area
BGS 1:50 000 sheets 1 and 3 The Rhins of Galloway
Route map: Figure 65

The Moffat Shale Group is exposed at both the north and south margins of Clanyard Bay. The northern exposure youngs to the north, as is generally the case in Moffat Shale inliers, but the southern exposure is

unusual in that it seems to young towards the south. This was formerly taken as evidence for a major anticlinal structure centred on Clanyard Bay, but more recently the complex thrust-related structure has become apparent. This is described in some detail as part of Excursion 15.   .

Grennan Quarries, nearby, afford an opportunity to collect graptolites from interbeds in the greywacke succession and can be visited at times when the tide covers exposures in Clanyard Bay.

Clanyard Bay

Take the A716 south from Stranraer and Sandhead towards Drummore, but about 2 km north of Drummore [NX 128 383] take the minor road to Clanyard, from which Clanyard Bay is a short walk (800 m). The exposures can only be studied in detail at low tide. The northern outcrop is the larger. The beds farthest from the northern margin of the bay are Upper Hartfell Shale, typically developed as grey 'barren' mudstone. They include black mudstone interbeds that have yielded *Dicellograptus*. Working towards the greywackes at the northern edge of the bay, you find Birkhill Shale, and from various beds in a general south-to-north sequence can collect graptolites of the *atavus, acinaces, triangulatus?, convolutus* and *sedgwickii* biozones. In addition, an old collection contains well-preserved fossils indicating a low level in the *turriculatus* Biozone; the exact locality is unknown but it is possible that, if careful collecting were undertaken, the *turriculatus* locality might be rediscovered and evidence obtained for the presence of other zones.

On the south side of the bay, the Birkhill Shale is exposed with associated beds of bentonite. Graptolites of the *cyphus* Biozone have been collected about 20 m from the base of the cliffs. Farther south, about 10 m from the cliff, the presence of the *convolutus* Biozone provides evidence for southward younging here.

Grennan Quarries

These quarries are situated just west of the A716, 3 km north of Drummore. One on

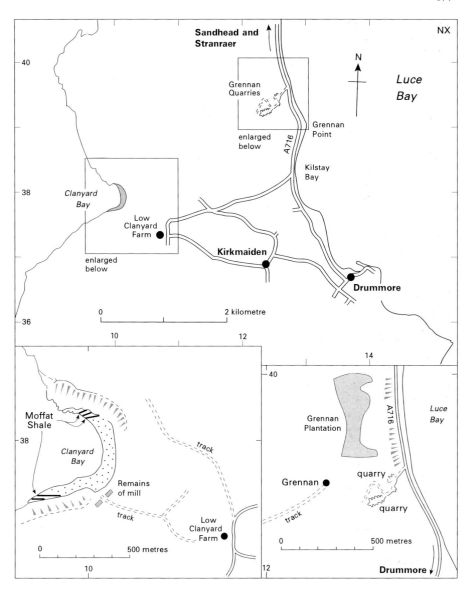

Figure 65 Locality map for Clanyard Bay and Grennan quarries (Locality 5).

the west of the track to Grennan [1267 3943] displays greywackes of Gala Group 8 (or Port Logan Formation), which here includes shaly interbeds. From these you can collect well-preserved graptolites of the *crispus* Biozone, including *Monograptus crispus, M. discus, M. marri, M. priodon* and *Streptograptus exiguus*. A larger quarry in the greywackes slightly farther SW [1258 3932] yields *M. crispus* and, on some bedding planes, an abundance of *S. exiguus*.

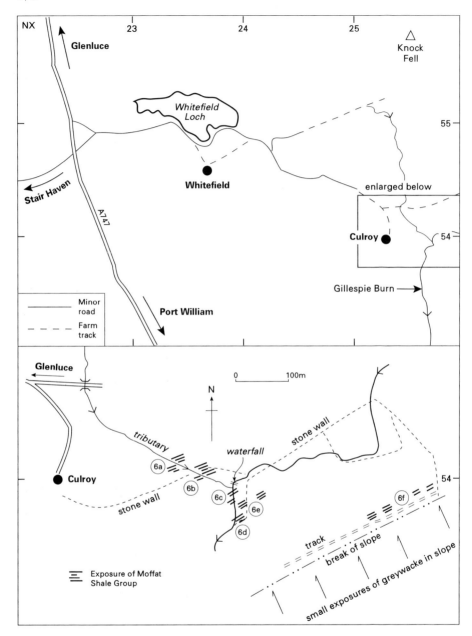

Figure 66   Locality map for Gillespie Burn (Locality 6).

6   Gillespie Burn [NX 257 539]

*OS 1:50 000 Sheet 82 Stranraer, Glen Luce
& surrounding area
BGS 1:50 000 Sheet 4 W Kirkcowan
Route map: Figure 66 with locality numbers
referenced in the text*

Gillespie Burn exposes an interesting succession of Upper Hartfell and Birkhill Shales. The Upper Hartfell 'Barren Mudstones' include richly fossiliferous black mudstone beds of the *D. anceps* Biozone, overlain by Lower Birkhill Shale which, unusually, here contains several beds of greywacke.
From Glenluce take the A747 south towards Port William. About 3 km SE from Glenluce, turn left down the minor road, past Whitefield Loch and Machermore, towards Culroy [253 540]. A car may be parked near the track-junction [NX 252 543] and Gillespie Burn approached over land farmed from Culroy, where prior permission for access and parking must be sought. From Culroy walk due east to the tributary stream which flows down to join the Gillespie Burn [257 539] where it flows through a small ravine.

Silurian

About 40 m upstream of the place where a stone wall crosses this tributary, the left (NE) bank displays greywacke beds with shale interbeds (**6a**). Graptolites from these interbeds include climacograptids (*Normalograptus* spp.) and *Atavograptus* spp. which represent the *atavus* Biozone and possibly also the *acinaces* Biozone. A few paces downstream greywackes on the right (SW) bank contain *Cystograptus vesiculosus* and *Parakidograptus acuminatus* which indicate that these greywackes are discernably older (*acuminatus* Biozone); it is noteworthy that nearer to Culroy a poorly exposed shale bed has yielded younger graptolites of the *cyphus* Biozone. On this evidence the ground between Gillespie Burn and Culroy is interpreted as being underlain by Lower Birkhill Shales which, exceptionally, here include beds of greywacke deposited during the *acuminatus, atavus* and possibly *acinaces* biozones. These are apparently overlain by massive greywackes of Gala Group 4 (the Sinniness Formation) deposited during *cyphus* Biozone times (Rushton and Stone, 1991).

Ordovician

Go downstream to where the stone wall crosses the tributary stream. Black Upper Hartfell Shales can be seen a few paces both upstream and downstream of the wall (**6b**). Graptolites of the *anceps* Biozone, particularly *Orthograptus abbreviatus,* can be collected from each outcrop.
Now descend the tributary to Gillespie Burn itself. It enters the ravine at a waterfall, below which the grey 'Barren Mudstones' of the Upper Hartfell Shales are well seen. For about 50 m downstream from the confluence of Gillespie Burn and the tributary, the 'Barren Mudstones' show interbeds of black mudstone (**6c**) from which faunas of the *Dicellograptus anceps* Biozone can be collected, most commonly *Climacograptus supernus* and *Orthograptus abbreviatus.* Further downstream, at a right-hand bend (**6d**), graptolites of the Lower Hartfell Shale (*clingani* or *linearis* Biozone) can be collected; the same strata are also seen in small exposures high on the east bank of the burn (**6e**). *Orthograptus* spp. are most commonly found but their preservation is not very good.
About 150 m SE of Gillespie Burn the ground rises where the greywackes of Gala Group 5 make a topographical feature. There are small exposures of Lower Hartfell Shale (**6f**) along the track at the foot of this slope and better-preserved graptolites of the *clingani* and *linearis* biozones can be collected.

A W A Rushton and S P Tunnicliff

Appendix 1

Metalliferous mineralisation

Most of the mineral locations in south-west Scotland are veins, many of which were trialled or mined for lead, copper and zinc in the 18th and 19th centuries, with limited work continuing in places until about 1920 (Wilson, 1921). Production of baryte from Barlocco probably continued until 1954.

Subsequently, uranium veins and both disseminated and vein occurrences of minerals of arsenic, molybdenum, lead, copper and zinc were discovered using modern techniques, but none has proved economic. Minor quantities of gold have also been discovered recently at several localities.

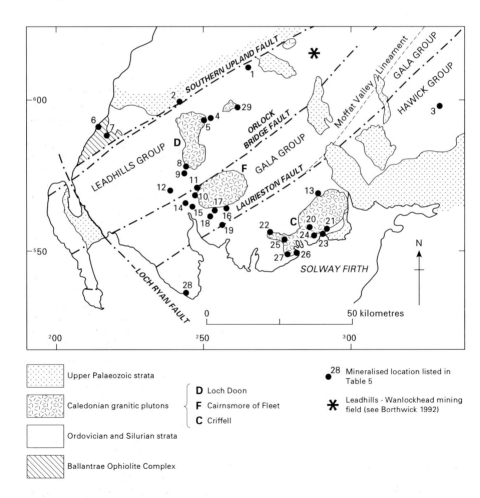

Figure 67 Location of significant metalliferous mineralisation in south-west Scotland. Full details are listed in Table 5.

The known mineral veins of south-west Scotland are concentrated at the southern and western margins of the granitic complexes of Cairnsmore of Fleet in the west, and Criffell in the east. The composition of the veins changes in a general way from dominantly lead-zinc in the west to copper, barium and uranium in the east. The veins are highly variable in trend (Table 5), cutting sedimentary rocks of Ordovician to Lower Carboniferous age and intrusions of diorite, granodiorite and granite dated isotopically at late Silurian to early Devonian (Stephens and Halliday, 1984; Stephens et al., 1985). The lead-zinc vein at Blackcraig may postdate a dyke of Permo-Carboniferous type (Gallagher, 1964) and pitchblende from one of the Dalbeattie veins has yielded a Mesozoic age (Miller and Taylor, 1966).

Eight types of mineralisation (A–H) are described in this account, with reference to 29 of the more significant mineral locations in the region (located on Figure 67). Much further information can be found in the geochemical atlas *Regional geochemistry of southern Scotland and part of northern England* (British Geological Survey, 1993c) which contains coloured distribution maps for many elements.

A   Associated with ultrabasic rocks

The oldest mineralisation known in south-west Scotland is of chrome-spinel, as concentrations in the early Ordovician Ballantrae ophiolite complex. Accessory quantities of chrome spinel occur widely in serpentinised harzburgite and dunite, the main rock types of the complex, and at Poundland Burn nodular chrome spinel is visible in outcrop (location 7, Table 5 and Figure 67). At Pinbain (6), true chromite forms 30–90 per cent of a small unit 4–5 m wide, most probably a chromitite pod (Stone et al., 1986).

B   Associated with Ordovician or Silurian sedimentary rocks

Two mineral occurrences very unusual to Scotland fall into this group. Ordovician siliceous mudstone and siltstone contain finely disseminated pyrite and sphalerite some 2 km SW of the Loch Doon granitic pluton in the vicinity of Penkiln Burn (9); thin quartz veinlets containing galena, sphalerite and pyrite cut across the strata (Stone and Leake, 1984; Stone et al., 1984). A third style of mineralisation in the same area contains lead and arsenic, in the form of plumbogummite–beudantite assemblages, both in the altered margins of dykes and in a gossan occupying a N–S fault zone.

Stratabound arsenopyrite and pyrite were intersected by drilling in Silurian greywackes on the north side of Glenshanna Burn close to the old Glendinning antimony mine (3) (Gallagher et al., 1983). The arsenopyrite is enriched in antimony and the pyrite in arsenic, thus providing a suitable source of metals for the later vein mined for stibnite (see Type F).

C   Associated with diorite and granodiorite

Base and precious metal mineralisation is located in or near the margins of several diorite–granodiorite intrusion in south-west Scotland. Three varieties can be recognised.

i   The Talnotry deposit (11) is the only instance of a magmatic copper-nickel orebody in the Southern Uplands. The host rock is a late Caledonian diorite sill in which a basal lens of sulphide, 4×20 m in size, contains pyrrhotite, pentlandite, chalcopyrite, nickeline and gersdorffite, plus numerous minor constituents including gold (Stanley et al., 1987).

ii   A second variety is that of volcanic porphyry Cu-Mo-Au-Ag mineralisation, exemplified by disseminations and veinlets of mineral in diorite complexes. The Fore Burn complex (2) is a Lower Devonian igneous assemblage lying immediately north of the Southern Upland Fault. Arsenopyrite, pyrite, chalcopyrite, gold, silver and tetrahedrite-tennantite occur in quartz-carbonate veins and in small intrusion breccias which are intensely tourmalinised. Gold is also present locally in quartz-arsenopyrite-chalcopyrite veins. Grades varying up to about 50 gm per tonne are reported by Charley et al. (1989). Porphyry-style copper mineralisation is weakly developed in a late Caledonian complex of intersecting porphyrite dykes, gran-

Table 5 Significant metalliferous mineral locations in south-west Scotland.

Location no.	Deposit name	Exposure type[1]	Commodity[2]	Mineralisation type[3]	Trend of vein	NGR	1:50 000 Geological Sheet	Key reference
1	Hare Hill	T	Sb Au	C, F	010	NS 658 104	15W	Dewey et al., 1920
2	Fore Burn	I	As Cu Au	C	—	NX 420 996	8E	Allen et al., 1982
3	Glendinning	M	**Sb** As Zn Pb Cu	B, F	045	NY 313 966	10E	Gallagher et al., 1983
4	Woodhead	M	**Pb** Zn Cu	E	110	NX 531 936	8E	Wilson, 1921
5	Carsphairn (near)	M	**Fe**	D	000	NX 504 929	8E	Macgregor et al., 1920
6	Pinbain	O	Cr	A	—	NX 138 917	7	Stone and Smellie, 1988
7	Poundland Burn	O	Cr	A	—	NX 170 882	7	Stone and Smellie, 1988
8	Glenhead Burn	I	As Pb Zn Au	C, F	000	NX 449 780	8E	Leake et al., 1981
9	Penkiln Burn	I	Pb Zn As Cu	B	000	NX 446 767	8E	Stone et al., 1984
10	Talnotry (near)	T	As	F	045	NX 480 702	4E	Dewey et al., 1920
11	Talnotry	T	Ni Cu	C	—	NX 477 704	4E	Wilson, 1921
12	Wood of Cree	M	**Pb Zn Cu**	E	155	NX 386 695	4E	Wilson, 1921
13	Beeswing	I	U Cu	H	135	NX 885 681	5E	Gallagher et al., 1971
14	Blackcraig	M	**Pb Zn** Cu Ba	E	110	NX 435 650	4E	Wilson, 1921
15	Cairnsmore	M	**Pb Zn** Ba	E	105	NX 463 636	4E	Wilson, 1921
16	Drumruck	T	Cu	F	110	NX 583 637	4E	Wilson, 1921
17	Dromore	T	Cu Zn	F	155	NX 537 622	4E	Wilson, 1921
18	Pibble	M	**Cu Pb** Zn Ba	E	110	NX 525 607	4E	Foster-Smith, 1967
19	Kings Laggan	T	Cu Pb Zn	F	105	NX 562 578	4E	Wilson, 1921
20	Ironhash Hill	I	Fe U	D	080	NX 858 563	5E	Gallagher et al., 1971
21	Needle's Eye	I	U Cu Bi Fe HC	H	135–170	NX 915 562	5E	Miller and Taylor, 1966
22	Black Stockarton Moor	I	Cu Mo	C	—	NX 725 555	5W	Brown et al., 1979
23	Powbrade Burn	I	U	H	045; 135	NX 902 554	5E	Miller and Taylor, 1966
24	Colvend	M	**Cu**	F	045	NX 869 538	5E	Wilson, 1921
25	Auchenleck	M	**Fe**	D	108	NX 773 525	5W	Macgregor et al., 1920
26	Auchencairn	M	**Ba** Cu	G	070	NX 821 485	5E	Wilson et al., 1922
27	Barlocco	M	**Ba** Cu	G	098	NX 788 475	5E	Wilson et al., 1922
28	Tonderghie	O	Cu Ba	F	080	NX 438 350	2	Wilson, 1921
29	Moorbrock Hill	I	As Au Cu Zn	C	045	NX 620 980	9W	Naden and Caulfield, 1989

1 **Exposure type:** M — old mine; T — old trial; O — outcrop; I — detected by modern investigation

2 **Commodity** (mined where bold): As — Arsenopyrite; Au — gold; Ba — baryte; Bi — native bismuth and secondary Bi — Cu minerals; Cr — chromite; Cu — chalcopyrite; Fe — haematite; HC — hydrocarbon; Ni — niccolite, nickeliferous pyrrhotite; Mo — molybdenite; Pb — galena; Sb — stibnite; bournonite; U — uraninite, secondary uranium minerals; Zn — sphalerite

3 **Mineralisation type:** A — associated with ultrabasic rocks; B — associated with Ordovician or Silurian sedimentary rocks; C — associated with diorite and granodiorite; D — haematite vein; E — lead-zinc vein; F — copper, antimony and/or arsenic veins; G — baryte vein; H — uranium vein.

odiorite intrusions and breccia pipes at Black Stockarton Moor (**22**) on the western margin of the Criffell granodiorite pluton (Leake and Cooper, 1983). Breccia veins are enriched in As, Sb and gold (maximum 0.06 ppm Au in samples) in association with molybdenite (350 ppm Mo) and with chalcopyrite and bornite (4400 ppm Cu). In one borehole, an average of 0.05 per cent Cu was maintained over 34 m (Leake and Brown, 1979).

iii Arsenic-antimony-gold mineralisation is a third variey, represented by mineral locations at Glenhead Burn, Hare Hill and Moorbrock Hill. These, together with the Fore Burn occurrences, are interpreted as mesothermal gold systems spatially related with regional strike-slip shears as well as with late-tectonic Caledonian intrusives (Boast et al., 1990). Quartz veins containing gold (8.8 ppm Au maximum), arsenopyrite (up to 3.5 per cent As) and pyrite cut Ordovician turbidites at Glenhead Burn (**8**) at the southern margin of the Loch Doon granitic pluton. The hornfelsed wallrocks are strongly sericitised and contain fine-grained, disseminated arsenopyrite. The mineralisation may be related, in part at least, to a swarm of dioritic dykes which are older than the pluton. At Hare Hill (**1**) (Excursion 6), gold is associated with a zoned As-Sb-Cu-Pb-Zn assemblage in fractured and sericitised granodiorite (Boast et al., 1990) adjacent to late-stage antimony veins (see Type F). At the margin of the Carsphairn intrusion at Moorbrock Hill (**29**), gold values of 1–3 ppm occur mainly in quartz-pyrite-arsenopyrite veins in a NE-trending zone of intense brecciation and hydrothermal alteration. Native gold forms isolated grains, 5–10 μm in size, adjacent to chalcopyrite-pyrite intergrowths and inclusions of graphitic Moffat Shale Group wall rock (Naden and Caulfield, 1989).

D Haematite veins

Fracture-bound haematite deposits are located at the margins of the Criffell granodiorite pluton (Phillips, 1956) and a weakly radioactive deposit occurs within the granodiorite (see Type H). The Auchenleck vein (**25**) was the most important economically, consisting of botryoidal haematite, quartz and baryte. The NE margin of the Loch Doon granitic pluton is transected by a haematite breccia vein, 0.5 m to at least 3 m in width, which has been prospected and/or mined over some 3 km of strike length. The occurrence lies about 7 km west of Carsphairn (**5**) and has yielded around 400 tonnes of haematite (Excursion 7).

E Lead-zinc veins

Numerous metalliferous veins were exploited in the past around Newton Stewart and lead mining near Carsphairn was important for a time (Excursion 7). In a little known review of the mines and trial workings in south-west Scotland (Foster-Smith, 1967), minimum productions of lead, zinc and copper in ore concentrates are given as 25.6, 1.3 and 0.24 thousand tonnes respectively.

Of this production, more than half the lead, almost all of the zinc and a proportion of the copper were recovered from the Blackcraig mines (**14**), some 5 km from the SW margin of the Cairnsmore of Fleet granodiorite pluton. Little can now be seen of this deposit, the most important in south-west Scotland, and the extensive dumps are mainly landscaped. Wilson (1921) recorded the presence of galena, sphalerite and chalcopyrite, set in a gangue of calcite, dolomite, baryte and some quartz. Mineralisation extended for 0.8 km along a fault zone trending ESE and up to 18 m wide in Silurian greywackes. The fault zone was evidently intruded by a Permo-Carboniferous dolerite dyke prior to mineralisation (Gallagher, 1964). The Cairnsmore lead-zinc vein (**15**) probably represents an extension of the vein at Blackcraig, as may also the copper-lead vein at Pibble (see Type F). The Wood of Cree mine (**12**) was sited on a wide line of fracture trending SSE and containing numerous stringers of sphalerite and galena, mingled with chalcopyrite and pyrite.

The Woodhead mines (**4**) near Carsphairn (Excursion 7) produced 6700 tonnes of lead ore from veins cutting Ordovician greywackes. Sphalerite and chalcopyrite are associated with the galena in a gangue of calcite, dolomite and quartz. The location is midway between the Loch

Doon and Carsphairn granitic bodies which are probably continuous at depth, providing a favourable structural and geochemical environment for mineralisation.

F   Copper, antimony and arsenic veins

Foster-Smith (1967) refers to Pibble Mine (**18**) as the dominant 19th century copper producer in south-west Scotland, although no production figures are given by Wilson (1921). The vein, about 1 m thick, cuts Silurian greywackes interbedded with black shales some 3 km south of the southern contact of the Cairnsmore of Fleet granitic pluton. It contains lenses of galena, sphalerite and chalcopyrite and, unusually for the veins of south-west Scotland, a variety of secondary minerals. These include linarite, pyromorphite, hemimorphite and malachite, all recorded from the upper levels of the mine. A variety of ruined mine buildings and spoil dumps remain at the site. Also to the south of the Cairnsmore of Fleet pluton, chalcopyrite-bearing veins have been trialled at Drumruck (**16**), Dromore (**17**) and Kings's Laggan (**19**).

Copper veins at Colvend (**24**) and Tonderghie (**28**) postdate Caledonian felsite intrusions in Silurian rocks. Chalcopyrite, in a calcite-quartz gangue, is accompanied by malachite and azurite at Colvend whereas at Tonderghie the gangue is baryte-quartz and the associate minerals are pyrite and malachite.

The Louisa mine at Glendinning (**3**) produced nealy 200 tonnes of antimony from narrow quartz-carbonate veins cutting Silurian greywackes. The remains of mine buildings, shafts, adits and crushing floors are still clearly visible. Stibnite and other antimony minerals (semsyite, bournonite and tetrahedrite) are accompanied by pyrite, arsenopyrite, galena, sphalerite and chalcopyrite. There is no evidence of Caledonian intrusive igneous activity in the area and the vein contents probably derive from the stratabound mineralisation nearby (see Type B) (Gallagher et al., 1983). Similarly, at Hare Hill (**1**), enrichments of metal in the granodiorite (see Type C) are probably the source of metals in later stibnite-galena veins, one of which has been trialled for antimony.

Modern investigations have demonstrated that arsenopyrite and geochemical enrichments of arsenic are much more widespread in the rocks of South-west Scotland than had previously been reported (Stone et al., 1995). Nevertheless only near Talnotry (**10**), at the west edge of the Cairnsmore of Fleet granodiorite, is there any record of recovery. A few tonnes of arsenopyrite were raised from a small shaft on a quartz vein about 1 m thick.

G   Baryte veins

A group of baryte veins south of Auchencairn underwent exploitation in the late 19th century and until just after World War 2 (cf. MacGregor et al., 1944). Some 2800 tons of baryte were produced from Barlocco Mine (**27**), mainly from the more northerly of two approximately east–west subvertical veins. The principal vein is 0.5–2.1 m thick and occupies a fault breccia traceable for at least 300 m in altered Silurian shale. The high-quality white baryte remaining on the dumps is accompanied by calcite and traces of chalcopyrite, malachite and bornite. At Auchencairn mine (**26**) '700 tons of baryte are said to have been taken out of one pocket' in the latter part of the 19th century, and a little more in 1916 (Wilson, 1921). The Auchencairn vein, which is 0.5 m thick at surface and reputedly widens at depth, cuts Lower Carboniferous conglomeratic sandstone and is accompanied by multiple thin stringers of baryte and a 0.5 m thick quartz vein seen in the foreshore exposures.

H   Uranium veins

Pitchblende is present in thin veins cutting hornfelsed Silurian turbidites at the southern margin of the Criffell pluton and cutting Lower Carboniferous strata at Needle's Eye (**21**), on the south side of the ENE-trending North Solway Fault. Over 30 anomalously radioactive veins are concentrated in a 400 m coastline section between Marbruie Cove and Powbrade Burn (**23**) which is one of the principal localities. Pitchblende is accompanied by black vitreous hydrocarbon, specular haematite, chalcopyrite, pyrite and native bismuth. Quartz and dolomite are the main gangue minerals with smaller amounts of calcite and baryte. Pitchblende from a vein at Steps gave a U-Pb isotopic age of 185 ± 20 Ma (reported in Miller and Taylor, 1966), that is Upper Triassic or Lower Jurassic and therefore the youngest vein mineralisation in Britain.

A uraniferous structure of similar NW trend also occurs at the northern edge of the Criffell pluton, at Beeswing (13), where joints in the greywackes adjacent to thin, im-persistent quartz-haematite veins are coated with uraninite and chalcopyrite. Within the granodiorite mass itself, a haematite-impregnated shatter zone at Ironhash Hill (20) is anomalously radioactive.

The presence of anomalous radioactivity in association with copper veins of Type F at King's Laggan (19) and Pibble (18) was observed by Miller and Taylor (1966).

M J Gallagher

Appendix 2

Earth science conservation

The dramatic coastline and landscapes of south-west Scotland are the product of almost 500 million years of geological evolution. Increasingly it is recognised that our ancient rock foundation provides the basis of an intricate ecological system upon which our soils, flora and fauna depend. In seeking to conserve a part of that system, whether it be the golden eagles of the Merrick or the salt marshes of the Solway, it is important to conserve the working system intact. To alter a part of the system is to affect the whole of it. This holistic approach to conservation is governed by the principle of sustainability: those activities we choose to operate within a landscape (agriculture, recreation, industry) should not permanently alter the systems already operating within that landscape. We face a choice whether to manage the landscape sustainably for present and future generations or to exploit it for short-term gain.

Within our landscape are geological and geomorphological features of particular importance to our understanding of how that landscape formed and operates. These locations are recognised as Sites of Special Scientific Interest (SSSIs). Prior to 1977 geological Sites of Special Scientific Interest were identified on an *ad hoc* basis with no systemised selection procedure. The Geological Conservation Review (GCR), completed between 1977 and 1989, was an attempt to rationalise the site selection process in Britain. Over 90 different subject areas were identified within British geology and, after wide consultation, the key sites critical to our understanding of each subject area were selected. A prerequisite for selection was that each site be of national or international importance. Over 50 geologi-

cal Sites of Special Scientific Interest were identified in south-west Scotland as a result of this process (Figure 68). These sites are listed in Table 6 under the Geological Conservation Review interest for which they were selected. Some sites such as the Girvan to Ballantrae Coast SSSI have multiple interests and appear in a number of categories. Other sites such as the Upper Solway Flats and Marshes SSSI are of joint geological and biological interest. By early 1994 all but three of the sites had been notified as Sites of Special Scientific Interest under the Wildlife and Countryside Act (1981) and as such are afforded a measure of legislative protection from activities that may damage their geological interest. Designation as a Site of Special Scientific Interest does not entail an automatic right of access and the landowners permission should be sought in the normal way before visiting a site. A detailed account of the geology of each site is being published in a series of volumes covering each of the Geological Conservation Review subject areas. Two volumes incorporating sites in south-west Scotland have already been published: *Caledonian Structures of Britain* (Treagus, 1992) and *Quaternary of Scotland* (Gordon et al. 1993). Although the network of sites selected as SSSI's will remain broadly intact, it is envisaged that through time advances in research will necessitate a re-evaluation of the network. The effects of such progress in research on the status of two pre-GCR Sites of Special Scientific Interest in south-west Scotland, at Portayew Bay and Corsewall Point, have recently been examined (McCurry, 1994).

J A McCurry

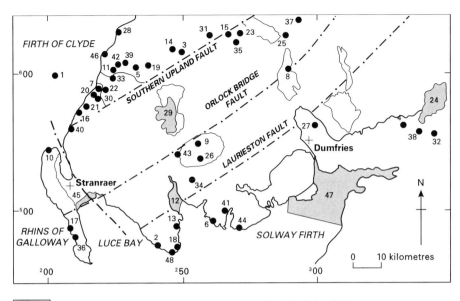

Site of Special Scientific Interest,
more than 500 hectares

● Site of Special Scientific Interest,
less than 500 hectares

Geological sites of Special Scientific Interest (G/B : joint geological/biological)

1	Ailsa Craig (G/B)	25	Leadhills-Wanlockhead
2	Back Bay to Carghidown (G/B)	26	Lea Larks
3	Benbeoch	27	Locharbriggs Quarry
4	Bigholm Burn	28	Maidens-Doonfoot (G/B)
5	Blair Farm	29	Merrick Kells (G/B)
6	Borgue Coast (G/B)	30	Millenderdale
7	Byne Hill	31	Nith Bridge
8	Carron Water and Hapland Burn	32	Penton Linns
9	Clatteringshaws Dam Quarry	33	Penwhapple Burn
10	Corsewall Point	34	Pibble Mine
11	Craighead Quarry	35	Polehote Burn and Polneul Burn
12	Cree Estuary (G/B)	36	Port Logan
13	Cruggleton Bay	37	Raven Gill
14	Dunaskin Glen	38	River Esk, Glencartholm
15	Fountainhead-Hare Hill	39	Roughneuk Quarry
16	Girvan to Ballantrae Coast	40	Sgavoch
17	Grennan Bay	41	Shoulder O'Craig
18	Isle of Whithorn Bay	42	South Threave
19	Knockgardner	43	Talnotry Mine
20	Knocklaugh	44	Torrs-Masons Walk (G/B)
21	Knockormal Hill	45	Torrs Warren-Luce Sands (G/B)
22	Laggan Burn	46	Turnberry Lighthouse-Port Murray
23	Lagrae Burn	47	Upper Solway Flats and Marshes (G/B)
24	Langholm-Newcastleton Hills (G/B)	48	West Burrow Head

For explanation of geological lines see Figure 67

Figure 68 Location of geological Sites of Special Scientific Interest (SSSIs) in south-west Scotland. Full details are listed in Table 6.

Table 6   Geological Sites of Special Scientific Interest, south-west Scotland

SSSI (located by number in Figure 68)	District	NGR	Excursion
ARENIG–LLANDEILO			
16 Girvan to Ballantrae Coast	Kyle and Carrick		
Balcreuchan Port, Bennane Head		NX 097 875	8
37 Raven Gill	Clydesdale	NS 923 199	
CARADOC–ASHGILL			
10 Corsewall Point	Wigtown	NX 000 729	15
11 Craighead Quarry	Kyle and Carrick	NS 232 012	8
16 Girvan to Ballantrae Coast	Kyle and Carrick		
Girvan Foreshore, Kennedy's Pass		NX 147 931	8
22 Laggan Burn	Kyle and Carrick	NX 204 947	
42 South Threave	Kyle and Carrick	NS 251 038	
ORDOVICIAN IGNEOUS			
7 Byne Hill	Kyle and Carrick	NX 180 945	
16 Girvan to Ballantrae Coast	Kyle and Carrick		
Balcreuchan Port to Port Vad		NX 100 878	8
Bennane Lea		NX 091 861	8
Games Loup		NX 103 880	
20 Knocklaugh	Kyle and Carrick	NX 168 920	
21 Knockormal Hill	Kyle and Carrick	NX 138 890	
30 Millenderdale	Kyle and Carrick	NX 177 905	
40 Sgavoch	Kyle and Carrick	NX 073 808	
LLANDOVERY			
5 Blair Farm	Kyle and Carrick	NS 325 024	
16 Girvan to Ballantrae Coast	Kyle and Carrick		
Woodland Point		NX 169 953	8
33 Penwhapple Burn	Kyle and Carrick	NX 230 984	
39 Roughneuk Quarry	Kyle and Carrick	NS 270 040	
WENLOCK			
6 Borgue Coast	Stewartry		
Meikle Ross		NX 640 449	5
19 Knockgardener	Kyle and Carrick	NS 355 036	
44 Torrs–Masons Walk	Stewartry	NX 676 465	11
CALEDONIAN STRUCTURES OF THE SOUTHERN UPLANDS			
2 Back Bay to Carghidown	Wigtown	NX 368 394	13
6 Borgue Coast	Stewartry		5
Barlocco		NX 585 485	
13 Cruggleton Bay	Wigtown	NX 477 448	
17 Grennan Bay	Wigtown	NX 074 438	15,18
18 Isle of Whithorn Bay	Wigtown	NX 476 365	13
48 West Burrow Head	Wigtown	NX 452 341	13
CALEDONIAN IGNEOUS			
9 Clatteringshaws Dam Quarry	Stewartry	NX 548 754	16
26 Lea Larks	Stewartry	NX 563 690	
29 Merrick-Kells–Loch Dee	Wigtown and Stewartry	NX 466 847	7,16
41 Shoulder O'Craig	Stewartry	NX 663 491	5

SSSI	District	NGR	Excursion
OLD RED SANDSTONE IGNEOUS			
28 Maidens–Doonfoot	Kyle and Carrick		
Culzean Harbour		NS 231 102	
Dunure Castle		NS 252 159	
46 Turnberry Lighthouse–Port Murray	Kyle and Carrick	NS 196 072	
DINANTIAN OF SCOTLAND			
28 Maidens-Doonfoot	Kyle and Carrick		
Bracken Bay–Longhill Point		NS 292 188	
32 Penton Linns	Annandale and Eskdale	NY 434 774	1
47 Upper Solway Flats and Marshes	Nithsdale		
Kirkbean		NX 987 563	10
WESTPHALIAN			
14 Dunaskin Glen	Cumnock and Doon Valley	NS 454 088	
23 Lagrae Burn	Nithsdale	NS 705 153	
35 Polehote Burn and Polneul Burn	Nithsdale	NS 688 123	
38 River Esk, Glencartholm	Annandale and Eskdale		
Byre Burn		NY 389 778	
ARTHROPODA			
38 River Esk, Glencartholm	Annandale and Eskdale	NY 376 796	
PALAEOZOIC PALAEOBOTANY			
14 Dunaskin Glen	Cumnock and Doon Valley	NS 454 088	
38 River Esk, Glencartholm	Annandale and Eskdale	NY 376 796	
PERMIAN–CARBONIFEROUS FISH/AMPHIBIA			
38 River Esk, Glencartholm	Annandale and Eskdale	NY 376 795	
PERMIAN–CARBONIFEROUS IGNEOUS			
3 Benbeoch	Cumnock and Doon Valley	NS 492 085	
8 Carron Water and Hapland Burn	Nithsdale	NS 887 024	2
24 Langholm–Newcastleton Hills	Annandale and Eskdale	NY 423 902	1
28 Maidens–Doonfoot	Kyle and Carrick		
Heads of Ayr		NS 279 183	
38 River Esk, Glencartholm	Annandale and Eskdale	NY 376 799	
PERMIAN–TRIASSIC			
8 Carron Water and Hapland Burn	Nithsdale	NS 887 024	2
27 Locharbriggs Quarry	Nithsdale	NS 990 810	9
TERTIARY IGNEOUS			
1 Ailsa Craig	Kyle and Carrick	NX 019 997	

SSSI		District	NGR	Excursion
QUATERNARY				
4	Bigholm Burn	Annandale and Eskdale	NY 316 812	
29	Merrick-Kells–Loch Dee			
	Loch Dungeon	Stewartry	NX 525 846	
	Round Loch of Glenhead	Wigtown	NX 450 804	
	The Tauchers	Kyle and Carrick	NX 462 876	
31	Nith Bridge	Cumnock and Doon Valley	NS 594 141	
36	Port Logan	Wigtown	NX 092 402	15
47	Upper Solway Flats and Marshes	Annandale and Eskdale		
	Newbie		NY 165 651	
	Redkirk Point		NY 301 652	
COASTAL GEOMORPHOLOGY OF SCOTLAND				
45	Torrs Warren–Luce Sands	Wigtown	NX 150 555	
SALTMARSH MORPHOLOGY				
12	Cree Estuary	Wigtown	NX 465 545	
47	Upper Solway Flats and Marshes	Nithsdale		
	Solway Firth North Shore		NY 003 668	
MINERALOGY OF SCOTLAND				
15	Fountainhead–Hare Hill	Cumnock and Doon Valley	NS 659 104	4, Appendix 1
25	Leadhills–Wanlockhead	Clydesdale	NS 881 158	
34	Pibble Mine	Wigtown	NX 524 607	Appendix 1
43	Talnotry Mine	Wigtown	NX 478 703	Appendix 1
47	Upper Solway Flats and Marshes	Stewartry		
	Southwick–Needle's Eye		NX 915 561	Appendix 1

Sites listed under the Geological Conservation Review interest for which they were selected. These are located on Figure 68. The excursion number is given where an SSSI is included in one of the itineraries.

Any questions about our earth science heritage in south-west Scotland should be directed to the relevant SNH Area Office or the Earth Science Branch in Edinburgh.

Dumfries and Galloway Area,
Scottish Natural Heritage,
106 High Street,
Dalbeattie,
Kirkcudbrightshire,
DG5 4HB

Tel: 01556 610086

Earth Science Branch,
Research and Advisory Services,
Scottish Natural Heritage,
2 Anderson Place,
Edinburgh,
EH6 5NP

Tel: 0131 447 4784

Note added in proof A recent addition to this list is Morroch Bay on the west coast of the Rhins of Galloway (Wigtown District), NX 017 525. The conservation review interest is Caradoc–Ashgill stratigraphy and the locality is examined by Excursion 18 (3).

References

Most of the references listed below are held in the libraries of the British Geological Survey at Keyworth, Nottingham and Murchison House, Edinburgh. Copies of the references can be purchased subject to the current copyright legislation.

ALLEN, P M, COOPER, D C, PARKER, M E, EASTERBROOK, G D, and HASLAM, H W. 1982. Mineral exploration in the area of the Fore Burn igneous complex, south-west Scotland. *Mineral Reconnaissance Report, Institute of Geological Sciences*, No. 55.

ANDERSON, T B, and OLIVER, G J H. 1986. The Orlock Bridge Fault: a major late Caledonian sinstral fault in the Southern Uplands terrane, British Isles. *Transactions of the Royal Society of Edinburgh: Earth Sciences*, Vol. 77, 203–222.

BAILEY, E B. 1926. Subterranean penetration by a desert climate. *Geological Magazine*, Vol. 63, 276–280.

BARNES, R P. 1989. Geology of the Whithorn district. *Memoir of the British Geological Survey*, Sheet 2 (Scotland).

BARNES, R P, ANDERSON, T B, and McCURRY, J A. 1987. Along-strike variation in the stratigraphical and structural profile of the Southern Uplands Central Belt in Galloway and Down. *Journal of the Geological Society of London*, Vol. 144, 807–816.

BARNES, R P, LINTERN, B C, and STONE, P. 1989. Timing and regional implications of deformation in the Southern Uplands of Scotland. *Journal of the Geological Society of London*, Vol. 146, 905–908.

BARNES, R P, PHILLIPS, E R, and BOLAND, M P. 1995. The Orlock Bridge Fault in the Southern Uplands of SW Scotland: a terrane boundary? *Geological Magazine*, Vol. 132, (in press)

BARNES, R P, ROCK, N M S, and GASKARTH, J W. 1986. Late Caledonian dyke-swarms in Southern Scotland: new field, petrological and geochemical data for the Wigtown Peninsula, Galloway. *Geological Journal*, Vol. 21, 101–125.

BERTHE, D, CHOUKROUNE, P, and JEROUZO, P. 1979. Orthogneiss mylonite, and non-coaxial deformation of granites: the example of the South Armorican shear zone. *Journal of Structural Geology*, Vol. 1, 31–42.

BLUCK, B J. 1978. Geology of a continental margin 1: the Ballantrae Complex. 151–162 *in* Crustal evolution in north-western Britain and adjacent regions. BOWES, D R, and LEAKE, B E (editors). *Special Issue of the Geological Journal*, No. 10.

BLUCK, B J, HALLIDAY, A N, AFTALION, M, and MacINTYRE, R M. 1980. Age and origin of Ballantrae ophiolite and its significance to the Caledonian orogeny and Ordovician time scale. *Geology*, Vol. 8, 492–495.

BLUCK, B J, and INGHAM, J K. 1992. The Girvan–Ballantrae district. 301–439 in *Geological excursions around Glasgow and Girvan*. LAWSON, J D, and WEEDON, D S (editors). (Glasgow: Geological Society of Glasgow.)

BOAST, A M, HARRIS, M, and STEFFE, D. 1990. Intrusive-hosted gold mineralization at Hare Hill, Southern Uplands, Scotland. *Transactions of the Institution of Mining and Metallurgy (Section B: Applied Earth Sciences)*, Vol, 99, B106–112.

BONNEY, T G. 1878. On the serpentine and associated igneous rocks of the Ayrshire coast. *Quarterly Journal of the Geological Society of London*, Vol. 34, 769–785.

BORTHWICK, G W. 1992. Leadhills and Wanlockhead. 192–202 in *Scottish Borders geology: an excursion guide*. McADAM, A D, CLARKSON, E N K, and STONE P (editors). (Edinburgh: Scottish Academic Press.)

BOTT, M H P, and MASSON-SMITH, D. 1960. A gravity survey of the Criffel granodiorite and the New Red Sandstone deposits near Dumfries. *Proceedings of the Yorkshire Geological Society*, Vol. 32, 317–332.

BOUMA, A H. 1962. *Sedimentology of some flysch deposits: a graphic approach to interpretation*. (Amsterdam: Elsevier.)

BRAND, P J. 1990. Pre-Westphalian biostratigraphy of the Thornhill Basin. Report on collections made in the field from locations on sheets NX89NE, NX89SE, NX99SW, NS80SE and NS80NE, forming part of the area of the Thornhill Basin, Sheets 9 and 15, Scotland. *British Geological Survey Technical Report*, WH/90/272R.

BRITISH GEOLOGICAL SURVEY. 1987. Whithorn. Scotland Sheet 2. Solid geology. 1:50 000. (Keyworth, Nottingham: British Geological Survey.)

BRITISH GEOLOGICAL SURVEY. 1992a. The Rhins of Galloway. Scotland Sheets 1 and 3 with parts of 7 and 4W. Solid geology. 1:50 000. (Keyworth, Nottingham: British Geological Survey.)

BRITISH GEOLOGICAL SURVEY. 1992b. Kirkcowan. Scotland Sheet 4W. Solid geology. 1:50 000. (Keyworth, Nottingham: British Geological Survey.)

BRITISH GEOLOGICAL SURVEY. 1992c. Wigtown. Scotland Sheet 4E. Solid geology. 1:50 000. (Keyworth, Nottingham: British Geological Survey.)

BRITISH GEOLOGICAL SURVEY. 1993a. Dalbeattie. Scotland Sheet 5E. Solid geology. 1:50 000. (Keyworth, Nottingham: British Geological Survey.)

BRITISH GEOLOGICAL SURVEY. 1993b. Kirkcudbright. Scotland Sheet 5W. Solid geology. 1:50 000. (Keyworth, Nottingham. British Geological Survey.)

BRITISH GEOLOGICAL SURVEY. 1993c. *Regional geochemistry of southern Scotland and part of northern England*. (Keyworth, Nottingham: British Geological Survey.)

BROOKFIELD, M E. 1977a. Field guide to the Permian rocks of the Dumfries and Lochmaben Basins. *Transactions of the Dumfries and Galloway Natural History and Antiquarian Society*, Vol. 52, 1–16.

BROOKFIELD, M E. 1977b. The origin of bounding surfaces in ancient aeolian sandstones. *Sedimentology*, Vol. 24, 303–332.

BROOKFIELD, M E. 1978. Revision of the stratigraphy of Permian and supposed Permian rocks of southern Scotland. *Geologische Rundschau*, Vol. 67, 110–149.

BROOKFIELD, M E. 1979. Anatomy of a lower Permian aeolian sandstone complex, southern Scotland. *Scottish Journal of Geology*, Vol. 15, 81–96.

BROOKFIELD, M E. 1980. Permian intermontane basin sedimentation in southern Scotland. *Sedimentary Geology*, Vol. 27, 167–194.

BROOKFIELD, M E. 1981. Field guide to the Permian rocks of the Thornhill and Moffat Basins. *Transactions of the Dumfries and Galloway Natural History and Antiquarian Society*, Vol. 56, 1–9.

BROOKFIELD, M E. 1984. Eolian sands. 91–103 *in* Facies models. WALKER, R G (editor). *Geoscience Canada, Reprint Series*, No. 1. 2nd edition.

BROWN, M J, LEAKE, R C, PARKER, M E, and FORTEY, N J. 1979. Porphyry-style copper mineralisation at Black Stockarton Moor, south-west Scotland. *Mineral Reconnaissance Report, Institute of Geological Sciences*, No. 30.

CHARLEY, M J. HAZELTON, R E, and TEAR, S J. 1989. Precious metal mineralisation associated with the Fore Burn igneous complex, Ayrshire, south-west Scotland. *Transactions of the Institution of Mining and Metallurgy (Section B: Applied Earth Sciences)*, Vol. 98, B48.

CLARKSON, C M, CRAIG, G Y, and WALTON, E K. 1975. The Silurian rocks bordering Kirkcudbright Bay, South Scotland. *Transactions of the Royal Society of Edinburgh*, Vol. 69, 313–325.

COCKS, L R M, and TOGHILL, P. 1973. The biostratigraphy of the Silurian rocks of the Girvan district, Scotland. *Journal of the Geological Society of London*, Vol. 129, 209–243.

COLMAN-SADD, S P, STONE, P, SWINDEN, H S, and BARNES, R P. 1992. Parallel geological development in the Dunnage

Zone of Newfoundland and the Lower Palaeozoic terranes of southern Scotland: an assessment. *Transactions of the Royal Society of Edinburgh: Earth Sciences,* Vol. 83, 571–594.

COWIE, J W, and BASSETT, M G. 1989. International Union of Geological Sciences 1989 Global Stratigraphic Chart. *Episodes,* Vol. 12, No. 2, Supplement.

CRAIG, G Y. 1956. The Lower Carboniferous outlier of Kirkbean, Kirkcudbrightshire. *Transactions of the Geological Society of Glasgow,* Vol. 22, 113–132.

CRAIG, G Y, and NAIRN, A E M. 1956. The Lower Carboniferous outliers of the Colvend and Rerrick shores, Kirkcudbrightshire. *Geological Magazine,* Vol. 93, 249–256.

CRAIG, G Y, and WALTON, E K. 1959. Sequence and structure in the Silurian rocks of Kirkcudbrightshire. *Geological Magazine,* Vol. 96, 209–220.

DAVIES, A. 1964. P.54 in *Summary of progress of the Geological Survey of Great Britain for 1963.* (London: Her Majesty's Stationery Office.)

DAVIES, A. 1970. Carboniferous rocks of the Sanquhar Outlier. *Bulletin of the Geological Survey of Great Britain,* Vol. 31, 37–87.

DAY, J B W. 1970. Geology of the country around Bewcastle. *Memoir of the Geological Survey of Great Britain.*

DEEGAN, C E. 1970. The petrology and sedimentology of the Lower Carboniferous rocks between White Port and Kirkbean, Kirkcudbrightshire. Unpublished PhD thesis, University College of Wales, Aberystwyth.

DEEGAN, C E. 1973. Tectonic control of sedimentation at the margin of a Carboniferous depositional basin in Kirkcudbrightshire. *Scottish Journal of Geology,* Vol. 9, 1–28.

DEWEY, H, FLETT, J S, and WILSON, G V. 1920. Arsenic and antimony ores. *Special Report on the Mineral Resources of Great Britain, Memoir of the Geological Survey of Great Britain,* Vol. 15.

ELDERS, C F. 1987. The provenance of granite boulders in conglomerates of the northern and central belts of the Southern Uplands, Scotland. *Journal of the Geological Society of London,* Vol. 144, 853–863.

ELDERS, C F. 1990. Discussion on detrital mineral ages from the Southern Uplands using ^{40}Ar–^{39}Ar laser probe. *Journal of the Geological Society of London,* Vol. 147, 882–884.

EVANS, J A, STONE, P, and FLOYD, J D. 1991. Isotopic characteristics of Ordovician greywacke provenance in the Southern Uplands of Scotland. 161–172 *in* Developments in sedimentary provenance studies. MORTON, A C, TODD, S P, and HAUGHTON, P D W (editors). *Special Publication of the Geological Society of London,* No. 57.

FLOYD, J D. 1982. Stratigraphy of a flysch succession: the Ordovician of W Nithsdale, SW Scotland. *Transactions of the Royal Society of Edinburgh: Earth Sciences,* Vol. 73, 1–9.

FLOYD, J D, and STONE, P. 1992. Tweedsmuir. 147–158 in *Scottish Borders geology: an excursion guide.* McADAM, A D, CLARKSON, E N K, and STONE, P (editors). (Edinburgh: Scottish Academic Press.)

FLOYD, J D, and TRENCH, A. 1989. Magnetic susceptibility contrasts in Ordovician greywackes of the Southern Uplands of Scotland. *Journal of the Geological Society of London,* Vol. 146, 77–83.

FOSTER-SMITH, J R. 1967. The non-ferrous metal mines of south-west Scotland. *Northern Cavern and Mine Research Society, Individual Survey Series,* No. 2.

FROLICHER, F J. 1977. The sedimentology and palaeoecology of the Dinantian outlier of Kirkbean, Kirkcudbrightshire, Scotland. Unpublished PhD thesis, University of Edinburgh.

GALLAGHER, M J. 1964. Rock alteration in some mineralized basic dykes in Britain. *Transactions of the Institution of Mining and Metallurgy,* Vol. 73, 825–840.

GALLAGHER, M J, MICHIE, U M, SMITH, R T, and HAYNES, L. 1971. New evidence of uranium and other mineralisation in Scotland. *Transactions of the Institution of Mining and Metallurgy (Section B: Applied Earth Sciences)*, Vol. 80, B150–173.

GALLAGHER, M J, and 10 others. 1983. Stratabound arsenic and vein antimony mineralization in Silurian greywackes at Glendinning, south Scotland. *Mineral Reconnaissance Report, British Geological Survey*, No. 59.

GEORGE, T N, and 6 others. 1976. A correlation of Dinantian rocks in the British Isles. *Special Report of the Geological Society of London*, No. 7.

GORDON, J E, SUTHERLAND, D G, BIRKS, H J B, JONES, V J, and STEVENSON, A C. 1993. Southwest Scotland. 589–613 in *Quaternary of Scotland. (Geological Conservation Review Series 6)*. GORDON, J E, and SUTHERLAND, D G (editors). (London: Chapman and Hall.)

HALLIDAY, A N, STEPHENS, W E, and HARMON, R S. 1980. Rb-Sr and O isotopic relationships in three zoned Caledonian granitic plutons, Southern Uplands, Scotland: evidence for varied sources and hybridization of magmas. *Journal of the Geological Society of London*, Vol. 137, 329–348.

HARKNESS, R. 1850. On the New Red Sandstone of the southern portion of the Vale of the Nith. *Quarterly Journal of the Geological Society of London*, Vol. 6, 389–399.

HARRISON, R K, STONE, P, CAMERON, I B, ELLIOT, R W, and HARDING, R R. 1987. Geology, petrology and geochemistry of Ailsa Craig, Ayrshire. *Report of the British Geological Survey*, Vol. 16, No. 9.

HEPWORTH, B C, OLIVER, G J H, and McMURTRY, M J. 1982. Sedimentology, volcanism, structure and metamorphism of the northern margin of a Lower Palaeozoic accretionary complex; Bail Hill–Abington area of the Southern Uplands of Scotland. 521–534 in Trench-forearc geology: sedimentation and tectonics on modern and ancient active plate margins. LEGGETT, J K (editor). *Special Publication of the Geological Society of London*, No. 10.

HITCHEN, K, and RITCHIE, J D. 1993. New K-Ar ages and a provisional chronology for the offshore part of the British Tertiary Igneous Province. *Scottish Journal of Geology*, Vol. 29, 73–85.

HOLROYD, J. 1978. The sedimentological and geotectonic significance of Lower Palaeozoic flysch rudites. Unpublished PhD thesis, University of Wales.

INCE, D. 1984. Sedimentation and tectonism in the Middle Ordovician of the Girvan district, SW Scotland. *Transactions of the Royal Society of Edinburgh: Earth Sciences*, Vol. 75, 225–237.

INGHAM, J K. 1978. Geology of a continental margin 2: middle and late Ordovician transgression, Girvan. 163–176 in Crustal evolution in northwestern Britain and adjacent regions. BOWES, D R, and LEAKE, B E (editors). *Special Issue of the Geological Journal*, No. 10.

KELLEY, S, and BLUCK, B J. 1989. Detrital mineral ages from the Southern Uplands using ^{40}Ar–^{39}Ar laser probe. *Journal of the Geological Society of London* Vol. 146, 401–403.

KELLING, G. 1962. The petrology and sedimentation of Upper Ordovician rocks in the Rhins of Galloway, south-west Scotland. *Transactions of the Royal Society of Edinburgh*, Vol. 65, 107–137.

KELLING, G, DAVIES P, and HOLROYD, J. 1987. Style, scale and significance of sand bodies in the Northern and Central belts, south-west Southern Uplands. *Journal of the Geological Society of London*, Vol. 144, 787–805.

KEMP, A E S. 1986. Tectonostratigraphy of the Southern Belt of the Southern Uplands. *Scottish Journal of Geology*, Vol. 22, 241–256.

KEMP, A E S. 1987a. Tectonic development of the Southern Belt of the Southern Uplands accretionary complex. *Journal of the Geological Society of London*, Vol. 144, 827–838.

KEMP, A E S. 1987b. Evolution of Silurian depositional systems in the Southern Uplands, Scotland. Chapter 7 in *Marine clastic sedimentology*. LEGGETT,

J K, and ZUFFA, G G (editors). (London: Graham & Trotman.)

KEMP, A E S, OLIVER, G J H, and BALDWIN, J R. 1985. Low-grade metamorphism and accretion tectonics: Southern Uplands terrain, Scotland. *Mineralogical Magazine*, Vol. 49, 335–344.

KEMP, A E S, and WHITE, D E. 1985. Silurian trench sedimentation in the Southern Uplands, Scotland: implications of new age data. *Geological Magazine*, Vol. 122, 275–277.

KERRICK, D M. 1991. Overview of contact metamorphism. 1–12 in Contact Metamorphism. Kerrick, D M (editor). *Mineralogical Society of America. Reviews in Mineralogy*, Vol. 26.

KIMBELL, G S, and Stone, P. 1992. Geophysical evidence for a concealed Caledonian intrusive body at Sandhead, Wigtownshire. *Scottish Journal of Geology*, Vol. 28, 19–25.

KING, B C. 1937. The minor intrusives of Kirkcudbrightshire. *Proceedings of the Geologists' Association*, Vol. 48, 282–306.

LAMBERT, R ST J, HOLLAND, J G, and LEGGETT, J K. 1981. Petrology and tectonic setting of some Ordovician volcanic rocks from the Southern Uplands of Scotland. *Journal of the Geological Society of London*, Vol. 138, 421–436.

LAPWORTH, C. 1878. The Moffat Series. *Quarterly Journal of the Geological Society of London*, Vol. 34, 240–346.

LEAKE, R C, AULD, H A, STONE, P, and JOHNSON, C E. 1981. Gold mineralisation at the southern margin of the Loch Doon granitoid complex, south-west Scotland. *Mineral Reconnaissance Report, Institute of Geological Sciences*, No. 46.

LEAKE, R C, and BROWN, M J. 1979. Porphyry-style copper mineralization at Black Stockarton Moor, south-west Scotland. *Transactions of the Institution of Mining and Metallurgy (Section B: Applied Earth Sciences)*, Vol. 88, B170–181.

LEAKE, R C, and COOPER, C. 1983. The Black Stockarton Moor subvolcanic complex, Galloway. *Journal of the Geological Society of London*, Vol. 140, 665–676.

LEEDER, M R. 1975. Lower Border Group (Tournaisian) stromatolites from the Northumberland basin. *Scottish Journal of Geology*, Vol. 11, 207–226.

LEEDER, M R. 1976. Palaeogeographic significance of pedogenic carbonates in the topmost Upper Old Red Sandstone of the Scottish Border Basin. *Geological Journal*, Vol. 11, 21–28.

LEEDER, M R. 1982. Upper Palaeozoic basins of the British Isles: Caledonide inheritance versus Hercynian plate margin processes. *Journal of the Geological Society of London*, Vol. 139, 479–491.

LEEDER, M R. 1988. Recent developments in Carboniferous geology: a critical review with implications for the British Isles and NW Europe. *Proceedings of the Geologists' Association*, Vol. 99, 73–100.

LEEDER, M R, and MCMAHON, A H. 1988. Upper Carboniferous (Silesian) basin subsidence in northern Britain. 43–52 in *Sedimentation in a synorogenic basin complex: the Upper Carboniferous of northwest Europe*. BESLEY, B M, and KELLING, G (editors). (Glasgow and London: Blackie and Son.)

LEGGETT, J K. 1987. The Southern Uplands as an accretionary prism: the importance of analogues in reconstructing palaeogeography. *Journal of the Geological Society of London*, Vol. 144, 737–752.

LEGGETT, J K, MCKERROW, W S, and EALES, M H. 1979. The Southern Uplands of Scotland: a Lower Palaeozoic accretionary prism. *Journal of the Geological Society of London*, Vol. 136, 755–770.

LINTERN, B C, BARNES, R P, and STONE P. 1992. Discussion on Silurian and early Devonian sinistral deformation of the Ratagain Granite, Scotland: constraints on the age of Caledonian movements on the Great Glen system. *Journal of the Geological Society of London*, Vol. 149, 858.

LISTER, G S, and SNOKE, A W. 1984. S-C mylonites. *Journal of Structural Geology*, Vol. 6, 617–638.

LONGMAN, C D, BLUCK, B J, and VAN BREEMEN, O. 1979. Ordovician conglomerates and the evolution of the

196

Midland Valley. *Nature, London,* Vol. 280, 578–581.

LOVELL, J P B. 1974. Sand volcanoes in the Silurian rocks of Kirkcudbrightshire. *Scottish Journal of Geology,* Vol. 10, 161–162.

LUMSDEN, G I, TULLOCH, W, HOWELLS, M F, and DAVIES, A. 1967. The geology of the neighbourhood of Langholm. *Memoir of the Geological Survey, Scotland.*

MACGREGOR, A G, MACGREGOR, M, and ROBERTSON, T. 1944. Barytes in Central Scotland. *Wartime Pamphlet of the Geological Survey of Great Britain,* No. 38.

MACGREGOR, M, LEE, G W, and WILSON, G V. 1920. The iron ores of Scotland. *Special Report on the Mineral Resources of Great Britain, Memoir of the Geological Survey of Great Britain,* Vol. 11.

MCADAM, A D, CLARKSON, E N K, and STONE, P. (editors). 1992. *Scottish Borders geology.* (Edinburgh: Scottish Academic Press.)

MCCURRY, J A. 1989. The geology of the Lower Palaeozoic rocks in the Mull of Galloway, SW Scotland: studies in an imbricate thrust terrane. Unpublished PhD thesis, University of St Andrews.

MCCURRY, J A. 1994. The Newfoundland connection: a cautionary tale in site denotification. *Earth Heritage,* Vol. 2. 10–12.

MCCURRY, J A, and ANDERSON, T B. 1989. Landward vergence in the lower Palaeozoic Southern Uplands–Down– Longford terrane, British Isles. *Geology,* Vol. 17, 630–633.

MCKEEVER, P J. 1994. A new vertebrate trackway from the Permian of Dumfries and Galloway. *Scottish Journal of Geology,* Vol. 30, 11–14.

MCKERROW, W S, and ELDERS, C F. 1989. Movements on the Southern Uplands fault. *Journal of the Geological Society of London,* Vol. 146, 393–395.

MCMILLAN, A A, and BRAND, P J. 1995. Depositional setting of Permian and Upper Carboniferous strata of the Thornhill Basin, Dumfriesshire. *Scottish Journal of Geology,* Vol. 31, 43–45.

MCMURTRY, M J. 1980a. Field guide to the Bail Hill area. *Southern Uplands Field Workshop Field guide (unpublished).*

MCMURTRY, M J. 1980b. The Ordovician rocks of the Bail Hill area, Sanquhar, South Scotland: volcanism and sedimentation in the Iapetus Ocean. Unpublished PhD thesis, University of St Andrews.

MCMURTRY, M J. 1980c. Discussion of: Evidence for Caledonian subduction from greywacke detritus in the Longford–Down Inlier. *Journal of Earth Sciences of the Royal Dublin Society,* Vol. 2, 209–212.

MENTEATH, J S. 1828. A short sketch of the geology of Nithsdale. *Edinburgh New Philosophical Journal,* 45–60.

MERRIMAN, R J, FORTEY, N J, and ROBERTS, B. 1991. An excursion guide to areas of very low grade metamorphism in the Lake District and Rhins of Galloway. *British Geological Survey Technical Report,* WG/91/8.

MERRIMAN, R J, and ROBERTS, B. 1993. The low grade metamorphism of Lower Palaeozoic strata on the Rhins of Galloway, SW Scotland. *British Geological Survey Technical Report,* WG/92/40.

MILLER, J M, and TAYLOR, K. 1966. Uranium mineralization near Dalbeattie, Kirkcudbrightshire. *Bulletin of the Geological Survey of Great Britain,* No. 25, 1–18.

MURPHY, F C. 1984. Fluidized breccias: a record of brittle transitions during ductile deformation. *Tectonophysics,* Vol. 104, 325–349.

MYKURA, W. 1960. The replacement of coal by limestone and the reddening of Coal Measures in the Ayrshire Coalfield. *Bulletin of the Geological Survey of Great Britain,* Vol. 16, 69–109.

MYKURA, W. 1967. The Upper Carboniferous rocks of south-west Ayrshire. *Bulletin of the Geological Survey of Great Britain,* Vol. 26, 23–98.

NADEN, J, and CAULFIELD, J B D. 1989. Isotopic and fluid inclusion studies of gold mineralisation in the Southern Uplands of Scotland. *Transactions of the Institution of Mining and Metallurgy (Section B: Applied Earth Sciences),* Vol. 98, B46–48.

NEEDHAM, D T. 1993. The structure of the western part of the Southern Uplands of Scotland. *Journal of the Geological Society of London,* Vol. 150, 341–354.

NILSEN, T H (translator). 1978. Turbidites of the northern Apennines: Introduction to facies analysis by MUTTI, E, and RICCI LUCCHI, F. 1972. *International Geology Review,* Vol. 20, 125–166.

OLIVER, G J H, and LEGGETT, J K. 1980. Metamorphism in an accretionary prism: prehnite-pumpellyite facies metamorphism of the Southern Uplands of Scotland. *Transactions of the Royal Society of Edinburgh: Earth Sciences,* Vol. 71, 235–246.

ORD, D M, CLEMMEY, H, and LEEDER, M R. 1988. Interaction between faulting and sedimentation during Dinantian extension of the Solway basin, SW Scotland. *Journal of the Geological Society of London,* Vol. 145, 249–259.

OWEN, A W, and CLARKSON, E N K. 1992. Trilobites from Kilbucho and Wallaces Cast and the location of the Southern Uplands during the late Ordovician. *Scottish Journal of Geology,* Vol. 28, 3–17.

PALMER, D, and RICKARDS, B (editors). 1991. *Graptolites: writing in the rocks.* (Woodbridge: The Boydell Press.)

PASSCHIER, C W, and SIMPSON, C. 1986. Porphyroclast systems as kinematic indicators. *Journal of Structural Geology,* Vol. 8, 831-843.

PEACH, B N, and HORNE, J. 1899. The Silurian rocks of Britain, Vol. 1: Scotland. *Memoir of the Geological Survey of the United Kingdom.*

PHILLIPS, E R. 1992. Microfabric analysis of a series of sheared metasandstones exposed within the Moniaive Shear Zone, Southern Uplands, Scotland. *British Geological Survey Technical Report,* WG/92/45.

PHILLIPS, E R, BARNES, R P, BOLAND, M P, FORTEY, N J, and MCMILLAN, A A. 1995. The Moniaive Shear Zone: a major zone of sinistral strike-slip deformation in the Southern Uplands of Scotland. *Scottish Journal of Geology,* Vol. 31 (in press).

PHILLIPS, W J. 1956. The Criffell–Dalbeattie granodiorite complex. *Quarterly Journal of the Geological Society of London,* Vol. 112, 221–239.

PICKERING, K T, HISCOTT, R N, and HEIN, F J. 1989. *Deep marine environments: clastic sedimentation and tectonics.* (Andover: Chapman and Hall.)

PLATT, J P. 1984. Secondary cleavages in ductile shear zones. *Journal of Structural Geology,* Vol. 6, 439–442.

PLATT, J P, and VISSERS, R L M. 1980. Extensional structures in anisotropic rocks. *Journal of Structural Geology,* Vol. 2, 397–410.

PRINGLE, J, and RICHEY, J E. 1931. Carboniferous rocks of the Thornhill Basin, Dumfriesshire. 25–33 in *Summary of progress of the Geological Survey of Great Britain for 1930.* (London: Her Majesty's Stationery Office.)

ROBERTS, B, MERRIMAN, R J, and PRATT, W. 1991. The influence of strain, lithology and stratigraphical depth on white mica (illite) crystallinity in mudrocks from the vicinity of the Corris Slate Belt, Wales: implications for the timing of metamorphism in the Welsh Basin. *Geological Magazine,* Vol. 128, 633–645.

ROBERTSON, A H F, OGAWA, Y, and STONE, P. 1990. *Field guide to the Ordovician Ballantrae Ophiolitic Complex and associated units, SW Scotland.* Field Guide No. 21. (Nottingham: 13th International Sedimentological Congress.)

ROCK, N M S, COOPER, C, and GASKARTH, J W. 1986a. Late Caledonian subvolcanic vents and associated dykes in the Kirkcudbright area, Galloway, south-west Scotland. *Proceedings of the Yorkshire Geological Society,* Vol. 46, 29–37.

ROCK, N M S, GASKARTH, J W, and RUNDLE, C C. 1986b. Late Caledonian dyke swarms in southern Scotland: a regional zone of primitive K-rich lamprophyres and associated vents. *Journal of Geology,* Vol. 94, 505–522.

RUSHTON, A W A, and STONE, P. 1991. Terrigenous input to the Moffat Shale sequence, Southern Uplands. *Scottish Journal of Geology,* Vol. 27, 167–169.

RUSHTON, A W A, STONE, P, SMELLIE, J L, and TUNNICLIFF, S P. 1986. An early Arenig age for the Pinbain sequence, Ballantrae Complex. *Scottish Journal of Geology*, Vol. 22, 41–54.

RUST, B R. 1965. The stratigraphy and structure of the Whithorn area of Wigtownshire, Scotland. *Scottish Journal of Geology*, Vol. 1, 101–133.

SIMPSON, J B, and RICHEY, J E. 1936. The geology of the Sanquhar Coalfield and adjacent basin of Thornhill. *Memoirs of the Geological Survey, Scotland.*

SMELLIE, J L, and STONE, P. 1992. Geochemical control on the evolutionary history of the Ballantrae Complex, SW Scotland, from comparisons with recent analogues. 171–178 in Ophiolites and their modern oceanic analogues. PARSON, L M, MURTON, B J, and BROWNING, P (editors). *Special Publication of the Geological Society of London*, No. 60.

SMITH, J. 1910. Carboniferous rocks of the Solway, Scotland. *Transactions of the Geological Society of Glasgow*, Vol. 114, 30–59.

SOPER, N J, and HUTTON, D H W. 1984. Late Caledonian sinistral displacements in Britain: implications for a three-plate collision model. *Tectonics*, Vol. 3, 781–794.

SOPER, N J, STRACHAN, R A, HOLDSWORTH, R E, GAYER, R A, and GREILING, R O. 1992. Sinistral transpression and the Silurian closure of Iapetus. *Journal of the Geological Society of London*, Vol. 149, 871–880.

STANLEY, C J, SYMES, R F, and JONES G C. 1987. Copper-nickel mineralisation at Talnotry, Newton Stewart, Scotland. *Mineralogy and Petrology*, Vol. 37, 293–313.

STEPHENS, W E, and HALLIDAY, A N. 1984. Geochemical contrasts between late Caledonian granitoid plutons of northern, central and southern Scotland. *Transactions of the Royal Society of Edinburgh: Earth Sciences*, Vol. 75, 259–273.

STEPHENS, W E, WHITLEY, J E, THIRLWALL, M F, and HALLIDAY, A N. 1985. The Criffell zoned pluton: correlated behaviour of rare earth element abundances with isotopic systems. *Contributions to Mineralogy and Petrology*, Vol. 89, 226–238.

STONE, P. 1988. The Permian successions at Ballantrae and Loch Ryan, south-west Scotland. *Report of the British Geological Survey*, Vol. 19, No. 2, 13–18.

STONE, P. 1995. Geology of the Rhins of Galloway district. *Memoir of the British Geological Survey*, Sheets 1 and 3 (Scotland).

STONE, P, COOK, J M, McDERMOTT, C, ROBINSON, J J, and SIMPSON, P R. 1995. Lithostratigraphic and structural controls on the distribution of As and Au in the SW Southern Uplands, Scotland. *Transactions of the Institution of Mining and Metallurgy (Section B: Applied Earth Sciences)*, Vol. 104, B111–120.

STONE, P, FLOYD, J D, BARNES, R P, and LINTERN, B C. 1987. A sequential back-arc and foreland basin thrust duplex model for the Southern Uplands of Scotland. *Journal of the Geological Society of London*, Vol. 144, 753–764.

STONE, P, GUNN, A G, COATS, J S, and CARRUTHERS, R M. 1986. Mineral exploration in the Ballantrae complex, southwest Scotland. 265–278 in *Metallogeny of basic and ultrabasic rocks*. GALLAGER, M J, IXER, R A, NEARY, C R, and PRICHARD, H M (editors). (London: Institution of Mining and Metallurgy.)

STONE, P, and LEAKE, R C. 1984. Disseminated and epigenetic Pb-Zn mineralisation in Ordovician mudstone, Galloway. *Scottish Journal of Geology*, Vol. 20, 181–190.

STONE, P, LEAKE, R C, JONES, R C, FORTEY, N J, and GALLAGHER, M J. 1984. Base metal mineralisation associated with Ordovician shales in south-west Scotland. *Mineral Reconnaissance Report, British Geological Survey*, No. 69.

STONE, P, and RUSHTON, A W A. 1983. Graptolite faunas from the Ballantrae Ophiolite Complex and their structural implications. *Scottish Journal of Geology*, Vol. 19, 297–310.

STONE, P, and SMELLIE, J L. 1988. *Classical areas of British geology: the Ballantrae area: description of the solid geology of parts of 1:25 000 sheets NX08, 18 and 19.* (London: HMSO for British Geological Survey.)

STYLES, M T, STONE, P, and FLOYD, J D. 1989. Arc detritus in the Southern Uplands: mineralogical characterization of a 'missing' terrane. *Journal of the Geological Society of London,* Vol. 146, 397–400.

STRINGER, P, and TREAGUS, J E. 1980. Non-axial planar S_1 cleavage in the Hawick rocks of the Galloway area, Southern Uplands, Scotland. *Journal of Structural Geology,* Vol. 2, 317–331.

STRINGER, P, and TREAGUS, J E. 1981. Asymmetrical folding in the Hawick Rocks of the Galloway area, Southern Uplands. *Scottish Journal of Geology,* Vol. 17, 129–147.

THIRLWALL, M F. 1988. Geochronology of late Caledonian magmatism in northern Britain. *Journal of the Geological Society of London,* Vol. 145, 951–967.

THIRLWALL, M F, and BLUCK, B J. 1984. Sr-Nd isotope and geochemical evidence that the Ballantrae 'ophiolite', SW Scotland, is polygenetic. 215–230 *in* Ophiolites and oceanic lithosphere. GASS, I G, LIPPARD, S J, and SHELTON, A W (editors). *Special Publication of the Geological Society of London,* No. 13.

TREAGUS, J E. 1992. Southern Uplands. 9–42 in *Caledonian structures in Britain south of the Midland Valley. (Geological Conservation Review Series 3).* TREAGUS, J E (editor). (London and Glasgow: Chapman and Hall.)

WALKER, R G, and MUTTI, E. 1973. Turbidite facies and facies associations. 119–157 in *Turbidites and deep-water sedimentation. Society of Economic Palaeontology and Mineralogy Pacific Section Short Course Notes.* MIDDLETON, G V, and BOUMA, A H (editors). (Anaheim: Society of Economic Palaeontology and Mineralogy.)

WEIR, J A. 1968. Structural history of the Silurian rocks of the coast west of Gatehouse, Kirkcudbrightshire. *Scottish Journal of Geology,* Vol. 4, 31–52.

WEIR, J A. 1974. The sedimentology and diagenesis of the Silurian rocks on the coast west of Gatehouse, Kirkcudbrightshire. *Scottish Journal of Geology,* Vol. 10, 165–186.

WEIR, J A. 1979. Tectonic contrasts in the Southern Uplands. *Scottish Journal of Geology,* Vol. 15, 169–186.

WHITE, D E, BARRON, H F, BARNES, R P, and LINTERN, B C. 1992 (for 1991). Biostratigraphy of late Llandovery (Telychian) and Wenlock turbiditic sequences in the SW Southern Uplands, Scotland. *Transactions of the Royal Society of Edinburgh: Earth Sciences,* Vol. 82, 297–322.

WHITE, S H, BRETAN, P G, and RUTTER, E H. 1986. Fault zone reactivation: kinematics and mechanisms. *Philosophical Transactions of the Royal Society of London Series A,* Vol. 317, 82–97.

WILLIAMS, A. 1959. A structural history of the Girvan district, south-west Ayrshire. *Transactions of the Royal Society of Edinburgh,* Vol. 63, 629–667.

WILLIAMS, S H. 1994. Revision and definition of the *C wilsoni* graptolite Zone (middle Ordovician) of southern Scotland. *Transactions of the Royal Society of Edinburgh: Earth Sciences,* Vol. 85, 143–157.

WILSON, G V. 1921. The lead, zinc, copper and nickel ores of Scotland. *Special Report on the Mineral Resources of Great Britain, Memoir of the Geological Survey of Great Britain,* Vol. 17.

WILSON, G V, EASTWOOD, T, POCOCK, R W, WRAY, D A, and ROBERTSON, T. 1922. Barytes and witherite (3rd edition). *Special Report on the Mineral Resources of Great Britain, Memoir of the Geological Survey of Great Britain,* Vol. 2.

Glossary

Acid: describes igneous rock containing more than 10 per cent quartz and having a chemical composition of more than 66 per cent silica, SiO_2 (cf. intermediate and basic).

Aeolian: describes deposits formed from wind-transported sediments.

Agglomerate: pyroclastic rock consisting of fragments greater than 2 mm in size (cf. tuff).

Alkali(-ne):   describes igneous rock in which the feldspar is mainly sodium and/or potassium rich (as against calc-alkaline in which feldspar is mainly calcium rich).

Amygdale (-oidal):   gas bubble in lava infilled with a mineral, e.g. quartz, calcite or zeolite.

Andesite: fine-grained intermediate igneous rock characterised by the presence of oligoclase or andesine as the feldspar; occurs as extensive lava flows often associated with subduction-related volcanicity, or may form small intrusive bodies.

Anticline: fold with the oldest strata in the core, generally but not necessarily convex-upwards (cf. syncline).

Antiform: convex-upwards fold with no available information on the direction of younging in the folded sequence (synform is convex-downwards).

Aphyric: a uniformly fine-grained texture in igneous rocks (cf. porphyritic).

Aplite: a fine-grained rock of granitic composition, usually occurring in veins or dykes.

Arenite (-aceous):   any detrital sedimentary rock consisting of particles in the sand size range.

Argillite (-aceous):   any detrital sedimentary rock consisting of particles of silt size or less.

Arkose: sandstone containing an abundance of detrital feldspar grains.

Aureole: the zone of thermally metamorphosed rock surrounding an igneous intrusion.

Autobreccia: a fragmentary rock produced by the process of igneous emplacement (usually extrusive) and not by subsequent erosion or tectonism.

Autolith: an inclusion in an igneous rock to which it is genetically related.

Axial plane: that plane passing through all points on a fold hinge, throughout the fold's development, and bisecting the angle between the fold limbs.

Axial-plane cleavage: cleavage, usually slaty, developed parallel to the axial plane of a fold.

Basalt: fine-grained basic igneous rock containing calcium-rich plagioclase feldspar and pyroxene (usually augite), and often also olivine, hornblende and magnetite in significant amounts; occurs as lava flows and in small intrusions where cooling has been rapid.

Basic: describes igneous rock containing no free quartz and having a chemical composition of between 45 and 55 per cent silica, SiO_2 (cf. acid, intermediate).

Bentonite: assemblage of clay minerals formed by the alteration of glassy volcanic ash.

Biostratigraphical zonal scheme: series of divisions of the age of rocks based on their fossil content.

Biozone: time range of a certain species or assemblage of species.

Bivalves: group of marine or freshwater invertebrates that secrete an exterior calcitic shell of two valves, usually the same size.

Boninite: an unusual variety of basalt lava with an exceptionally high content of magnesium, chromium and nickel, coupled with high levels of silica.   Such lavas are characteristic of the frontal zones of oceanic volcanic island arcs.

Botryoidal: describes minerals occurring as aggregates with rounded surfaces.

Boudinage: the stretching of a planar layer or body of rock to produce a series of lenses separated by narrowed necks.

Breccia: (1) detrital sedimentary rock containing angular fragments greater than 2 mm in size, either laid down in water or subaerially; angularity indicates that fragments have not been transported very far. (2) a zone of shattered rock, usually recemented, produced tectonically by fault movement.

Chert: finely crystalline silica, SiO_2, occuring as bands or nodules in sedimentary sequences.

Cleavage: parting imposed on a rock during tectonism, either by alignment of recrystallised minerals or by physical microdeformation.

Crenulation cleavage: cleavage planes, whether micaceous layers or sharp breaks, which are separated by thin slices of rock containing an earlier, cross-cutting planar fabric which is deformed between the new crenulation planes.

Slaty cleavage: a penetrative fabric caused by mineral orientation in closely spaced layers throughout a rock.

Transecting cleavage: cleavage planes genetically related to a fold structure to which they are nevertheless not axial planar. Typically the cleavage planes are parallel to the axial plane in cross-section but cut obliquely across the fold in plan view. Generation in a varying stress field is the likely explantion.

Conglomerate: detrital sedimentary rock containing rounded fragments greater than 2 mm in size, usually deposited in water, the roundness of the fragments resulting from erosion during transportation.

Conjugate: applied to faults or joints which formed during the same deformation episode but which intersect at an acute angle.

Convoluted: describes irregular folds produced in soft sediments by slumping.

Crinoid: marine echinoderm with calcite-plated skeleton surrounded by soft tissue consisting of a stem and five free arms.

Cross-lamination; cross-bedding: inclined bedding with a relationship to the direction of current flow during deposition, cut across by subsequent bedding laminae deposited during different flow conditions.

Cupola: an upward projection of a large igneous intrusion beyond the general level of its roof.

Cyclothem: a sequence of beds which, although of different lithology, were all deposited during a single sedimentary cycle.

Décollement: plane of detachment, usually gently dipping or horizontal, which allows different styles of deformation to develop above and below; typically the basal sole structure in a thrust complex.

Detrital: relates to particles that have been part of a pre-existing rock.

Diagenesis: the processes affecting, or the changes imposed on, a sediment at low temperature and pressure prior to its deeper burial and lithification.

Distal: describes sedimentary lithologies deposited a long way from the source of the sediment (cf. proximal).

Dolerite: medium-grained basic igneous rock compositionally equivalent to basalt; usually occurs in larger intrusions where cooling has been relatively slow.

Dolomite: either the common rock forming mineral CaMg $(CO_3)_2$ or a sedimentary rock formed mainly of that mineral.

Downthrow: direction in, and/or distance by, which a rock unit is moved down across a fault.

Drumlin: mound of boulder clay elongated in the direction of ice flow.

Dyke: sheet-like, often vertical, igneous intrusion (cf. sill).

Esker: long, winding ridge of sand and gravel deposited by a subglacial stream or one issuing from a retreating glacier.

Euhedral: well-formed crystal shape (cf. subhedral).

Facies: general aspect of a suite of sedimentary rocks, from which its environment of deposition may be determined.

Fault: fracture in a rock along which there has been movement.

Feldsparphyric: an igneous rock texture in which large feldspar crystals are contained in a fine-grained groundmass.

Felsic: an acronym from feldspar and silica, used to describe pale-coloured rocks formed mainly of those minerals (cf. mafic).

Felsite: pale-coloured, fine-grained acid or intermediate igneous rock, often forming dykes.

Ferromagnesian: describes silicate minerals rich in iron and/or magnesium such as olivine, pyroxene, amphibole or biotite.

Fissile: breaks along closely spaced bedding planes.

Flame structure: feature produced when a layer of soft sediment is disrupted and forces its way upwards into an overlying layer, usually through loading, giving the appearance of flames.

Flute mark (cast): asymmetrical groove eroded in a sediment surface by a turbidity current, then filled with sediment and subsequently exhumed as a positive feature; a sole mark.

Flysch: general term for the sedimentary rock assemblage produced by deposition from turbidity currents.

Fold axis (= hinge): line joining the highest points within the axial plane of the same bed or layer in an antiform or the lowest points in a synform.

Forearc: in a volcanic arc formed above a subduction zone, that area between the arc and the adjacent trench.

Foreset: in a cross-bedded unit, one of the inclined layers deposited on an advancing frontal slope.

Gabbro: coarse-grained basic igneous rock compositionally equivalent to basalt and dolerite; forms in large intrusions where cooling has been very slow.

Gangue: that part of a mineral vein which is not the economically valuable material. Common gangue minerals are quartz and calcite.

Ganister: a hard, fine-grained quartz-rich sandstone or quartzite found as a seatearth to some coal seams.

Gouge: the soft, tectonically comminuted rock material found in some fault planes.

Graded bedding: unit of sedimentary rock which shows evidence of sorting with coarsest material at the base and finest material at the top.

Granite: coarse-grained acid igneous rock with quartz, sodium- and potassium-rich feldspars and micas; forms in large intrusions where cooling has been very slow.

Granodiorite: coarse-grained intermediate igneous rock compositionally equivalent to andesite and/or dacite with calcium-rich feldspar, hornblende and biotite; forms in large intrusions where cooling has been very slow.

Graptolite: colonial marine invertebrate, now extinct, which consisted of a branched organism with individuals living in `cups' (thecae) along the branches.

Greywacke: matrix-rich sandstone with a mixed, angular clast assemblage including a high proportion of rock fragments.

Groove mark (cast): groove eroded in a sediment surface either by current flow or by an object being dragged along by the current, then filled with sediment and subsequently exhumed as a positive feature; a sole mark.

Half-graben: an extensional basin bounded on one side by a normal fault.

Hanging wall: the overlying side of an inclined fault; the underlying side is the footwall.

Hawaiite: a variety of olivine basalt containing andesine as the main plagioclase.

Hemipelagite: a sedimentary rock formed by the slow accumulation on the sea floor of biogenic and fine terrigenous particles.

Hinge zone: that part of a fold in the vicinity of the axial plane.

Hornfels: fine- to medium-grained rock produced by partial recrystallisation during thermal metamorphism.

Iapetus Ocean: former ocean between Scotland and England and the continental masses to which they were once attached; it developed and closed during the early Palaeozoic era.

Imbricate thrust: one of a series of thrusts whose dip decreases with depth towards a common basal sole thrust (cf. *décollement*).

Inlier: area of older rocks completely surrounded by younger rocks.

Intermediate: describes igneous rock containing less than 10 per cent quartz and having a chemical composition of between 55 and 66 per cent silica, SiO_2 (cf. acid, basic)

Intermontane: situated between or surrounded by mountains.

Isoclinal fold: fold in which the two limbs are approximately parallel.

Isocryst: a line on a metamorphic map joining points of equal low-grade metamorphism as quantified by white mica crystallinity.

Isotopic dating: see radiometric dating.

Lamprophyre: medium-grained basic and intermediate igneous rock with pyroxene, amphibole and/or biotite phenocrysts in a groundmass which also contains orthoclase and/or plagioclase. Commonly found as dykes or small intrusive bodies.

Lapilli: a pyroclastic fragment in the size range 2 to 64 mm.

Leucocratic: describes igneous rocks containing mainly light-coloured minerals such as quartz, feldspar and muscovite.

Lithic: made of rock, as in a fragment or clast within a greywacke or conglomerate.

Lithoclast: an eroded and redeposited rock fragment larger than 2 mm in diameter.

Mafic: a general term used to describe the dark-coloured ferromagnesian minerals (pyroxenes, amphiboles etc.) or rocks composed principally of such minerals (cf. felsic).

Magma: molten rock derived from great depth within the Earth's crust or mantle, that solidifies to form an igneous rock,

either as an extrusive lava or as an intrusion.

Mélange: an internally chaotic body of rock in which clasts of various sizes and compositions are contained in a foliated, fine-grained matrix. May be produced by slumping of unlithified sediment or by tectonism.

Metabentonite: a lithified volcanic ash in which the clay minerals have mostly been altered to illite.

Metamorphism: the alteration of rocks within the Earth's crust by heat and/or pressure.

Metasomatism: a metamorphic change which involves the introduction of material from an external source.

Microdiorite: medium-grained intermediate igneous rock, compositionally equivalent to andesite, with andesine plagioclase feldspar, some sodium or potassium feldspar and biotite, hornblende and augite, with minor amounts of quartz.

Monocline: asymmetric fold with one limb dipping steeply and the other dipping gently.

Mugearite: a variety of alkali-basalt usually containing oligoclase, olivine or clinopyroxene.

Mylonite: a fine-grained, banded rock produced by tectonic shearing and granulation of rocks that have been pulverised and rolled during thrusting or faulting.

Obduction: the overthrusting of oceanic crust on to the leading edge of a continental lithospheric plate.

Olistolith: an exotic rock fragment carried within a major submarine slump. The accumulation of such blocks in a fine-grained matrix is termed an olistostrome.

Oncolite: concentrically laminated ball produced by the action of algae in trapping sediment on the surface of a mobile grain.

Oolith: spherical particle, usually less than 2 mm diameter, formed by the concentric deposition of carbonate rings around a mobile grain.

Ophiolite: a group of mainly mafic and ultramafic igneous rocks with a common origin as oceanic crust. A relic 'stratigraphy' may be preserved with ultramafic rock at the base followed, in upward succession, by gabbro, a sheeted basalt dyke unit, and pillow lavas. There is often a cap of oceanic chert and shale.

Outlier: area of younger rocks completely surrounded by older rocks.

Palaeocurrent: ancient current from which sediment was deposited; its direction and flow-rate may be determined from sedimentary structures.

Palaeosol: a buried and lithified soil layer.

Pegmatite: an exceptionally coarse-grained igneous rock usually forming a dyke or vein.

Pelagic: (1) mode of life of animals which live permanently in the upper waters of the ocean, e.g. fish, jellyfish. (2) fine-grained sediment deposited on the deep ocean floor.

Pelite: metamorphosed argillaceous rock.

Pericline: fold in which variation in hinge plunge produces either a basin or a dome or an alternation of both.

Phenocryst: relatively large, usually well-formed crystal set in a groundmass of much smaller crystals.

Phyllonitic: a foliated texture formed by the mechanical degradation of initially coarser rocks.

Phyllosilicate: a class of minerals characterised by a sheet-like crystal structure. Mica is a typical example.

Pillow lava: a globular mass of lava extruded under water. As the semi-solidified pillows accumulate they flatten and sag into distinctive shapes that indicate the attitude of the original lava pile.

Plunge: direction and/or amount of downwards slope of a fold axis or lineation relative to the horizontal.

Pluton: large intrusion originally formed deep in the Earth's crust.

Porphyritic: texture in an igneous rock in which large crystals (phenocrysts) are set in a fine-grained groundmass.

Porphyroblast: a large crystal in a rock formed by metamorphic recrystallisation.

Porphyry: medium-grained acid or intermediate igneous rock containing phenocrysts usually of plagioclase feldspar.

Pressure shadow: aggregate of new grains growing on opposite sides of an original clast or crystal and producing an elongate structure; generally aligned parallel to a foliation.

Provenance: the source area from which the constituent grains in a sedimentary rock were originally derived.

Proximal: describes sedimentary lithologies deposited near to the source of the sediment (cf. distal).

Pseudomorph: a mineral produced by alteration which has assumed the crystal form of its precursor mineral.

Pyroclastic: describes a rock consisting of fragmental volcanic material blown into the air by an explosive volcanic eruption.

Radiolarian: single-celled marine planktonic protistan, secreting a lacy siliceous shell.

Radiometric dating: method for providing an age of a rock using radioactive decay rates.

Recumbent: describes an overturned fold in which both limbs and the axial plane are near horizontal.

Roche moutonnée: glacially smoothed rock with a gradual slope on the ice advance side and a steep, rough slope on the other side plucked by the ice.

Rodingite: a pale-coloured, fine-grained rock produced by the alteration of, and the addition of calcium to, an original basic igneous rock. The process is genetically associated with the conversion of ultramafic rock to serpentinite which may produce excess calcium (cf. metasomatism).

Rudite: a general name for clastic sedimentary rocks mainly composed of grains larger than sand size.

Scoria(-cious): lava full of empty vesicles.

Seatearth: fossil soil, commonly underlying a coal seam; palaeosol.

Shale: detrital sedimentary rock consisting predominantly of clay minerals and characterised by a marked bedding-plane fissility.

Sill: subhorizontal sheet-like igneous intrusion, often parallel to bedding.

Sinistral: left-lateral movement across a wrench fault (opposite is dextral).

Skarn: a thermally metamorphosed carbonate rock into which has been introduced additional silica, iron, aluminimum and magnesium (cf. metasomatism).

Slickenfibres: fibrous growths of quartz or calcite parallel to the direction of movement in a fault plane.

Slickensides: grooves produced by the fault movement of two rock surfaces against each other.

Sole mark: irregularity preserved on the base of a greywacke bed, e.g. flute mark and groove mark.

Spilite: basaltic rock containing albite as the plagioclase feldspar and chlorite replacing augite and olivine; generally found as submarine lava which reacted with sodium in the sea water.

Strike fault; strike-parallel fault: fault trending parallel to the regional strike of a layered sequence.

Strike-slip shear: lateral movement parallel to the regional strike along a strike fault.

Stromatolite: a layered structure produced by trapping and binding of sediment during the growth of algae; the forms produced may be sheets, domes or columns.

Subduction (-ing): where two continental or oceanic crustal plates move towards one another, the more dense plate sinks and moves below the other and consequently melts; the line of subduction is usually marked by a deep ocean trench and a linear volcanic belt often forms parallel to the margin of the overriding plate.

Subhedral: poorly formed crystal shape (cf. euhedral).

Syncline: usually convex-downwards fold with the youngest strata in the core (cf. anticline).

Thermal metamorphism: alteration of rocks by the action of heat alone, usually from an igneous intrusion.

Tholeiite: type of basalt containing calcium plagioclase and pigeonite, a pyroxene that forms on rapid cooling, with interstitial glass or intergrowths of quartz and alkali feldspar.

Thrust: gently or moderately dipping fault with a reverse sense of movement emplacing older rocks above younger; reversed fault.

Trace fossil: feature resulting from biological activity in sediment, e.g. footprint, burrow, trail.

Trachyte(-ic): fine-grained intermediate igneous rock dominated by lath-like plagioclase crystals, characteristically aligned during the flow of the original viscous lava.

Tuff: a general term for consolidated pyroclastic rocks consisting mainly of fine-grained fragments (cf. agglomerate).

Turbidity current: slurry of sediment that behaves as a fluid when it flows down an underwater slope; initially erosional, becomes depositional as current slackens.

Ultramafic: describes very dark igneous rocks composed principally of olivine and pyroxene minerals.

Unconformity: depositional surface above an angular break in bedding attitude; the beds above are approximately parallel to the depositional surface whereas the strata beneath may be at any attitude or even intensely folded.

Vent: volcanic pipe from which lava and ash are ejected; subsequently filled by solidified lava or volcanic agglomerate.

Vergence: (1) the direction of overturning in asymmetric or recumbent folds. (2) the direction in which a major anticline might be expected to exist, based on the geometry of a minor fold pair of anticline and syncline.

Vesicle(-cular): cavity in lava formed by gas bubbles (cf. amygdale).

Xenolith: inclusion of a fragment of older rock within an igneous rock.

Mineral table

Details of some of the more unusual minerals mentioned in the text.

Main groups

Amphiboles: Group of common rock-forming Mg-Fe silicate minerals widespread in igneous and metamorphic rocks.

Feldspars: Group of very important rock-forming silicates, the major constituent of igneous and metamorphic rocks and common as detrital grains in sedimentary rocks.

Garnets: Group of cubic Fe-Mg minerals found in many metamorphosed rocks, in some igneous rocks and commonly as detrital grains in sedimentary rocks.

Micas: Group of layer-lattice minerals consisting of sheets of silicates which produce a fine lamellar cleavage, occurring mainly in igneous and metamorphic rocks.

Pyroxenes: Group of rock-forming silicate minerals, with the general formula ZSi_2O_6, where Z is most commonly Mg, Fe, Ca or Al; common in basic and ultrabasic igneous rocks.

Spinels: Group of cubic, oxide minerals with the general formulae XY_2O_4 where X may be Mg, Fe^{2+}, Mn or Zn; Y may be Al, Fe^{3+} or Cr; common accessory minerals in igneous rocks and as detrital grains in sedimentary rocks. Fe- and Cr-rich varieties are important as ore minerals.

Individual minerals

Actinolite: *amphibole group.* Calcium-rich Mg-Fe silicate occurring as a fibrous, pale green alteration product or in metamorphic rocks.

Apatite: calcium-rich phosphate mineral found in igneous rocks, usually white.

Arsenopyrite: sulphide ore mineral, FeAsS, usually found in veins, as aggregates, or as disseminations of silvery needles.

Azurite: secondary ore mineral, $2CuCO_3.Cu(OH)_2$, forms blue replacement masses after primary copper ore, usually associated with other oxidised Cu minerals.

Baryte: very heavy, massive or fibrous white mineral $BaSO_4$ found in veins; economically important.

Beudantite: greenish black secondary mineral, $PbFe_3(AsO_4)(SO_4)(OH)_6$, formed by the oxidation of primary lead ores such as galena in mixed sulphide mineral veins.

Biotite: *mica group.* Complex Fe-Mg layer lattice mineral, the iron-rich form of mica; brown in colour and common in igneous and metamorphic rocks.

Blende: zinc blende or sphalerite (ZnS), the principal ore of zinc.

Bornite: sulphide ore mineral, Cu_5FeS_4, found as massive aggregates within hydrothermal copper veins; readily tarnishes on exposure to air.

Bournonite: mixed sulphide ore mineral, $CuPbSbS_3$, dark grey and, through twinning, found as curious, wheel-shaped crystals; usually occurs with other copper minerals.

Chalcopyrite: sulphide ore mineral, $CuFeS_2$, the main ore of copper; widely distributed in mineral veins and as brassy yellow disseminations in some igneous rocks.

Chlorite: one of a series of mainly green secondary minerals consisting of hydrated Mg-Al-Fe aluminium silicates, formed by the alteration of primary ferromagnesian minerals.

Cordierite: silicate mineral formed mainly during thermal metamorphism of argillaceous rocks. It occurs as ovoid crystals crowded with inclusions and often forms the spots in a hornfels.

Epidote: green, Ca-Fe silicate mineral most commonly formed during regional metamorphism or by the hydrothermal alteration of feldspar.

Galena: sulphide ore mineral, PbS, usually found as dense, black masses in hydrothermal mineral veins. The principal ore of lead.

Gersdorffite: silvery grey ore mineral, NiAsS, found in veins or as disseminations in basic and ultrabasic rock.

Gypsum: white to pink evaporite mineral, $CaSO_4.2H_2O$, commonly forming nodules and layers within sedimentary sequences of tropical, shallow-marine origin.

Hemimorphite: secondary ore mineral, $Zn_4Si_2O_7(OH)_2.H_2O$, a white alteration product found in the oxidised zones of zinc ore deposits or mineral veins.

Hornblende: *amphibole group*, black or green-black, complex Na- and K-rich, Fe-Mg silicate mineral, common in igneous and metamorphic rocks.

Jasper: red, haematite-rich variety of chert, the massive form of SiO_2.

Linarite: rare, blue secondary mineral, $(Pb,Cu)SO_4.(Pb,Cu)(OH)_2$, found as an oxidation product of primary ore in lead-copper veins.

Malachite: secondary ore mineral, $Cu_2CO_3(OH)_2$; a bright green mineral seen as coatings and encrustations in the oxidised zone of copper deposits and on copper-rich rocks generally.

Molybdenite: sulphide ore mineral, MoS_2, soft, silvery grey mineral forming plates or scales in hydrothermal veins and as disseminations in some igneous rocks.

Muscovite: *mica group.* complex K-Al layer-lattice mineral, the iron-free form of mica; colourless flakes very common in igneous and metamorphic rocks.

Nickeline: pale reddish brown mineral NiAs, usually found in hydrothermal veins. An important nickel ore.

Olivine: a series of mineral variations with the general formulae X_2SiO_4 where X is most commonly Fe, Mg or Mn or a combination of these; widespread in basic and ultrabasic igneous rocks, usually as the common form $(Mg.Fe)_2(SiO_4)$.

Orthoclase: *feldspar group.* Potassium-rich variety $KAlSi_3O_8$, with monoclinic crystal form; common in igneous rocks.

Pentlandite: sulphide ore mineral, $(Fe, Ni)_9S_8$, usually found in hydrothermal veins or as disseminations in basic and ultrabasic igneous rocks.

Phlogopite: *mica group.* Complex K-Mg-Fe layer lattice mineral similar to biotite but containing more magnesium; found in some basic and ultrabasic igneous rocks.

Pitchblende: a massive, impure variety of uranium oxide; radioactive.

Plagioclase: *feldspar group.* A series of feldspars forming a triclinic solid-solution series from pure sodium feldspar (albite, $NaAlSi_3O_8$) to pure calcium feldspar (anorthite, $CaAl_2Si_2O_8$). Plagioclase is the commonest component of igneous rocks.

Plumbogummite: complex secondary mineral, $PbAl_3(PO_4)_2(OH)_5.H_2O$, usually forming a brown alteration replacement of primary lead ore such as galena.

Pyromorphite: secondary ore mineral, $(PbCl)Pb_4(PO_4)_3$, a greenish yellow encrustation on the primary ore minerals in the oxidised zone of lead deposits.

Pyrrhotite: sulphide ore mineral, Fe_7S_8-FeS, a reddish bronze accessory disseminated in basic igneous rocks and concentrated as granular masses in hydrothermal veins.

Semseyite: dark grey or black mixed sulphide ore mineral, $Pb_9Sb_8S_{21}$ usually occurring in hydrothermal veins together with other lead and antimony minerals.

Sericite: intermediate between the micas and the clay minerals, usually an alteration product of other silicate minerals; common in weathered and slightly metamorphosed rocks.

Serpentine: green hydrated magnesium silicate mineral, $Mg_6Si_4O_{10}(OH)_8$; massive or fibrous habit, formed by the alteration of olivine and some other ferromagnesian minerals in basic and ultrabasic rock.

Sillimanite: aluminium silicate mineral, Al_2SiO_5, generally found as white needle-shaped crystals or fibrous aggregates in high-grade metamorphic rocks.

Sphalerite: sulphide ore mineral, ZnS, usually black or dark brown aggregates or masses in hydrothermal veins. The principal ore of zinc.

Stibnite: sulphide ore mineral, Sb_2S_3; forms silvery grey bladed crystals, usually in hydrothermal veins. The principal ore of antimony.

Tennantite: complex sulphide ore mineral $(Cu.Fe)_{12}As_4S_{13}$, occurring as black, massive aggregates in veins. Forms a continuous series with **tetrahedrite**.

Tetrahedrite: complex sulphide ore mineral, $(Cu.Fe)_{12}Sb_4S_{13}$, occurring as dark grey massive aggregates in hydrothermal veins, usually with copper minerals.

Tourmaline: complex boron-rich silicate mineral, very variable in colour and forming columnar crystals with unusual triangular cross-sections; associated with volatile, gaseous phases and found in some acid igneous rocks and high-grade metamorphic rocks.

Uraninite: black, massive, radioactive mineral, UO_2, usually found in hydrothermal veins, granites and pegmatites.

Zircon: common accessory mineral, $ZrSiO_4$, found in acid igneous rocks and as a resistate grain in sedimentary rocks derived therefrom.

Index

Lie Mullin farm Quarry on 701 nr Loch Urskun

Southern Upland Fld sequence p8.

D_1 early Thrust related deformation D_1 produced F_1 and S_1

D_2 accommodation in hinterland (structures)

D_3 the late sinistral shear

F   fold hinges (specific)

S   cleavage plane (specific)